W9-BPS-298

THE IMPACT OF THE CIVIL WAR

A Series Planned by the Civil War
Centennial Commission

Among the Volumes in Preparation

ON WOMEN
by Mary Elizabeth Massey

ON THE MILITARY THOUGHT AND PRACTICES OF EUROPE
by Cyril Falls

ON PHILANTHROPY AND WELFARE
by Robert H. Bremner

THE NORTH TO POSTERITY
by James I. Robertson, Jr.

Agriculture and the Civil War

THE
IMPACT
OF
THE
CIVIL
WAR

[THE CIVIL WAR CENTENNIAL COMMISSION SERIES]

Edited by Allan Nevins

AGRICULTURE
AND THE
CIVIL WAR

by Paul W. Gates

WEST VIRGINIA LIBRARY COMMISSION
2004 QUARRIER STREET
CHARLESTON, WEST VIRGINIA

104530

New York: Alfred · A · Knopf

1 9 6 5

L. C. catalog card number: 65–13461

THIS IS A BORZOI BOOK,
PUBLISHED BY ALFRED A. KNOPF, INC.

Copyright © 1962 by the Michigan Historical Commission. © 1963 by the University of Nebraska Press. © 1964 by the Agricultural History Society. © 1965 by Paul W. Gates. All rights reserved. No part of this book may be reproduced in any form without permission in writing from the publisher, except by a reviewer, who may quote brief passages and reproduce not more than three illustrations in a review to be printed in a magazine or newspaper. Manufactured in the United States of America, and distributed by Random House, Inc. Published simultaneously in Toronto, Canada, by Random House of Canada, Limited.

FIRST EDITION

The map "Major Crop Areas of the United States, 1860" appeared in slightly different form in *The Farmer's Age,* by Paul W. Gates, published by Holt, Rinehart and Winston, Inc., 1960, and is reprinted here with the permission of the publisher.

Portions of Chapters 10 and 11 have appeared in somewhat different form in *Agricultural History* (April 1964), *Michigan History* (December 1962), and *Land Use Policy and Problems in the United States,* edited by Howard O. Ottoson, published by the University of Nebraska Press, 1963.

Introduction

by Allan Nevins

Out of the Civil War slowly rose a new nation; a nation that differed nearly as much from its past, in spirit, intent, and ideas, as the country of Jefferson and Hamilton had differed from colonial America. The process was necessarily slow. The war had swiftly destroyed slavery and erased the old opposition of the states to federal supremacy, but otherwise the new order represented an evolution, not a revolution. The Civil War upheaval had generated few forces that were totally novel. But it released some movements that had been dormant, stimulated some that had been sluggish, and reshaped others in more effective form; the public health movement, the woman's rights movement, and the movement toward realism in literature are examples of the three types of change. It gave well-organized efforts and well-nationalized enterprises their first real chance in a land all too individualistic, and all too divided.

The fighting and its attendant demands upon industry, finance, medicine, and law also helped train a host of leaders who during the next thirty-five years, to 1900, made their influence powerfully felt on most of the social, economic, and cultural fronts. It broke down barriers of parochialism; it ended distrust of large-scale effort; it hardened and matured the whole people emotionally. The adolescent land of the 1850's, streaked in some areas by sentimentalism and false values, coarsened in other areas by brutal violence, oscillating between Brook Farm dilettantism and Kansas border-ruffianism, rose under the blows of battle to adult estate. The nation of the post-Appomattox generation, though sadly hurt (especially in the South) by war losses, and deeply scarred psychologically (especially in the North) by war hatreds and greeds, had at last the power, resolution, and self-trust of manhood.

374605

The emergence of an adult and awakened country out of the war can be understood only if the most important elements of its new strength are studied separately. Nathaniel Hawthorne had written from Washington during the war of his fear that bullet-headed generals would take control of the country's destinies. So they did in the political sphere, though "bullet-headed" is an ungenerous term for Hayes, Garfield, and McKinley. But it was men who felt the shock of war at second hand, and who saw from peaceable vantage points its release of a thousand new energies, who gave the republic most of its fresh leadership. Rockefeller in industry, Morgan in finance, Henry James and William Dean Howells in letters, Whistler and St. Gaudens in art, gained many advantages from the new earnestness and wider intelligence born during the battle years; but they and half their fellows were not sons of the battlefield. It was the new spirit, the new toughness, the more sophisticated alertness, to which they responded. This new maturity and sterner drive become visible only when each department of national life is studied in analytic detail.

This analytical study may be termed the grandest theme of the crowded war period, and the most profitable task of its historians. Nobody would maintain that the writing of truly excellent military history has been overdone. It is the production of bad histories and biographies that has been pushed to excess. Despite the plethora of books a few important gaps remain to be filled. In well-worn paths authors as incisive as Henderson and as thorough as Douglas Freeman can always give new color and significance to old subjects. Nor would any sensible critic argue that truly excellent political studies of the Civil War era have grown too numerous. Again gaps remain to be filled and vital topics can be imbued with original life. Nevertheless, it can be asserted that military and political aspects of the far-felt convulsion have received an attention disproportionate to that given the social, the economic, the ideological, the cultural, and the administrative aspects of the era.

In this conviction the United States Civil War Centennial Commission has planned the fifteen volumes of its Impact Series, devoted to as many different facets of wartime development: challenge and response, retardation and growth, short-term influence and long-term impact. The gamut ranges from constitutional and statutory law to poverty, crime, and charities, from business organization to medicine and surgery. The Commission hopes that it may help correct the disproportionate emphasis thus far given political and military history, and open to view some of the riches of civil history still to be explored. We are happy to bring before the public, as the first book in the Series, so masterly a work as this one by Paul W. Gates, *Agriculture and the Civil War*.

When Sumter fell, agriculture was basic. About half of the 31,400,000 people listed by the census of 1860 dwelt on farms, more than half of the gainfully employed worked on them, and three quarters of the national exports came from them. In the United States as in other countries farming had a leisurely rhythm of its own, which did much to give the population its stable outlook. Three farm families out of four owned the acres they tilled. In the North and the border states the farms were mainly self-sufficient units. As land was cheap (the average value of an acre in 1860 being only $16.32) and implements were horse-drawn or mule-drawn, the total capital invested in agriculture fell short of seven billion dollars. Yet it was increasing fast, as successive censuses revealed. As Mr. Gates shows, farming was full of vitality and, outside static one-crop areas of the South, was charged with a remarkable amount of variety. It was responding to some great new impulses. It was busy developing both the Northwest and the Southwest, and spilling across the Missouri and Red rivers. it was meeting drastic changes in marketing created by the fast-lengthening fingers of railroads—particularly the railroads that knit the prairie states to the East. In some areas of the Middle West it was shifting from wheat to corn, or vice versa; some districts of the South were beginning to supplement slave labor with sharecropping.

What would the war do to this great lively, vital part of American society and the national economy? This question Mr. Gates answers with authority and clarity. He answers it with original data drawn from a thousand sources, and with a mass of human material that makes his story sometimes poignantly tragic, sometimes exhilarating, and always gripping. In few books is the "war as ordeal" more real.

For the North the ordeal, however cruel in some places, was triumphantly surmounted. Not merely did corn move toward the throne once occupied by cotton, but a passion for crop diversification seized the North, and with it a new specialization. Dairy farming felt an increased vigor. Large-scale truck gardening flourished near the fast-growing cities. New crops like sorghum, a temporary substitute for Southern molasses, appeared. The increased production of flax, hemp, and wool to take the place of cotton met a clear need, and gave the farmers money that efforts at cotton growing in southern Illinois and Kansas failed to yield. The number of livestock in the North, Mr. Gates shows, declined (except for sheep) in the war years, but only because the insistent demands of the War Department, of wage earners with increased incomes, and of overseas markets, kept depleting the supply.

To all parts of this varied picture in the North, Mr. Gates does justice. He treats the role of wheat, corn, and cured meats in international politics, and in supplying the United States with gold and international credits. He deals with the rise of rural organizations as farmers felt "the need for associational meetings at which group objectives could be framed, and plans for achieving them laid." He does not neglect such seeds of a greater farm revolution to come as agricultural science and Mr. Morrill's act for land-grant universities. Always, however, he humanizes his story with novel information of illuminating character. Diversification? He quotes the unpublished diary of a farmer living near Geneva, New York, who during the war sold oxen, a horse, a heifer, poultry, wood, and corn. "He exchanged labor with neighboring farmers, hired some hands at $8 to $18 a month, and worked at pulling stumps, picking stones, clearing hedges, butchering, making some farm implements, drawing 230 loads of manure, plowing, reaping, threshing grain, husking corn, and . . . cutting wood."

Northern agriculture came out of the war to face the anguish of crop gluts, falling prices, and mounting costs. Yet it had met the test of war with resourcefulness, it had made decent profits in stormy times, and it was ready to face new problems with the energy, initiative, and hopefulness long characteristic of the American yeomanry.

Far different is the picture Mr. Gates has to paint of the South under the harrow of war. Planters, farmers, slaves, and their dependents met myriad adversities, which he vividly depicts. The immense displacements of population, as refugees took to the roads and slaves were herded from state to state for safety, were quite new in American experience. Hardly until the two world wars were they matched in any Western nation. The Confederate government had to organize an impressment of farm products, a tax administration, and a tithing system, which bore cruelly upon all planters and farmers. All this broke down of its own weight, as Mr. Gates shows, so that meat rotted and grain spoiled because it could not be housed, transported, and distributed. Farmers saw their tools wearing out with no chance of replacement. They saw horses and mules indispensable to cavalry, artillery, and farm operations slowly starve to death. Invading armies, with torch, sword, and wagons laden with pillage, cut ever deeper into the Confederacy. While houses, barns, and gins burned, fields went without fertilizers, lacked seed, and with ill-managed labor grew up in weeds. The emancipation and escape of slaves steadily drained the labor supply.

Worst of all was the internecine strife that laid parts of the South in moral as well as material ruin. Guerrillas preyed on Unionists and Confederates alike, robbed and ravaged without mercy, and in areas like Tennessee, the disputed zones of Mississippi, and Missouri cut the throats of innocent folk and committed other appalling outrages. No wonder that many farmers and planters, without essential implements, animals, and hands, without credit or transportation to markets, by 1865 gave up hope. In a pregnant sentence Mr. Gates puts his finger on the three main causes of the Confederate downfall. "The scarcity of food, felt in all parts of the South and in the army from Virginia to Texas, desertion from and attrition in the army, and a disastrous currency combined to defeat the South."

This rich book throws a flood of new light upon rural life and economics as two of the most important sides of American life in the Civil War period. It does not fail to examine the reasons why the Negro fared so badly in the post-bellum reorganization of the Southern economy. It offers significant information on the relationship of agriculture to labor and the new capitalism in the years after the war. We may feel sure that it and the fourteen volumes which follow will demonstrate that much of the true history of the Civil War period has remained to be brought to light.

Contents

PART I: THE SOUTH

1 · *Corn Becomes King*   3
2 · *Shortages and Inflation*   28
3 · *Impressment and Tithing*   46
4 · *Tightening of the Screws*   73
5 · *The Belt of Desolation*   109

PART II: THE NORTH

6 · *Diversity*   129
7 · *Livestock Farming*   157
8 · *Dairy Farming*   188
9 · *Farm Labor and Machinery*   222

PART III: THE UNITED STATES

10 · *Beginnings of Agricultural Education*   251
11 · *Achievement of Homestead*   272
12 · *Government Patronage of Agriculture*   301
13 · *Groundswells of Agrarianism*   324
14 · *War's Aftermath*   356

Note on Sources and Acknowledgments   381

Index   follows page 383

Illustrations

The illustrations are grouped after page 174

1 THE COTTON FAMINE IN ENGLAND
>   FROM *The Illustrated London News*, NOV. 22, 1862.
>   YANKEE SOLDIERS GOING INTO CAMP
>   FROM J. D. BILLINGS: *Hardtack and Coffee* (BOSTON, 1887).

2 THE MILK RATION
>   FROM *Hardtack and Coffee.*
>   YANKEE SOLDIERS FORAGING IN LOUISIANA
>   FROM *Leslie's Illustrated Famous Leaders and Battle Scenes of the Civil War* (NEW YORK, 1896).
>   COTTON HOARD IN SOUTHERN SWAMPS
>   FROM *Harper's Pictorial History of the Great Rebellion,* VOL. II (CHICAGO, 1868).

3 SEIZURE AND HANDLING OF COTTON IN MISSISSIPPI
>   FROM *Harper's Weekly,* MAY 2, 1863.
>   CONFEDERATE CALL FOR GRAIN AND FORAGE, 1863
>   FROM L. BUCHANAN: *Pictorial History of the Confederacy* (NEW YORK, 1951).
>   ASSESSMENT FORM FOR CONFEDERATE TAX-IN-KIND
>   COURTESY NORTH CAROLINA DEPARTMENT OF ARCHIVES AND HISTORY

4 DROVE OF VIRGINIA CATTLE
>   FROM D. H. STROTHER: *The Old South Illustrated* (CHAPEL HILL, N.C., 1959).
>   A FARM ROAD
>   FROM [WILLIAM CLIFT] *The Tim Bunker Papers; or Yankee Farming* (NEW YORK, 1868).

VIRGINIANS DRAWING RATIONS FROM THE FEDERAL GOV-
ERNMENT
FROM *Harper's Weekly*, FEB. 11, 1865.

5 CRADLING AND LOADING WHEAT
FROM *American Agriculturist*, JULY 1861.
PENNSYLVANIA GERMAN FARMER PACKED TO FLEE FROM
CONFEDERATES
FROM *Harper's Weekly*, AUG. 13, 1864.

6 HUBBARD'S MOWER
FROM OHIO STATE BOARD OF AGRICULTURE: *Eigh-
teenth Annual Report*, 1863.
SEYMOUR, MORGAN AND ALLEN SELF-RAKING REAPER
FROM NEW YORK STATE AGRICULTURAL SOCIETY:
Transactions, 1868.
EMERY'S PATENT CHANGEABLE RAILROAD HORSE POWER AND
THRASHING MACHINE
FROM *Cultivator*, JUNE 1862.

7 IOWA LAND FOR SALE AT $1.50 AN ACRE
BROADSIDE IN BURLINGTON ARCHIVES, NEWBERRY
LIBRARY; COURTESY NEWBERRY LIBRARY.
ILLINOIS CENTRAL RAILROAD ADVERTISEMENT
FROM *Harper's Weekly*, NOV. 23, 1863.

8 PERSONNEL OF THE U.S. DEPARTMENT OF AGRICULTURE,
1867
COURTESY U.S. DEPARTMENT OF AGRICULTURE.
HENRY S. RANDALL
FROM *Atlas Map of Cortland County* (PHILADELPHIA,
1876).

I

THE SOUTH

MAJOR CROP AREAS
OF THE UNITED STATES, 1860

Cotton   Corn   Wheat

Tobacco   Sugar cane   Rice

Hay and dairying ---- Important railroads ---- Important canals

Prairies

0   MILES   500

B R I T I S H

W A S H I N G T O N

Columbia River

T E R R.

OREGON
TERRITORY

NEBRASKA
TERRITORY

Missouri River

C A L I F O R N I A

Great Salt Lake

U T A H
TERRITORY

Colorado River

KANSAS
TERRITORY

UNORGANIZED
TERRITORY

Red River

NEW MEXICO
TERRITORY

PACIFIC
OCEAN

T E X A S

M E X I C O

Rio Grande

50°

40°

30°

20°

120°

50°

LAKE SUPERIOR

MAINE

St. Lawrence River

MINNESOTA

WISCONSIN

LAKE MICHIGAN

LAKE HURON

VT. N.H.

NEW YORK

MASS.

Boston

La Crosse

L. ONTARIO

Buffalo

Rochester

Troy

CONN.

RHODE ISLAND

Milwaukee

LAKE ERIE

Erie

40°

IOWA

Chicago

Toledo

PENNSYLVANIA

New York

INDIANA

OHIO

Columbus

Pittsburgh

Lancaster

Philadelphia

NEW JERSEY

St. Joseph

Indianapolis

Cincinnati

Potomac R.

Baltimore

DELAWARE

MARYLAND

ILLINOIS

Evansville

Scioto R.

VIRGINIA

Richmond

St. Louis

Ohio

Louisville

MISSOURI

River

KENTUCKY

Norfolk

Raleigh

Nashville

NORTH CAROLINA

ARKANSAS

Memphis

TENNESSEE

Chattanooga

Wilmington

Mississippi

Atlanta

SOUTH CAROLINA

ALABAMA

GEORGIA

Charleston

Jackson

Montgomery

Savannah

MISS.

LOUISIANA

Natchez

30°

Atchafalaya

Mobile

Pensacola

Houston

New Orleans

FLORIDA

ATLANTIC   OCEAN

GULF OF MEXICO

90°

80°

20°

I

Corn Becomes King

To a foreigner, the sectional strife in the halls of Congress before 1861, the angry philippics of the fire-eaters on each side, and the accounts of the bushwacking and jayhawking, the pillaging, horse stealing, and murder in Kansas, might have been clear signs that America was fast approaching civil war. Yet, aside from the charges then made, though since exploded, that Buchanan had permitted John Floyd, Secretary of War, to remove to the South important military supplies, there is no evidence that either side, or that leading partisans on either side, had done anything to prepare for war. Most amazing of all is that the South, which was so deficient in the means of producing the instruments of war, should have continued the struggle for four years and that the North, despite its terrific losses in killed and wounded, should have persisted until victory was won. The courage of the South and the perseverance of the North constitute the greatness of the American people during this unhappy Civil War.

Eleven Southern states, hopefully expecting that four others would join them, undertook to set themselves up as an independent nation and to resist all efforts to force them to return to the Union. Those states, and thus the new confederacy they sought to create, were made up of rural-agricultural communities dependent upon the production of cotton, sugar, rice, tobacco, and

3

wheat and their ability to sell them outside their boundaries. The export of these staples accounted for 59 per cent of the total value of the exports of the United States in the fifties. Moreover, they earned credits upon which the South could draw indirectly for the purchase of foodstuffs which it was not producing in sufficient quantities. Between one third and one half of the pork of the upper Mississippi Valley was sold in the South and quantities of corn, flour, beef, hay, apples, butter and cheese, and a variety of other items flowed southward by keelboat, flatboat, and steamboat.[1]

The economy of the upper Mississippi Valley was closely linked to the South and, reinforced by political ties, it tended to align the Northwest with the South on sectional issues, at least until the rise of Stephen A. Douglas and the building of railroads from the East to Chicago, Cincinnati, and St. Louis. The railroads did much to reverse the sectional ties and to bring the upper Mississippi Valley into closer relations with the Northeast, though great quantities of food continued to be marketed in New Orleans, Memphis, and Nashville.[2]

The agricultural units of the South varied greatly in size— ranging all the way from small family farms to plantations of thousands of acres operated on a commercial basis by hundreds of slaves under the management of overseers. The great plantations were located in the richly endowed Delta counties of Arkansas, Louisiana, and Mississippi, in the river valleys (the Alabama, Tombigbee, Chattahoochee, Savannah, and Roanoke) of Alabama, Georgia, North Carolina, South Carolina, and Virginia, and in the coastal region of Georgia and South Carolina. These plantations produced most of the South's staples, employed most of the slaves, and, of course, owned most of the wealth. Yeoman farmers, with or without a family or two of slaves, were common in these rich areas and their production constituted a considerable proportion of the cotton and tobacco but little of the rice and sugar crops. Elsewhere, on the poorer lands and

---

[1] L. B. Schmidt: "Internal Commerce and the Development of National Economy before 1860," *Journal of Political Economy,* XLVII (December 1939), 798 ff. The *New Orleans Price Current* for the years just before the war is invaluable.

[2] W. E. Dodd: "The Fight for the Northwest, 1860," *American Historical Review,* XVI (July 1911), 774 ff.

in the pine barrens and foothills, away from transportation, were the low-income families working land that yielded little more than was sufficient for their own subsistence. The rich planters with their many slaves, the yeoman farmers, and the poor whites were all to play vital parts in the war.[3]

The South relied heavily upon the upper Mississippi Valley for foodstuffs and lumber because it could buy them more cheaply than it could produce them and could obtain them in the needed quantities only from the states in that region. *De Bow's Review* and other ardently sectional papers of the South had long deplored its dependence upon the states of the upper Mississippi Valley and advocated regional self-sufficiency, even though that meant higher costs. When these economic ties were severed in 1861 the South found, to its regret, that its reliance on the old Northwest had placed it in a poor position for a long-sustained conflict. It was not accustomed to feeding itself, though it had a more favorable ratio of livestock to humans than did the North.

On the other hand, the upper Mississippi Valley farmers faced great distress in 1861 and 1862, when the natural market for much of their goods was blocked. Depression, perhaps as bad as anything the West had endured, came upon Illinois, Iowa, and Wisconsin, and it was relieved only when their economic ties with the East were strengthened and when England and France absorbed produce previously marketed in the South.

That neither the North nor the South had, before the war, considered the logistical problems of their armies is clear. Had the South done so it might well have made a different decision. One may wonder too whether some of the people in Illinois, Iowa, or Wisconsin who voted for Lincoln might have acted differently if they could have foreseen the economic difficulties their section was to go through before war purchases brought them higher prices and the return of prosperity.[4]

---

[3] L. C. Gray: *History of Agriculture in the Southern United States to 1860* (2 vols., Washington, 1933), II, *passim;* Willard Range: *A Century of Georgia Agriculture, 1850–1950* (Athens, Ga., 1954), pp. 3 ff.; J. H. Moore: *Agriculture in Ante-Bellum Mississippi* (New York, 1958).

[4] G. F. Warren and F. A. Pearson: *Wholesale Prices for 213 Years, 1720–1932,* Cornell University Agricultural Experiment Station, *Memoir,* 142 (Ithaca, N.Y., 1932), p. 9, shows that the wholesale price index for November 1860 stood at 93, fell to 92 in March 1861 and to 83 that July, did not

The war necessitated drastic and far-reaching changes in the farming operations of both sections. The South, first unwilling and then unable to ship its cotton to Europe, found it a drug on the market and expensive to store. To keep the cotton out of the clutches of the invading Yankee armies the South was eventually driven to destroy it. After harvesting a bumper cotton crop in 1861 the Confederacy turned increasingly to the production of foodstuffs, which, as the war progressed and the area controlled or devastated by the North increased, became ever more vital.

Any analysis of the capacity of both North and South to produce food during the war must be based on the census data collected in 1860 for the crop year 1859. To determine the per capita yield of various crops we must use figures for 1859, but to find the number of livestock per capita we have to depend on data for 1860. Although the census takers and computers of 1860 were anything but experts and their methods something less than precise, their calculations, in the absence of anything better, are indispensable. What was the relative position of the two sides with respect to actual food supplies and potential production? (The analysis given here is based on the assumption that the production of foodstuffs in remote areas not economically integrated with or adjacent to the North or South may be disregarded. For this reason California and Oregon and the territories, save Nebraska, are omitted.[5])

Most vital to the South was its great supply of hogs and cattle. Its ratio of hogs to humans was double that of the North, and if the border states are included with the South, this still holds good (1.85 to .90). Much of this advantage was more apparent than real, however, for it was offset by a greater dependence upon pork and the inferiority of Southern livestock. Outside of Maryland, Virginia, and Kentucky, livestock breeding had not made the progress it had in the North. Fewer purebred animals had been introduced, hogs still ran wild throughout most of the South, subsisting on mast, roots, and grass and getting little

---

pass the election-month level until December, and only reached prosperity levels in August 1862.
[5] *Eighth Census of the United States, 1860, Agriculture* (Washington, 1864), *passim.* Cf. "Resources of the North and South," *The Knickerbocker Magazine,* in W. B. Hesseltine: *The Tragic Conflict. The Civil War and Reconstruction* (New York, 1962), p. 324.

or no corn, and neglect and poor food prevented them from attaining the size and quality of the hogs in states such as Ohio. Frederick Law Olmsted, who had encountered hogs running wild in the woods of Virginia, called them "bony, snake-headed, hairy, wild beasts," while an Ohio soldier stationed in western Virginia declared that the local hogs were the "longest, lankiest, boniest animals in creation." Georgia's hogs, more numerous than those of any other state in the Confederacy except Tennessee, have been described as "mainly long-headed, long legged, fleetfooted 'piney woods rooters' used to depending on Providence for food." Colonel L. B. Northrop, Commissary General of Subsistence, was aware at the outset that there were not sufficient hogs in the Confederacy to meet the needs of the army and to supply the three pounds a week of bacon generally allotted to plantation slaves, and he made every effort to bring in hogs from Union territory and to safeguard the supplies in Southern areas.[6]

As with hogs, the ratio of Southern cattle to humans seemed favorable, for the South boasted 1.5 per head of population to .66 for the North. This ratio seemed even less favorable to the North, for a much larger proportion of the cattle was kept for dairy purposes in the North (35%) than in the South (22%). Since dairy cattle were not sent to the slaughterhouse until they were seven to ten years old, whereas beef cattle were slaughtered in the third or fourth year, a smaller amount of meat could be expected from the dairy cows in any one year than from the same number of beef cattle. On the other hand, the North had the advantage of superior breeding stock. To Solon Robinson, who was a skilled judge of livestock, the average cattle of Virginia, North Carolina, Georgia, and other Southern states were "scrubby" and so small, in a day when fat cattle were favored, as to be called "pony cattle," dressing off a mere 400 to 600 pounds of beef to the animal. Georgia beef cattle, second in numbers only to those of Texas, were "lean and bony-rumped," and her dairy cows were "mostly

---

[6] *Official Records of the Rebellion* (hereafter cited as O.R.), ser. 4, I, 870 ff.; F. L. Olmsted: *A Journey in the Seabord Slave States* (New York, 1856), pp. 65, 76; Range: *Century of Georgia Agriculture*, p. 18. The ratios of livestock and crops to people are computed from *Eighth Census of the United States, 1860, Agriculture.* Also see E. D. Genovese: "Livestock in the Slave Economy of the Old South," *Agricultural History*, XXXVI (July 1962), 143 ff.

starvelings, producing less than a third as much milk per head as the national average." Texas steers were light in weight, thin, not easy to fatten, and not possessed of the quantity and quality of meat found on the Scioto Valley Shorthorns or even on the grade stock of the North. A recent writer has declared that the Texas cattle, "poor even by Southern standards . . . were largely semi-wild and probably worth only one-half as much as animals in other Southern states." Worse still, they were far distant from transportation facilities and the areas where they would be needed.[7]

Sheep were less important for the meat they supplied. Possibly the greater proportion in the North of Merino sheep, not noted for the amount or quality of their mutton, would bring the actual meat value of sheep in the two sections closer together. In the North the ratio of sheep to humans was .81 and in the South .68. Sheep were to be more important in providing wool for winter clothing and blankets and for use as a substitute for cotton in the North.

The marching armies of the South depended on corn bread and salted or pickled beef and pork. Those of the North were given regular rations of pork, bacon, salt or fresh beef, hardtack, and corn meal, in addition to vegetables.[8] Beef and pork were and long had been standard items of army diets; so also were corn bread and some form of bread or crackers made of wheat flour. The statistics of grain production of 1859 help to explain why corn bread was so vital a part of the diet of the Southern states and why hardtack was so commonly used in the North.

The North exceeded the South in per capita production of wheat but the South produced more corn. The North raised four times as much rye, three times as much oats, seventeen times as much buckwheat, nineteen times as much barley, but on a per capita basis the difference was not so great. On the other hand, the South produced practically all the rice in the country, and far outdistanced the North in beans and peas. The North had an advantage in potatoes.

In dairy products the North far exceeded the South. It had

---

[7] Solon Robinson: *Facts for Farmers* (New York, 1870), p. 14; Genovese: "Livestock in the Slave Economy of the Old South," p. 145.
[8] B. I. Wiley: *Life of Billy Yank* (Indianapolis, 1951), p. 224.

PER CAPITA PRODUCTION IN BUSHELS

Product	North	South
Wheat	5.57	4.78
Corn	25.55	31.05
Oats	7.03	2.18
Rice	—	.35
Rye	.87	.24
Potatoes (white and sweet)	5.97	4.35

SOURCE: *Eighth Census of the United States, 1860, Agriculture.*

62 per cent of the milk cows and produced 99 per cent of the cheese and 86 per cent of the butter.

Notwithstanding its apparently favorable position with respect to hogs, cattle, and corn, the South bought from the states of the upper Mississippi Valley huge amounts of grain, meat, and other items, as is partly shown by the table of imports to New Orleans from the interior in the year 1859–60. Not all this produce was retained in the South.[9] Some was shipped

IMPORTS TO NEW ORLEANS FROM THE INTERIOR,

1859–60

Flour	965,860	barrels
Corn	5,266,000	bushels
Wheat	29,511	bushels
Beef	6,062,766	pounds
Butter	441,000	pounds
Potatoes	207,698	bushels
Pork	58,332,559	pounds
Bacon and Ham	77,678,662	pounds
Lard	419,619	kegs
Hides	163,568	
Oats	1,978,650	bushels
Onions	26,410	barrels
Hay	213,665	tons

SOURCE: *New Orleans Price Current,* Sept. 8, 1860.

[9] L. B. Schmidt minimizes the importance of grain exports from New Orleans as of 1860 in "The Internal Grain Trade of the United States, 1850–1860," *Iowa Journal of History and Politics,* XVIII (January 1920), 111.

abroad, but produce which came into the South by other routes or which halted at Memphis, Vicksburg, Natchez, or Nashville more than compensated for the exports.[1]

If we allow ten pounds of corn to produce a pound of beef or pork, we find that the corn equivalent of the pork and beef imports into New Orleans amounted to 23,593,000 bushels, which, added to the 5,266,000 bushels of corn brought to New Orleans, makes a total of 28,859,000 bushels. This was roughly equivalent to 10 per cent of the entire Southern crop of corn. Though the South was far from self-sufficiency, it had several million acres in cotton and tobacco which in an emergency could be turned to corn.[2]

The eleven Southern states had a great reservoir of cleared and improved land which they used to produce the cash staples of tobacco, cotton, rice, and sugar in addition to the food staples of corn, wheat, and hay. The ratio amounted to 6.23 acres to each inhabitant as compared with 4.59 acres for each inhabitant in the North. The land that had been devoted to cash staples, when shifted to corn during the war, made it possible for the South to prolong the struggle.

Carl Russell Fish has described the agriculture of the South as "efficient and productive and more highly organized than that of the North."[3] Better organized the South certainly was for normal peacetime production, but it is questionable whether it remained so during the war. The South's labor force was less dependable and less efficient; large numbers of its active laborers, slave and free, were withdrawn for military work; its farm implements were crude, and irreplaceable in wartime; and it was cut off from its normal markets and sources of capital. Furthermore, the South's advantage in livestock, improved land, and supplies of corn and rice was more apparent than real, as events were swiftly to show. Few Texas cattle were to reach the areas where food was in shortest supply. Control of the Mississippi by the North early in the war and the gradual tightening of the blockade made it difficult, if not impossible, to draw upon the

[1] F. L. Olmstead: *A Journey in the Back Country* (New York, 1860), p. 340.
[2] Schmidt: "Internal Commerce and the Development of National Economy," pp. 604 ff.
[3] C. R. Fish: *The American Civil War* (London, 1937), p. 157.

supplies of Arkansas and Louisiana and to make effective use of surpluses elsewhere, particularly as attrition was reducing the effectiveness of the railroad network. Sheridan's raiders and Sherman's bummers destroyed vast quantities of food and forage and Sherman's living off the land during his march through Georgia, South Carolina, and North Carolina used up additional amounts of food that otherwise would have been available for Lee's famished troops.

The statesmanship of President Lincoln is nowhere better seen than in his efforts to keep the border states in the Union. Their manpower and the strategic advantage that control of their cities, highways, rivers, and railroads would give were of vital importance. The wheat production of the four border states was approximately equal to that of all the seceded states, excluding Virginia; Missouri surpassed all Southern states, save Texas, in numbers of cattle; and the quality of Kentucky cattle was better than that of any Southern state. Finally, both Missouri and Kentucky had more horses and mules than any state in the South. Access to and control of the surplus corn, hogs, horses, and mules of these states would surely have made considerable difference to the South, at least in prolonging the war. As the war dragged on, the leaders of the Confederacy had ample reason to regret that Lincoln had outwitted them in dealing with the people of the border communities.

Both North and South erred in believing that war, if it came, would be short, the North holding that unionist sentiment would soon prevail over the warmongers in the Confederacy and the South counting on the efficacy of King Cotton to win aid abroad. Early planning, therefore, was short-range and took little account of the possibility of a war of several years' duration. True, special efforts to import pork and bacon from the North were made early in 1861 by state authorities, by individuals, and by an official of the Confederate Subsistence Department, which resulted in bringing into the Confederacy the equivalent of 1,200,000 hogs out of a total of 3,000,000 packed in the United States in the 1860–1 season. A second step, taken by the Provisional Congress of the Confederacy, reveals the South's awareness of its dependence on food from the Northwest. In an act of February 18, 1861, the Provisional Congress provided that all foodstuffs previously imported from the Northwest should continue to be admitted to the Confederacy. Among these items were barley, rye, wheat, corn, oats, bacon, pork, beef, flour, and livestock.[4]

Texas, long a major supplier of cattle for the Southern markets, continued to ship and drive cattle to New Orleans after the outbreak of war. Some 38,000 Texas cattle reached New Orleans in the period from the firing on Fort Sumter through December 1861, and 15,000 more came in 1862 before the fall of the city. The figures suggest no acceleration in buying, though the Commissary General, Colonel L. B. Northrop, stated he made every possible effort to get cattle moving eastward. Whether or not he had actually placed orders for as many as 200,000 steers, as he claims, he was greatly handicapped by the failure of the Treasury Department to furnish him with sufficient money to make large purchases and get them under way with advance payments.

Smaller orders were placed and the fall of New Orleans did not stop the drives. A contract made with R. A. Howard of San Antonio on October 25, 1861, which called for 20,000 beeves and involved an expenditure of half a million dollars, may have been the one which began to pay off just a year later when Mississippi papers announced that cattle in droves of 400 to 600 had reached the state. It subsequently appeared that counterfeit Confederate currency was used by the drivers en route, but, as the *Hinds County Gazette* said, "honest men might not try to bring in cattle so great was the danger from Union forces." Texas steers that never saw corn and whose beef was "poor, mean, stringy," without fat enough to make gravy so that "people might think . . . [they] died of disease," continued to cross into Mississippi at Natchez until the town was threatened with destruction if the traffic was not stopped. Hogs also brought from Texas constituted the principal source of meat for the troops which held out so successfully at Port Hudson.[5]

---

[4] O.R., ser. 4, I, 873; *Acts and Resolutions of the First Session of the Provisional Congress of the Confederate States* (Richmond, 1861), p. 41.

[5] *New Orleans Picayune*, 1861–2;

O.R., ser. 4, I, 870, 1101; *Natchez Daily Courier*, Oct. 25, 1861, Nov. 29, 1862, Feb. 4, Mar. 20, July 7, 1863; *Hinds County Gazette*, Sept. 3, Oct. 15, 1862; A. R. Childs (ed.): *The Private*

At the outset of the war planters were of two minds concerning the big surplus of cotton left from the 1860 crop and the new and very large acreage they had sown in 1861. The notion that cotton was King, that by withholding cotton from England and France the South could compel those countries to recognize the Confederacy and come to its aid, was widespread. As the *Charleston Courier* put it, the South could "make the foreign nations who require our cotton . . . our allies against the United States, to put an end to the war which interferes with their necessities and welfare." To bring this about the Confederacy decided to withhold cotton, and steps were taken by the states to ban exports and even to prevent the shipment of cotton from plantations to ports. The scarcity of cotton did not, however, induce the English and the French to grant the aid the South expected. Later, when the South began to exchange its cotton for guns, powder, and other scarce items, including food, by shipping it through the blockade, it found that some of that cotton was getting to the North through Nassau and Bermuda, thus relieving the shortage there to some extent.[6]

War and scarcity abroad were sure to increase the price of cotton, and Southern nationalists feared that the expected price rise would encourage the further production of Indian cotton. The *Southern Cultivator* expressed the belief, long held by some planters and nationalists, that England's desire to free itself of dependence on American cotton by stimulating its production in India was a serious menace to the dominance of the American crop. Such a view showed a lack of appreciation of the superior qualities of American cotton, which, the London *Economist* declared, were so outstanding as to assure for it certain recovery of the market when it was again available in unlimited amounts.[7]

Journal of Henry William Ravenel, 1859–1887 (Columbia, S.C., 1947), p. 136.

[6] *Charleston Courier* in *National Intelligencer*, Aug. 27, 1861. Earlier a writer in *De Bow's Review* (new ser., V, January 1861, 93), had said secession "must necessarily be a peaceful one, because England, France, the rest of commercial Europe, and the western and northwestern States of the Union require that it should be." Also see *Richmond Enquirer*, May 10, 1861; and F. L. Owsley: *King Cotton Diplomacy* (Chicago, 1959), p. 34.

[7] *The Economist*, XX (Jan. 25, 1862), 85. American cotton was longer, stronger, silkier, cleaner. It produced more cloth per pound of fiber, required less twisting for

The *Cultivator* maintained that planters should not abandon cotton entirely since there was little prospect of making money out of foodstuffs, for which, it claimed, cotton land was ill-adapted. Cotton, on the other hand, would enable planters to meet their taxes and other costs and would keep their hands busy as corn and wheat would not. A writer in the *Mobile Advertiser and Register* pointed to the great progress Southern planters had made in the efficiency of their operations. In 1810 it was customary to plant five acres in cotton to the hand, with each hand picking 60 pounds a day and the usual output per hand ranging from 800 to 1,000 pounds of ginned cotton, whereas in 1850–60 ten acres to the hand were common, the usual picking was well over 100 pounds a day, and the output ranged from 2,000 to 2,500 pounds to the hand. This greater efficiency came from the use of improved plows, more and better teams, superior organization, and, as he might have added, better seed. Planters were proud of this improvement and were certain that they could not do as well with other crops.[8]

Southern agricultural leaders were quite troubled about the advisability of planting cotton. Many favored a sharp reduction in cotton in favor of corn but were uncertain whether the change should be required by law. At the Secession Convention of Mississippi in January 1861, a committee was appointed to draft an appeal to planters to curtail production of cotton, and the Southern papers gave some attention to the problem, but generally too late to have much effect that year. Yet aroused Southerners, angry at Lincoln's effort to provision Fort Sumter and his subsequent call for troops, and convinced that the North would try to starve the South into submission, did plant corn extensively and were encouraged by reports that a large crop was expected. Accounts of a 50 per cent increase in the acreage of corn planted and of planters who expected to harvest crops that would be double their year's needs were frequently published, and the *Memphis Appeal* took much pleasure in saying: "It is not at all likely that Southern men will be starved out." It was even said

---

yarn, and could be made into yarn faster.
[8] *Southern Cultivator*, XIX (1861), 104–5; *Mobile Advertiser and Register*, Feb. 14, 1864.

in a dispatch in the *Mark Lane Express*, and copied in the *Genesee Farmer*, that planters had put in such a large acreage of corn and wheat that the army was abundantly supplied and corn was actually being shipped to the West Indies. If there is anything to the story, it was the last time the South could feel so confident of its food supplies.[9]

After the initial war excitement had subsided, leaders turned more seriously to plans for increasing and diversifying food and provision crops. On all sides farmers and planters were urged to raise corn, and some fields that had been planted to cotton were plowed up and put in corn. They were advised to plant peas, to save pea vines, to husband all grass that might be useful for forage, including crab grass, not to neglect turnips, and to give the utmost care to young pigs and to plant, between rows of corn or in orchards, the groundnuts of chufa and peanuts that were relished by hogs.[1]

In anticipation of the 1862 crop, planters were advised that the unsold cotton and tobacco of the previous year threatened, if further supplemented, to depress prices; no more was needed. Corn should be substituted in the Deep South, wheat in Virginia. The legislature of Mississippi, in a resolution of November 1861 deploring the "studied neglect of mixed husbandry heretofore, and too much engrossment in the production of cotton," urged planters to reduce their acreage in cotton by three fourths, to increase the amount of land in grain and grasses, and to give more attention to livestock and fruits. In other states there was much argument concerning the place of cotton in a war economy. Meantime, the Confederate Congress adopted a resolution urging

---

[9] J. K. Bettersworth: *Confederate Mississippi. The People and Policies of a Cotton State in Wartime* (Baton Rouge, La., 1943), pp. 148–9; *Carrollton* (Miss.) *Democrat*, Houma, La., *Civic Guard*, and *Memphis Appeal*, in *New Orleans Price Current*, May 8, 22, 25, 1861; *Atlanta Southern Confederacy*, May 28, Sept. 20, 1861; *Charleston Courier*, Aug. 3, 1861; Barnwell, S.C., *Sentinel*, Aug. 24, 1861; W. H. Russell: *My Diary North and South* (2 vols., Boston, 1863), I, 383; *Genesee Farmer*, 2d ser., XXIII (January 1862), 22.

[1] Executive order of Gov. A. B. Moore, Sept. 26, 1861, Governors' Correspondence, Alabama Dept. of Archives and History; Mrs. C. P. Spencer: *The Last Ninety Days of the War in North Carolina* (New York, 1866), p. 17.

that no cotton be planted in 1862 and gave serious consideration to a measure to prohibit the cultivation of that crop.[2]

By early 1862 newspapers throughout the South had taken up the cry: plant corn. The *Richmond Enquirer* urged that the usual rotation plans be set aside for corn and that the best land be put in this grain, since all that could be raised would be needed. Farmers in areas endangered by Union troops were asked to move their laborers elsewhere to help others produce more. The *Lynchburg Republican*, published in the heart of the tobacco country, advised farmers to concentrate upon the production of corn and oats instead of tobacco until independence was established. "Plant Corn and Be Free, or plant cotton and be whipped," declared the Columbus, Georgia, *Sun*. All the valor of Southern soldiers, it held, "will be powerless against grim hunger and gaunt famine, such as will overwhelm us if we insanely raise Cotton instead of corn." Alabama papers pointed out that those who planted cotton crippled the resources of the country; one writer held that planters who insisted on raising their usual crop of cotton were meaner than the meanest Yankee, guilty of treason, and should be hanged. In the planting season of 1862 the *Charleston Courier* gave almost as much space to advice to farmers and planters— telling them what crops they should cultivate in place of cotton— as it did to war news. Where cotton or tobacco had already been planted, it was urged that the crops be destroyed or plowed under, either voluntarily by the planter or by his neighbors.[3]

Perhaps H. H. Parks, writing in the *Columbus Times*, best summarized the need for concentrating on provision crops. Southern food production in 1861 was the largest ever known, but it was not more than half of what was needed. The wheat crop had been fine, but nearly all the wheat then at the mills came from Missouri, Kentucky, and Tennessee, which could no longer be counted on for further aid. Meat available in the Con-

---

[2] Atlanta *Southern Confederacy*, Oct. 21, Dec. 28, 1861; J. K. Bettersworth (ed.): *Mississippi in the Confederacy as They Saw It* (Baton Rouge, La., 1961), p. 216. Owsley: *King Cotton Diplomacy*, p. 45, maintains that these early measures were designed more as part of the effort to induce Eng-

land and France to aid the South.
[3] *Richmond Enquirer*, Mar. 3, Apr. 4, 1862; *Lynchburg Republican*, May 10, 1862; *Charleston Courier*, Mar. 18, 22, 25, 27, 28, 29, 31, Apr. 8, 1862; *Southern Cultivator*, XX (March–April 1862), 72, 77, quoting the *Tuscaloosa Observer* and the *Montgomery Advertiser*.

federacy was no more than half the requirement and a large amount was damaged. Cotton was not needed; in fact, it was a liability. Therefore, plant corn! A Confederate-subsidized organ in London, which exchanged material with Southern papers, remarked that it was criminally remiss to plant cotton, for only by vastly increased production of grain and forage could the South raise more hogs and cattle and thereby enlarge the supplies of bacon and beef and leather for shoes. William Ravenel was pessimistic about the food situation. On March 21 he confided in his diary that with Tennessee, Missouri, and the Northwest— "our granary"—cut off from the South, and with grain-growing parts of North Carolina in the hands of the enemy, and Virginia and Maryland harassed by marching armies, the Confederacy might be faced with famine unless the planters of the Deep South concentrated on corn and hay. He was gratified to note that planters were aware of the needs and were curtailing their cotton crop.[4]

Patriotic Southerners were not inclined to leave it up to the individual planters to decide how much land should be shifted from cotton to provisions. Governor Joseph E. Brown of Georgia urged residents of his state to double their usual corn crop, increase their land in potatoes, triple the usual acreage planted to beets, peas, and other vegetables, give close attention to their hogs and cattle, and plant cotton only for domestic use. Meetings were held in principal cotton-growing areas and fiery speeches were delivered in condemnation of those planters who did not cooperate by reducing their acreage in cotton. Moreover, publicity was given to planters who had turned chiefly to corn—such as T. M. Furlow, an "intelligent and patriotic Senator from Sumter County," who declared that he would place 1,200 acres in corn and only 20 acres in cotton, and Colonel Leonidas A. Jordan of Baldwin County, cited as the largest cotton planter in the state, whose usual crop was 2,000 bales and who now intended to cover his extensive plantations with grain and other food crops.[5]

Where admonitions and publicity proved insufficient, legal

---

[4] *Columbus Times*, Mar. 14, 1862; *The Index* (London), May 15, 1862; Childs: *The Private Journal of Henry William Ravenel*, p. 129.

[5] *Southern Cultivator*, XX (March–April 1862), 68; *Milledgeville Recorder* in *Charleston Courier*, Mar. 20, 1862.

measures were adopted. The Arkansas legislature decreed that no person should plant or cultivate more than two acres in cotton to the hand and made violation of the measure a misdemeanor subject to a fine of from $500 to $5,000. The Georgia legislature tried to limit the acreage in cotton to three acres for each hand between the ages of 15 and 55 and to three acres for each two hands under 15 or over 55. The governor was instructed to transmit a copy of the measure to the chief executive of every cotton-growing state in the hope that the act would be widely copied. South Carolina followed Georgia's example, establishing a ratio of three acres of short-staple cotton and one and a half acres of long-staple cotton to each hand between 15 and 45 years of age; for slaves between 12 and 15 and 55 and 65 the ratio was half that for prime slaves. Alabama tried a different expedient by imposing a tax of ten cents a pound on all seed cotton over 2,500 pounds to the full hand, and Mississippi levied a tax of five cents per pound on seed cotton after exempting 500 pounds of ginned cotton per laborer. Virginia, where the pressure on the food supply was felt most severely, experimented with restrictive legislation by establishing a maximum of 2,500 tobacco plants for each hand of 16 to 55 years and 80,000 for any plantation, but allowed each person to have at least 10,000 plants. Texas, revealing an attitude that was later to be characteristic of that state, could not bring itself to tell "a man what he should not plant."[6]

Throughout the Confederacy corn was substituted for tobacco, cotton, and sugar cane on a large scale. Only in Texas, the most remote of the Confederate states, where opportunities for trading across the line were numerous, was cotton planted in substantial amounts, if not in the same proportion as earlier. Texas planters were required to turn in to the army one half their cotton to be used "for items essential for the war effort." Colonel Fremantle, crossing the state from Brownsville via San Antonio and Houston in 1863, commented on the many cotton and corn

---

[6] Act of Mar. 21, 1862, *Laws of Arkansas*, 1862, p. 8; Act of Dec. 11, 1862, *Laws of Georgia*, 1862, p. 5; *National Intelligencer*, Mar. 17, 1863; *Mobile Advertiser and Register*, Mar. 22, 1863; Betters-worth: *Confederate Mississippi*, p. 152; Act of Mar. 12, 1863, *Acts of the General Assembly of Virginia*, Adjourned session, 1863, p. 70; *Austin State Gazette*, Feb. 11, Mar. 4, 1863.

fields he passed and was told that land in cotton had been cut to one third.[7]

However, not all the advice offered to farmers called for the sharp contraction or complete abandonment of cotton and tobacco for the duration of the war. The *Richmond Enquirer* and the Augusta, Georgia, *Chronicle & Sentinel* argued that both tobacco and cotton should be planted to give employment to the Negroes and to keep a supply of seed, as older seed would not germinate. An editor of the only Southern farm journal to survive the war declared that the cultivation of corn, a four months' labor crop, left the Negroes, horses, and other capital idle, "eating their heads off," for much of the year.[8]

Though dissent continued to be voiced against contracting the acreage in cotton, the tide of opinion in support of the policy forced those who disagreed to take evasive action. One practice was to plant corn along the highways and railroad lines while putting in cotton well back where prying eyes might not see what was being done. The *Mobile Advertiser and Register,* an ardent supporter of sharp reduction of cotton planting, condemned this practice, declaring that no one could conceal his cupidity and grasping acquisitiveness.[9]

Best known of those who insisted on planting cotton, not corn, no matter what the need, were Robert Toombs, Colonel A. P. Rood, and other owners of plantations on the Chattahoochee, who were "influenced by Avarice" rather than by patriotism. The committee of public safety of Cuthbert, Georgia, expressed "unqualified indignation" at the failure of these planters to increase their production of food crops and requested that they withdraw their Negroes from the cotton fields and place them in charge of the committee to superintend the defense of the river. A similar committee of Eufaula, Alabama, on the other side of the Chattahoochee, adopted a like resolution. Toombs, replying to the charges of the "cowardly miscreants," refused to give them a single hand. His insistence on planting cotton in the face of ad-

---

[7] *Houston Daily Telegraph,* July 20, 1864; Lieut-Col. Fremantle: *Three Months in the Southern States* (New York, 1864), p. 62.
[8] *Richmond Enquirer,* Mar. 6, 1862; Augusta *Chronicle & Sen-*tinel in *Southern Cultivator,* XX (January 1862), 10–11, 13.
[9] Mar. 26, 1863. The *Advertiser and Register* gave much attention to the scarcity of food in Mobile in 1862 and 1863.

verse public opinion was an expression of his dislike of the use of government to coerce individuals, but his action was later said to be his greatest political liability.[1]

Charles Allen, a well-to-do Mississippi planter who lived some twenty-five miles from Vicksburg and had 121 slaves, has left interesting data in his diary concerning the way he adapted himself to wartime needs. In 1860 he planted 200 acres in corn and 566 in cotton after manuring his land with cow dung and guano and harvested "splendid corn" averaging 32 bushels to the acre. His cotton yield of 375 bales does not indicate equal success with that crop. In 1861 he planted 220 acres in corn and 566 in cotton but had to replant some cotton, lost considerable from the cotton worm, and produced only 245 bales. In late 1861 meat was becoming scarce, his hogs were in danger of being stolen, and he was increasing the molasses ration in place of other food. A new venture was the marketing of hay. In 1862 he planted 430 acres in corn and 300 in cotton. Lack of salt made it impossible to dress off his hogs at the normal time and instead he had to kill them one at a time and consume the pork and bacon before it spoiled. The burning of cotton was a live issue and when orders came to burn all in the vicinity of the Mississippi he and other planters protested, but without effect. In 1863 he planted 235 acres in corn and smaller amounts in peas, potatoes, and other vegetables, and made no mention of cotton, but he no longer had the full use of his slaves, as a portion of them were impressed for work on fortifications in Vicksburg. As late as April 7, he was still spreading manure on his land but soon was

---

[1] *Mobile Tribune* in *Clarke County Democrat,* Sept. 18, 1862; *National Intelligencer,* July 1, 1862; Toombs to George Hill and others, June 11, 1862, U. B. Phillips: "The Correspondence of Robert Toombs, Alexander H. Stephens and Howell Cobb," American Historical Association, *Annual Report, 1911* (2 vols., Washington, 1913), II, 595. Joseph E. Brown, Milledgeville, Mar. 16, 1863, to Stephens, *ibid.,* p. 614. Toombs thought Governor Brown had "done some very foolish things" in attempting to restrict whiskey production and to cut down on cotton planting. These showed that he had "a want of knowledge of the first principles of political economy." In using unconstitutional powers "he is running a fool's race with Davis . . . robbing the sick and oppressing the poor. . . . Extortion is a crime against God and man; punish that and let the production and distribution of wealth alone. Producers have nothing to do with morality." *Ibid.,* p. 609.

hiding his remaining cotton in a swamp, packing up his pictures and books for removal, shipping off eighteen Negroes to work in the iron mines in Alabama, and looking for a safer place on which to employ the balance of his hands.

Allen's records reveal the gradual tightening of the Federal pincers in Mississippi. Salt, cotton cloth, osnaburgs, shoes, corn, and guano were becoming hard to find and the women turned to spinning and weaving. Allen sold some hay and logs, exchanged pork for cloth, and probably received some income from the hire of his hands, though he was reluctant to let them go, for he knew they were given better care on his own plantation than in the iron mines, on defense construction, or at the saltworks.[2]

In 1862 Georgia's comptroller compiled statistics of the land in corn, other grain, and cotton which provide some indication of the change the war had brought to agriculture by this early date. He found 4,349,080 acres of land in corn, 1,349,417 acres in other grain—wheat, rye, oats, and barley—and 236,198 acres in cotton. He estimated that the land in cotton would produce 125 pounds of the ginned staple to the acre, which would make the crop about one seventh of that of 1860. Corn, which yielded 16 bushels to the acre in 1849, might average 12½ bushels, but he thought it would be nearer 14 bushels. His final estimate of the crop was 55,000,000 bushels as compared with a little over 30,000,000 bushels in both 1849 and 1859. The comptroller's estimates were quite out of line with later information. That cotton planting was down, none would deny, but by somewhat less than two thirds, not by six sevenths. Moreover, the comptroller's prediction that the acreage in corn, which was also generously estimated, would yield from 12½ to 14 bushels to the acre was well in excess of figures suggested by members of the Georgia Senate, which ranged from a low of 5 to a high of 10 bushels to the acre.[3]

If the more cautious estimates of the yield of corn in Georgia

---

[2] Plantation book of Charles Allen, in Mississippi State Archives.
[3] Atlanta *Southern Confederacy*, Nov. 1, 1862; Milledgeville *Southern Recorder*, Jan. 9, 1863. The *Memphis Daily Appeal* of Atlanta, May 15, 1864, announced that the amount of land in wheat, corn, and potatoes in 1862 was only 3,000,000 acres, which was the same as 1860. Cf. *Charleston Courier*, Aug. 23, 1862.

have any validity, and they do seem to be closer to general average figures, it may be concluded that the state had not sufficiently increased its output to meet the needs of the Confederacy. This was the opinion of a writer in the Mobile *Advertiser and Register* of March 18, 1863. Though his estimates do not add up correctly, he arrived at the conclusion that the eleven Southern states needed to produce 480,000,000 bushels of corn to provide the essential amount of meal, bacon, and beef for human consumption and for horses, mules, and oxen. Comparing this with the 277,000,000 bushels produced in 1860 suggests that a 70 per cent increase in corn was essential. It should be remembered that by 1862 not only were corn imports from the Northwest, Kentucky, and Missouri mostly shut off but Arkansas, much of Tennessee, and part of the grain-growing portions of Virginia were overrun by the Northern forces or were so close to the lines as to be put out of active farming. The conclusion of the *Advertiser* was that every planter should put in ten acres of corn for each hand.[4]

If agriculture in the South was going through a major change in shifting from the basic staples which had constituted such a large part of American exports to grain, forage, and livestock, it was making the change under trying conditions that grew worse as the Union armies advanced. Local iron foundries, forges, and small-implement factories had provided some of the simple plows, harrows, shovels, hoes, rakes, corn shellers, and other tools of farming used in the South, although more of these tools had come from the North. Whatever the source, forges and foundries now had to concentrate upon implements of war, not implements for farmers. Particularly needed on Southern farms were plows, plow points, scythes, axes, spades, corn shellers, nails, carpenter's tools, and baling materials. Tools were so scarce and so expensive that some were brought through the blockade. Small farmers had to learn to do without or to get along with dull, broken, or inefficient implements. Planters who had forges and skilled operatives could improvise longer, but when their

---

[4] An estimate that makes sense gave 330,000,000 bushels of corn in 1862 as compared with 279,000,000 in 1859, or much less than the *Advertiser and Register* thought necessary. *Memphis Daily Appeal*, May 15, 1864.

supply of iron was exhausted all they could do was to sharpen dull hoes, scythes, axes, and shovels. Southern agriculture, never efficient, became less so as implements deteriorated.[5]

Labor problems on farms and plantations became increasingly serious until they were impossible to solve. Most of the effective white boys and men between eighteen and fifty were inducted into the army, if they were not exempt because of public office or because they were managing plantations with twenty or more Negroes. In the North, laborsaving machines helped replace farm labor but such machines were not available in the South. The Negroes remained at work on most plantations away from marching armies well after their emancipation had been proclaimed, but where military raids were being made the Negroes were carried off or induced to leave in large numbers. Furthermore, it was found necessary to draft slaves from plantations to aid in constructing the defenses of Savannah, Mobile, and many other places. Howell Cobb complained to the Secretary of War in August 1862 that Negroes were being impressed to work on Savannah fortifications just when they were needed to harvest corn, fodder, and other provisions. The hands might or might not be returned when the work had been accomplished, but all such drafts, combined with seductions and runaways, contributed to the demoralization of farming operations. Farmers suffered particularly from the loss of horses and mules—the result of impressment, theft, or patriotic contribution to the armies. Crops planted late, cultivation neglected, slow harvesting, and early frosts and late rains all contributed to damage or destroy crops that might have been saved with more reliable hands.[6]

On the plantations and farms, agriculture had been geared to the production of a major cash crop, whether tobacco, rice, cotton, or sugar cane. With each of these crops Negroes could be employed, in an inefficient way it is true, but throughout the year; whereas corn, wheat, and forage crops required less attention, did not use the labor of the Negroes as constantly, and, it may be added, were not well adapted to the use of slave labor. While the North was improving and extensively introducing

---

[5] Milledgeville *Southern Recorder,* Jan. 21, 1862; *Richmond Whig,* Mar. 31, 1864.

[6] Howell Cobb, Aug. 5, 1862, to the Secretary of War, O.R., ser. 4, II, 35.

drills, harrows, cultivators, mowers, and reapers, the South continued to rely on manual labor to accomplish most of the work on its farms. A considerable portion of the corn was grown as food for hogs and cattle, to which farmers were being urged to give greater care so as to increase their numbers. But hogs and cattle, unlike tobacco, cotton, rice, and sugar cane, were an invitation to depredations, being much sought after by Negroes and marauding bands of stragglers from both sides.

Serious harm was done to the Southern war effort and to the food supply of the South by the scarcity of salt. Before the war salt had come largely from England. Some salt had been produced in the Confederacy and every effort was made to develop new supplies, but Northern raids reduced the output and the need was never adequately met. Abundant evidence exists that quantities of insufficiently salted meat spoiled and that army horses, domestic livestock, and human beings alike suffered from the lack of salt.[7]

Since the larger part of the planters' capital was invested in slaves, they naturally did everything possible to prevent them from falling into Union hands or becoming influenced by the Federals. Early in the war, as danger neared, planters began moving their slaves to safer locations where they might be immune from seizure and less inclined to flee. When Northern troops made their raids on the Sea Islands off the coast of South Carolina and Georgia, some planters succeeded in moving their hands inland, where they hoped to find land on which to use their labor. Upcountry Georgia and parts of Florida soon were so flooded with transplanted slaves that the governors of these states, fearing insurrection, forbade further immigration. With the capture of New Orleans, slaves on the great sugar and cotton plantations of the Mississippi Delta were started up the Red River and treked overland to Texas. The English Colonel Fremantle, touring from Brownsville, Texas, to New York in 1863, found the road through northern Louisiana "alive with Negroes, who are being 'run' into Texas. . . . We must have met hundreds of them and many families of planters," trying to save their prop-

---

[7] Ella Lonn: *Salt as a Factor in the Confederacy* (New York, 1933), p. 40 and *passim*.

erty from capture. The "mass exodus of planters and Negroes" mounting into the thousands from the Teche region of Louisiana into Texas was noted.

Other planters took their slaves to what they thought were safe regions in Georgia, Alabama, and Louisiana. Even Governor Joseph E. Brown had to take time off in January 1864 to go to southwestern Georgia to arrange for a place to which his Negroes could be moved. Each success of the Federals started new movements of planters and slaves. States benefiting most from these flights from the older Confederate states were Texas and Florida, which were the only Southern commonwealths to have any substantial growth in the sixties.[8] The movement of Federal troops into eastern North Carolina led to the flight of thousands of Negroes with their owners into the interior, leaving provisions behind which were needed to support them. Planters were urged to bring out their corn and livestock, but their panic as well as their lack of wagons made this difficult.[9]

At the same time, the "tide of exiles and refugees" setting in toward Richmond, Charleston, Columbia, Savannah, and Augusta added seriously to the pressure on the cities' already meager food supplies. By the second year of the war it was said that the floating population of Richmond equaled its regular inhabitants, and the tide was still flowing strongly. All such movements left productive land behind which could ill be spared, and the migration to new areas and use of the slaves in creating new farms never compensated for this loss.[1]

[8] *Charleston Courier*, Nov. 6, 1862; Frances Fearn: *Diary of a Refugee* (New York, 1910), pp. 14 ff.; Fremantle: *Three Months in the Southern States*, pp. 87 ff.; J. D. Bragg: *Louisiana in the Confederacy* (Baton Rouge, La., 1941), pp. 150, 217, 300; J. C. Sitterson: *Sugar Country: The Cane Sugar Industry in the South, 1753–1950* (Lexington, Ky., 1953), p. 215; Bettersworth: *Confederate Mississippi*, p. 173; F. M. Brodie: *Thaddeus Stevens: Scourge of the South* (New York, 1959), p. 235; M. E. Massey: *Refugee Life in the Confederacy* (Baton Rouge, La.,

1964), *passim;* Phillips: "Correspondence," p. 632.

[9] A. J. Battle, Nov. 12, 1862, to Gov. Vance, Governors' Correspondence, North Carolina Archives; *North Carolina Standard*, Oct. 10, 28, 31, 1862. The *Standard* declared that the twelve counties being threatened by the Federals had produced 4,500,000 bushels of corn in 1859 and great quantities of pork, beef, and mutton.

[1] S. A. Putnam: *Richmond during The Confederacy* (New York, 1961), p. 320.

Further migration and demoralization resulted from General John C. Pemberton's plea that families leave Vicksburg before the city became surrounded by Federals and from the urgent appeal of the governor of Alabama in February 1864 that noncombatants, women, and children leave Mobile before the expected attack. Equally important was General William T. Sherman's order, preparatory to the destruction of Atlanta, that the people leave the city. Each such migration added to relief burdens in the areas to which the refugees went, and it proved difficult to adapt the refugees to productive use elsewhere.[2]

It is not easy to appraise the effect on Southern agriculture of the estimated 400,000 people who were driven out of Kentucky, Missouri, Tennessee, and elsewhere and who sought refuge in the diminishing portion of the South which remained free of invaders and loyal to the Confederacy. Included in this number were doubtless many whites who served in the Southern army and many slaves who, once they had been settled upon farms, could again produce essential foodstuffs. But the migration of such large numbers of people created additional pressure on the diminishing supply of food, and even where they settled down to farming again, it was with diminished interest and capability. A recent student of Florida in the Confederacy concluded that the refugee farmer usually became little more than a subsistence farmer, "forced to survive as much by his wits as by his means."[3]

Other factors tending to cripple agriculture and lead to further government controls were the steady disintegration of the transportation system, the failure to establish a unified policy of operation and a system of priorities of use, the growing feeling, bitterly entertained by many, that it was the small farmer who

---

[2] *Vicksburg Daily Whig*, Feb. 5, 1863; *Mobile Advertiser and Register*, Feb. 16, 1864. In her very fine study of *Refugee Life in The Confederacy*, which quite refutes Page Smith's animadversions against the intensive kind of research being done in academic circles today, Massey offers practically no statistics of the number of refugees within the Confederacy, but in her final sentence she mentions: "Tens of thousands of . . . Southerners voluntarily displaced themselves and floundered around the contracting Confederacy for months and years, but they paid a high price for the privilege" (p. 282).

[3] Mobile *Advertiser and Register*, Nov. 1, 1863; J. E. Johns: *Florida during the Civil War* (Gainesville, Fla., 1963), p. 147.

was doing most of the fighting and whose family back home was suffering the most from inadequate food, and the virtual civil war within a Civil War between the Unionists and Confederates in eastern Tennessee and parts of North Carolina and Georgia.

At the end of 1862 the South could feel that it had not done at all badly in resisting Northern military advances, despite the loss of New Orleans, Nashville, and some coastal points. It had also made progress in the hard struggle to convert a plantation economy into a self-sufficient one. But there was much to worry its leaders in the increasing effectiveness of the blockade and the possibility that the Confederacy might be starved into submission.

2

Shortages and Inflation

GENERAL SCOTT'S ANACONDA PLAN for crushing the South by a naval blockade of its ports, conquest of the Mississippi, and the movement of enveloping armies by land was regarded by Confederates as a plan to starve the Confederacy into submission. The strategy of starvation, so it was held, included the capture or closing of the Atlantic and Gulf ports, establishment of control on the Mississippi, retention of the border states which had abundant supplies of food on which the South had long drawn, early conquest of Tennessee, the leading corn-producing state, and the cutting of rail connections with the lower South. Few Southerners, however, believed that the Confederacy could be starved into submission. Thus writers in the *Charleston Courier* and *De Bow's Review* maintained that "Lincoln's humbug of a blockade" never could achieve its objective because of the South's abundant supply of food.[1]

---

[1] J. D. Gladney, Aug. 6, 1862, to Jefferson Davis, *O.R.*, ser. 4, II, 39. It was this plan to starve the South into submission, some Confederates believed, that caused Stanton and others to refuse to exchange prisoners, preferring to leave Union prisoners in Andersonville to "eat Confederate corn," though "thousands of their own men starved and rotted with scurvy." Edward Younger (ed.): *Inside the Confederate Government. The Diary of Robert Garlick Hill Kean* (New York, 1957), p. 230; *Charleston Courier*, July 29, 1861; *De Bow's Review*, cited in *Richmond Enquirer*, Oct. 11, 1861; E. M. Coulter: "The Movement for Agricultural Reorganization in the Cotton South during the Civil War," *Agricultural History*, I (January 1927), 16.

Provisions in abundance existed in some parts of the South throughout the war but in other parts they became increasingly scarce. From the army came reports in 1863 that it was living on quarter rations of meat, that the artillery horses were in poor condition because of reduced rations (Douglas Freeman's expression was "this slow starvation of the horses"), and that numerous cases of dysentery had occurred, partly as the result of the wet season and partly from the scanty and unwholesome food. Even as early as November 1862, officials of the Commissary Department were troubled about the scarcity of wheat in Virginia, the drought which had seriously reduced the forage so that the cattle were too thin to slaughter, and the inadequate supply of fresh beef for the army of Virginia.[2]

To prevent attention being given to disasters, military or otherwise, that might shake the confidence of people in their leaders and encourage peace sentiment, Southern newspapers subjected themselves to voluntary censorship which was more rigid than the censorship imposed in the North. Even individuals writing relatives or friends about food scarcities, the half rations of soldiers, or the lack of green vegetables were cautious about revealing the plight of the people. "Don't mention this, as it will do harm to let it get abroad," said Senator Clement C. Clay, when writing about the near starvation which prevailed in Richmond in 1863. Southern newspapers frequently denied that food was scarce, yet at the same time editors did their utmost to induce farmers to raise an ever greater volume of provisions. Although the shortage of food was not admitted in the public press as a rule, references to it can be found. The steps taken to provide aid for the poor through control of prices and extensive public and private relief are in themselves evidence of the critical food situation in certain areas.[3]

---

[2] *Richmond Whig*, Mar. 20, 1863; *Atlanta Commonwealth* in *Charleston Courier*, July 24, 1863; D. S. Freeman: *R. E. Lee* (4 vols., New York, 1935), III, 252; L. B. Northrop, Nov. 3, 1862, to G. W. Randolph, and F. G. Ruffin, Nov. 3, 1862, to Northrop, *O.R.*, ser. 4, II, 158.

[3] *Nashville Dispatch*, May 5, July 10, 1863; *Lynchburg Republican*, Jan. 28, 1865; Mrs. C. C. Clay: *A Belle of the Fifties. Memoirs of Mrs. Clay of Alabama* (New York, 1905), p. 194. In his *Thirteen Months in the Rebel Army* (New York, 1862), pp. 135–7, W. G. Stevenson said: "The Confederate authorities have complete control of the press, so that nothing is

Planters and farmers increasingly concentrated their operations on provision crops during 1862, despite the general fear that these would not prove as profitable as their usual staple crops. Yet their uncertainty about what their neighbors were doing and their desire to profit from increasing prices for cotton tended to make the changeover somewhat less than was hoped or needed.

Charges were common in 1861 that not all planters were doing their part in meeting the South's pressing need for food. When restrictive legislation was adopted in late 1862 and 1863 limiting cotton planting to three or four acres to the hand, a critic in the *Charleston Mercury* calling himself "Clodhopper" (but who, readers were informed by the editor, was a distinguished citizen) declared that planters were not living up to the spirit of the law, for they selected their best acres for the staple, put all their manure on them, and gave them "garden culture," to the neglect of corn and other grain. Clodhopper maintained that the ratio of cotton planted to the hand should have been one-half acre, but he announced that, after making an analysis of the difficulties facing the planter, he had decided to plant one acre to the hand. That some planters were embarrassed and perhaps ashamed of the amount of cotton they had put in is seen in a news item about hundreds of acres in the staple being plowed up and planted to corn.[4]

Another *Mercury* writer put the cotton-corn issue and planter management even more concretely. Consider, he said, a plantation with 50 hands where ordinarily 15 acres were planted to the hand. Of these, 450 would be in cotton and 300 in corn. All the manure and the cotton seed would be put on the corn land, which would make 10 bushels to the acre or 3,000 bushels. But in the current year (1863) planters had selected their best land for cotton and put all the manure on it. On such a plantation 600 acres of the worst land would be put in corn and would yield 4 to 5 bushels to the acre or 3,000 bushels—just enough to pro-

---

ever allowed to appear in print which can give information to the North or dishearten their own men. . . . if a Southern paper would publish such information of their movements, as do the Northern of theirs, the editor's neck would not be safe for an hour."

[4] *Tri-Weekly Mercury*, Feb. 28, Apr. 21, 1863.

vide for domestic consumption with none to spare. But on the 150 acres in cotton, by careful husbandry the planter might make only slightly less cotton than formerly.[5]

Though the statistics of cotton production in the South do not bear out the charge that planters ignored the need of their section for grain, the reiteration of the charge at least reveals suspicion and distrust. Even Susan Dabney Smedes in her highly romantic account of her father, Thomas Dabney of Hinds County, Mississippi, who owned or managed a number of plantations on which there were more than 500 slaves and who was himself a Unionist before the war, declared that while Dabney insisted on putting all his land into corn, his neighbors planted half cotton crops. A young Louisiana officer told his father that "planting or not planting cotton" was a major topic of discussion in the army, with the officers being about equally divided on the question. He recommended that his father plant all the cotton he could cultivate.[6]

The most severe indictment of planter management came from L. B. Northrop, Commissary General. He charged that on his way to a conference with Governors Joseph E. Brown of Georgia, John G. Shorter of Alabama, and Zebulon B. Vance of North Carolina to consider problems of production and distribution, he passed through one of the best corn areas of Georgia but found not one in five acres in corn or being prepared for it. The production of wheat, he feared, would not be half as great as had been anticipated. Restrictive measures which permitted planters to clear fresh land and put it into cotton while raising corn on worn-out land were indefensible. Famine threatened, he contended, unless more effective controls were introduced and larger crops of grain assured. At this conference General Braxton Bragg presented three proposals for use of governmental powers to put farming on a complete war basis. The first called for a presidential proclamation prohibiting the planting of either cotton or tobacco or the use of labor to clear new land, which was

---

[5] *Tri-Weekly Mercury*, Apr. 16, 1863; P. F. Walker: *Vicksburg. A People at War, 1860–1865* (Chapel Hill, N.C., 1960), p. 134.
[6] F. M. Green (ed.): *Memorials of a Southern Planter*, by S. D. Smedes (New York, 1965), pp. 181–2; F. P. Connor: "Letters of Lieutenant Robert H. Miller to His Family, 1861–1862," *Virginia Magazine of History and Biography*, LXX (January, 1962), 66.

generally put in cotton. The second provided for a proclamation requiring every planter to put a certain amount of his cultivated land in corn and other grains. The third proposal was that the state governments should operate the plantations. It was the last proposal which Northrop, driven by the increasing difficulties of providing minimum—even substandard—rations for the army and aware of food scarcity in Richmond and other points, came to favor, although he probably did not believe that he could persuade Jefferson Davis to support such drastic action.[7]

Governor Brown, who was sensitive about any threat to state powers, was quite willing to tighten restrictive measures on planter management by making it "highly penal" to plant more than a quarter acre in cotton to the hand. It was deplorable, he felt, that producers, anxious to make a little more money, would plant the last seed allowed by law without realizing how they were endangering the liberties of the people by failing to raise more provisions. Similarly, Governor Shorter felt that the Alabama statute did not exert sufficient pressure upon planters to turn to food crops. The North, in its effort to starve the South into submission, was ravaging or gaining control of much of the South's productive area and to offset this he urged closer restriction of the land in cotton and generous treatment of slaves to get them to produce more grain.

Virginia patriots were hard put to know what to do about planting tobacco. It was clear in early 1863 that greater efforts must be made to produce wheat and corn or the South would be starved into submission. Reluctantly, then, the *Richmond Whig* came to the conclusion that all planting of tobacco in Virginia and North Carolina should be interdicted by the states. War's necessity thus brought conservatives to support far-reaching interference in the private affairs of individuals. In the same issue, however, the *Whig* fulminated against evidences of "Yankee Despotism" in the North.

In the absence of drastic state action to limit the planting of cotton and tobacco and to require large-scale grain planting,

---

[7] L. B. Northrop, Apr. 25, 1863, to J. A. Seddon, *National Intelligencer,* Nov. 12, 1863.

the Congress of the Confederacy tried to grapple with the issue in 1862. Senator A. G. Brown of Mississippi proposed a measure that would have prohibited the production of more than three bales of cotton plus one for each plantation hand employed in cultivation. In presenting this proposal Brown said he was ready to go even further and advocate burning all Southern cotton and raising no more until it could be sold. Opposition on constitutional grounds prevented action, however. In 1863 the Congress merely adopted a resolution declaring that many people thought the war was near an end and were turning back to cotton and tobacco planting, but that they should "subordinate the hope of gain to the certain good of the country" by planting only food crops. Regulations affecting land use and the degree to which nonfood staples could be raised were left to the states, in accordance with the views of the more extreme states' rights advocates.[8]

Plantation and farm management was becoming involved with other questions of profound importance for the Confederacy. Conscription, which in the North was to produce so much bitterness, class feeling, hatred of the Negro, and draft riots, had serious consequences in the South also. The exemption of a white man for every twenty slaves owned was easy to justify on the grounds that planters had to have overseers who would keep the Negroes under control, but this provision enabled planters to keep one or more sons out of the army and led to the oft-repeated charge that those who had precipitated the war were evading their obligations to fight in it. Another method by which men of influence could gain exemption for themselves or their sons was to secure appointment to a Confederate or state post. As the burden of supplying the army grew, the government needed increasing numbers of civilian employees, all of whom were exempt from military service. Many of these employees were regarded

---

[8] *Richmond Whig*, Feb. 20, 1863; *Mobile Advertiser and Register*, Mar. 22, 1863; Augusta *Chronicle & Sentinel*, Mar. 18, 1864; "Proceedings of the First Confederate Congress," *Southern Historical Society Papers*, XLIV (June 1923), 147–8; *Statutes-at-Large of the Confederate States* (Richmond, 1863), p. 166; W. B. Yearns: *The Confederate Congress* (Athens, Ga., 1960), p. 131.

by the public as supernumeraries who held their posts solely to avoid service.

Not only were planters able to gain exemption for themselves and their sons, but they were accused of refusing to allow their Negroes to be used for defense work. People said that the planters talked much about patriotism and loyalty as well as about the pernicious encroachments of the Confederate government upon the just powers of the states, but that they were glad to have army service chiefly done by the independent farmer class. It was, said many of the latter with deep bitterness, a rich man's war but a poor man's fight.[9]

By 1862 and 1863 these criticisms were affecting the morale of many in the army. Confederate soldiers complained about the inadequacy of their rations, about their allowance, which had so little value because of inflation, about conscription that allowed exemption to privileged groups. One soldier, on returning home after eleven months' absence in the army, reported that his family could not buy bread or corn and charged that planters were shipping grain to cities where they could get better prices. He was troubled that a farmer who never had employed an overseer was able to declare his son an overseer and thus keep him out of military service. A rigorous enforcement of conscription with "prominent, rich and influential men being swept into the ranks" would tend to allay the growing feeling of discontent, said a Mississippi correspondent of Jefferson Davis.

A few bitter criticisms directed at planters who held their grain for excessively high prices, at speculators who bought essential items for modest prices and held them for rises, and at draft evaders were allowed to appear in some papers. The *Mobile News* had a particularly sharp editorial condemning speculators:

> Alas, poor human frailty! Excited by the reports of sudden fortunes realised upon small means, urged on by greed and love of gain, eminent physicians, distingushed lawyers and politicians, liberal and hospitable planters, high minded

---

[9] Thomas North: *Five Years in Texas; or What You Did Not Hear during the War . . . in Texas and Mexico* (Cincinnati, 1871), p. 167; *Memphis Appeal* (Atlanta), Nov. 14, 1863; *Army Argus and Crisis* (Mobile), Jan. 14, 1865; A. B. Moore: *Conscription and Conflict in the Confederacy* (New York, 1924), pp. 70 ff.

merchants, lowered the high standards of Southern chivalry, out-Jewed Jews, out-traded the sharp Yankee trader, and descended from that exalted position known on earth —Southern gentlemen—to become nothing better than common hucksters.

The *Hillsborough Recorder* of North Carolina (May 7, 1862), under the caption "Who Are the Traitors" excoriated those who lived at home in ease and comfort, speculating in corn, leather, bacon, and whiskey, who transported corn out of the state when it was needed at home, who paid farmers low prices for hides but charged fantastically for the finished shoes, who in their cotton factories paid their workers low wages but sold their cloth at inflated levels.[1]

Governor Brown, who has not been treated altogether kindly by historians because he insisted on carrying the doctrine of states' rights to its logical extreme, came close to stating the concept of a rich man's war and a poor man's fight in a message to the legislature of Georgia on April 6, 1863:

> The armies of the Confederate States are composed, in a great degree, of poor men and non-slaveholders, who have but little property. . . . Upon their labor their families at home have depended for support, as they have no slaves to work for them. They receive from the Government but *eleven dollars per month*, in depreciated currency, which, at the present high prices, will purchase very little of the necessaries of life. The consequence is, that the wives of thousands of them are now obliged to work daily in the field to make bread. . . . Many are living upon bread alone, and feel the most painful apprehension lest the time may come when enough even of this cannot be afforded them. . . . A large proportion of the wealthy class . . . have avoided the fevers of the camp and the dangers of the battle field. . . .

The governor's only proposal to relieve these inequities, however, was to ask for an increase in the soldiers' pay to $20 a month, likewise in depreciated currency. At about the same time, green

---

[1] *Richmond Enquirer*, Mar. 31, 1863; *Mobile News*, Aug. 29, 1863; *Natchez Weekly Courier*, May 20, 1863; *Savannah Republican*, Sept. 29, 1862, Feb. 23, 1864; *Charles-* *ton Courier*, Feb. 1, 1864; *Memphis Appeal*, Dec. 26, 1863; James Phelan, Dec. 9, 1862, to Davis, *O.R.*, ser. 2, XVII, part 2, 788.

peas were quoted in Savannah at $10 a half peck, beef at $2.50 a pound, pork and mutton at $3 a pound, and fowl at $5 to $8 a pair. On July 15, 1863, the exchange value of Confederate currency in terms of gold was ten to one.[2]

Mrs. James Chesnut, an able diarist and the best-known purveyor of Southern gossip, relates sectional differences in South Carolina to the concept of a rich man's war and a poor man's fight:

> The Up Country men were Union men generally, and the Low Country were seceders. The former growl; they never liked those aristocratic boroughs and parishes, they had themselves a good and prosperous country, a good constitution, and were satisfied. But they had to go—to leave all and fight for the others who brought on all the trouble, and who do not show too much disposition to fight for themselves.[3]

The view that it was a rich man's war and that the small farmer or workingman in the towns and cities did the fighting was expressed most often in the areas which had the greatest scarcities. Heartrending letters came to soldiers telling of the difficulty of buying grain and flour and of the need for help in getting in the crops. A Virginia soldier writing home in 1862 of the distressingly high prices said "I begin to hear a good deal of murmuring & complaint among the soldiers & reproaches thrown at 'the rich' who have no mercy in grinding every cent out of the poor." Loyal soldiers had a most difficult decision to make when pitiful letters came from home telling of sickness, food scarcity, and no one to tend to crops, stock, or the ill. Desertion became so widespread that General Longstreet issued an order allowing a thirty-day furlough to any soldier who himself or through the instrumentality of others would deliver to him any deserter.[4]

---

[2] Herbert Fielder: *A Sketch of the Life and Time and Speeches of Joseph E. Brown* (Springfield, Mass., 1883), pp. 278–9; *Raleigh Daily Confederate*, May 3, 1863; *Rural New Yorker*, XVI (July 8, 1865), 218.

[3] B. A. Williams (ed.): *A Diary from Dixie by Mary Boykin Chesnut* (Boston, 1949), pp. 54, 193.

[4] *Savannah Republican*, Feb. 23, 1864; J. A. Graham, Feb. 1, 1864, Mar. 8, 1865, to his mother, in H. M. Wagstaff (ed.): *The James A. Graham Papers* (*The James Sprunt Historical Studies*, XX

Deplorable conditions existed behind the lines in some areas. Northern Arkansas was destitute, with almost no food available; Natchez was practically out of meat, with little prospect of supplies coming in. In six Georgia counties, provisions were nearly consumed by Union and Confederate troops, the entire livestock was gone, and without compensation, and the people were destitute, said a resolution of the Georgia legislature of November 1863. Even in Texas the scarcity of corn sent the price to $16 a bushel in 1863 and the poor, it was said, were close to starvation.[5]

J. B. Jones, who later styled himself a "rebel war clerk," was driven by anxiety over providing food for his family in Richmond to accuse the farmers of Virginia and North Carolina of a conspiracy to hoard foodstuffs to raise prices. Jones had harsh feelings toward slaveowners and larger landowners who, immune from military service, were making a mockery of the war that was being fought to defend their peculiar institution. Soon, he thought, the South would have an army of the "poor and ignorant" with "nothing to fight for," while the "higher class" stayed at home making money. He also declared that quartermasters were acquiring fortunes from speculating in food and bringing the Southern cause to ruin. He claimed that there was abundant grain and meat in the South but that mismanagement and failure to use the railroads efficiently caused maldistribution. Corn, he pointed out on April 19, 1864, sold for $1.25 a bushel in Georgia whereas in Richmond it brought $40.[6]

The transportation facilities of the South were stretched to their limit early in the war and soon were unable to perform all the necessary hauling for the army. Any major errors in the use of railroads were therefore serious. One was the shipping of

(Chapel Hill, N.C., 1928), 178, 211; Williams: *Diary from Dixie*, p. 413; G. C. Eggleston: *A Rebel's Recollections* (Bloomington, Ind., 1959), p. 89.

[5] J. B. Jones: *A Rebel War Clerk's Diary at the Confederate States Capital* (2 vols., Philadelphia, 1866), II, 277, 281; Augusta *Chronicle & Sentinel*, Apr. 4, June 27, 1863; *Memphis Appeal*, Dec. 1, 1863; *Natchez Weekly Courier*,

Mar. 13, 20, 1863; *Richmond Whig*, Apr. 7, 1863; *Richmond Enquirer*, Oct. 13, 1863; *Charleston Courier*, Mar. 4, 1864; *New Orleans Bee* in *Nashville Dispatch*, Oct. 6, 1863; *Laws of Georgia*, 1863–4, pp. 107, 110; *Houston Telegraph* in Charleston *South Carolinian*, Jan. 31, 1863.

[6] Jones: *Diary*, II, 173, 188, 277, 281.

20,000 bushels of corn from Macon to Savannah for Beauregard's army at the same time that 20,000 bushels were shipped from Savannah to Macon for Bragg's army, in each case on the Central Railroad. Another case of mismanagement tied up shipping on the Mississippi and the railroads in Alabama and Mississippi with nonessential goods. It occurred after the fall of New Orleans, when planters and factors, anxious to save their sugar and molasses from the invaders, brought them by steamboats running night and day to Vicksburg, using space that was needed to bring in corn. When Vicksburg was endangered, this same sugar and molasses was shipped by rail to Mobile, using space needed to provision that city. Widespread complaints were made that private interests had been placed above public welfare, as the people of Mobile were having to pay "starvation prices" for food in late 1862.[7]

Further aggravating the problem of the movement of private goods, which consisted mostly of food needed in deficit areas, was the order of General Pemberton confining the freight-carrying capacity of the Mobile & Ohio Railroad to military supplies, thus creating food shortages in numerous places. A principal cause of friction between the government of Mississippi and the Richmond authorities was over the use of the M & O. Food going south on the M & O was impressed to such an extent that the people of Mobile feared starvation and began to think, "We are pretty near the end of our struggle."[8]

Progressively worsening food conditions, including scarcity, poor quality, and what were generally regarded as "extortionate prices," produced a rash of riots and disorderly attacks upon wholesale and retail stores and quartermasters' depots in numerous centers. One of the first occurred in Greenville, Alabama, forty miles from Montgomery, in December 1862, when twenty women descended on the railroad agent crying "Salt or blood!" The agent was collared and forced to divide a large sack of salt

---

[7] Sumter, S.C., *Watchman* in *Mobile Advertiser and Register*, Feb. 3, 1864.

[8] *Raymond Gazette* in Jackson *Daily Southern Crisis*, Mar. 13, 1863; Greensboro *Alabama Beacon*, Nov. 21, 1862. Much was made of the attention to the sugar and molasses brought to Vicksburg and the neglect leading to heavy losses of corn and meal. *Mobile Advertiser and Register*, Mar. 6, 10, Oct. 29, 1863.

among the participants. The next raid took place in Bladensboro, North Carolina, where a group of self-styled "regulators," having searched for food without success, raided a government depot where the grain was stored and took six sacks of corn and a sack of rice for their starving families. In March 1863 raids occurred in Atlanta, Georgia, and Salisbury, North Carolina. The Salisbury raid was by a "company of females" protected by an armed leader, who compelled a storekeeper to share his food with them. Forty or fifty "respectable women," mostly wives of soldiers, led on by hunger and hatred of speculators, armed themselves with hatchets and swarmed into a number of stores whose proprietors were forced to turn over to them twenty-three barrels of flour, two sacks of salt, a half barrel of molasses, and some money.[9]

The most dangerous of the bread riots occurred in April 1863 in Richmond, where prices were generally well above levels elsewhere and Lee's army absorbed most of the available food supplies. Shouting "Bread or Blood," a mob of 60 women, according to the *Richmond Enquirer* (but according to the *North Carolina Standard*, a mob of 600 which increased to 2,000 men, women, and boys), plundered stores of bacon, flour, shoes, and other scarce items. The ringleaders were severely punished, and efforts were made to suppress news of the riot. It was one thing to have small food riots occur in remote and unimportant communities, but for a near revolt to take place in the capital of the Confederacy —and to be followed swiftly by another in Petersburg—was alarming and called for swift reprisal and punishment.[1]

Threats of severe punishment and obloquy did not deter people inadequately clothed, pinched with hunger, and unable to buy enough food with the pittance of relief allowed them. In September 1863 a group of women marched into a store in Talladega, Alabama, and seized shoes they badly needed. The

---

[9] *Natchez Weekly Courier*, Dec. 11, 1862; letter of the "Regulators," Feb. 18, 1863, M. C. Moore, Mar. 21, 1863, Mrs. L. R. Shryock, Apr. 7, 1863, and H. M. Brown, Mar. 18, 1863, to Gov. Vance, Gov. Corr., N.C. Arch.; Augusta *Chronicle & Sentinel*, Apr. 4, 1863; Raleigh *North Carolina Standard*, Mar. 20, 24, 1863, quoting the *Charlotte Bulletin*.

[1] *North Carolina Standard*, Apr. 7, 22, 1863; *Richmond Whig*, Apr. 7, 1862, Feb. 20, 1863; *Richmond Examiner*, Oct. 13, 1863. Cf. W. J. Kimball: "The Bread Riot in Richmond, 1863," *Civil War History*, XII (June 1961), 149 ff.

next month people in Wilmington, North Carolina, plundered a blockade runner and appropriated most of its cargo. When the Home Guard was called out, it refused to fire on the pillagers. In Mobile a formidable riot occurred, with people carrying banners on which were inscribed "Bread or Blood" and "Bread or Peace" and helping themselves to food and clothing. As in Wilmington, local troops refused to fire on the mob. Raleigh had its riot when some twenty soldiers' wives who could not purchase corn, wheat, or flour with Confederate money raided a government tithing depot, seized flour and grain, and then attempted a raid on a gristmill. Other raids took place in Savannah, Georgia, Waco, Texas, and Barnwell, South Carolina. More ominous was a "bread riot" in a Georgia brigade, two hundred of whose members, dissatisfied with their rations, plundered the post commissary of 75 sacks of flour, 700 pounds of bacon, 10 casks of bran, and quantities of candles.[2]

Clearly, food was becoming scarce and difficult to obtain at prices within the reach of the poorer class in many portions of the South. The situation called for action, though perhaps not of the bread-riot type. Runaway inflation resulting from the issue of great quantities of currency hurt the soldier and his dependent family most, for his monthly allotment was only $11. At the outbreak of the war this sum was not bad, but as the value of gold rose and prices in Confederate currency rose spectacularly, it became practically valueless. Hay sold for $70 a ton in New Orleans in May 1862 and for $400 a ton in Richmond on April 18, 1863. Butter brought $1.25 in Richmond in January 1863 and $6.25 on March 1, 1864. In the same period flour went from $20 to $250 a barrel. Just before the fall of Atlanta, milk sold there for $5 a quart, but on Christmas Day of that year in Richmond it brought $10 and was "nearly half water at that." Eggs sold

---

[2] Talladega *Democratic Watchtower*, Sept. 28, 1863; *Nashville Union*, Nov. 10, 1863; *New Orleans Bee* in *Nashville Union*, Oct. 6, 1863; *Raleigh Progress* in *Memphis Appeal*, Mar. 10, 1864; Turnwold, *The Countryman*, May, 3, 1864; *Houston Telegraph*, Sept. 21, 1864; *Charleston Courier*, Mar. 4, 1864. Another soldier's riot at Danville, Va., in which the threat was made to tear down the jail, brought appeals for quick aid. T. P. Atkinson, telegram, Jan. 7, 1863, to Gov. Letcher, Confederate War Dept., Letters Received, National Archives.

for $1.75 a dozen in Mobile in April 1863; in Richmond in February 1865 they sold for $6.[3]

Many were convinced that speculators had a major share in pushing prices upward. People condemned the activities of the speculator, the monopolist, the selfish individual who put greed above all else and wished to make a killing by cornering local supplies of scarce items. Storekeepers, butchers, wholesalers, farmers, and planters—all were accused of withholding their goods from market until they could get high prices. A continuous debate was carried on in the press concerning responsibility for the runaway inflation, with every element trying to lay the blame on others.

Farmers and planters were criticized severely. As early as November 23, 1861, the Atlanta *Southern Confederacy* took the farmers to task for the exorbitant prices they charged for their provisions—200 to 400 per cent greater than before the war—although they cost no more to raise than formerly and crops were abundant. The *Richmond Whig*, published in a city where the food scarcity was most seriously felt and where prices had advanced outrageously, charged on August 18, 1863, that it seemed to be the "desire of every farmer—the only class that can accumulate a surplus—to obtain the very highest prices for every necessary of life, whether from his neighbor, the Government, or the soldier who is fighting to defend his most tangible wealth." Sharp replies from equally angry planters led the paper to agree that the Confederacy's unfortunate policies were partly to blame, but it continued to complain about the planters' selfishness.[4]

J. B. Jones, who was greatly troubled that his income did not permit him to buy adequate food for his family, wrote bitterly in his diary about the landed proprietors, who were exempt from army service and were growing rich from the high prices they

---

[3] Prices of commodities are from many papers of Richmond, Savannah, Charleston, and Mobile. The quotation is from B. I. Wiley: *Letters of Warren Akin. Confederate Congressman* (Athens, Ga., 1959), p. 54. For Confederate finance see E. M. Lerner: "The Monetary and Fiscal Programs of the Confederate Government, 1861–1865," *Journal of Political Economy*, LXII (December 1954), 506 ff.; and R. C. Todd: *Confederate Finance* (Athens, Ga., 1954).

[4] *Richmond Whig*, Aug. 18, 28, Oct. 23, 1863.

were receiving while the poorer classes were doing their fighting for them. Another diarist wrote: "Shame! on the farmers & planters who are now asking four or five dollars per bushel for corn & seven & eight dollars for wheat! . . ." In a Georgia paper "Flint Lock" denounced the farmers who "in their greediness and meanness" were hoarding corn, wool, pork, potatoes, butter, bacon, and peanuts for higher prices. The *Tuscaloosa Observer*, under the caption "The Hoarding of the Wheat Crop," declared that the granaries of the farmers were bursting while the soldiers were starving and asked if the farmers intended to continue placing avarice above patriotism. Similarly, the *Lynchburg Republican* accused the farmers of Roanoke County of unpatriotically hoarding flour and refusing to let either the government or the people buy any, though most farmers had a three years' supply. What made it possible for farmers to hoard foodstuffs instead of selling them when harvested, as they had been accustomed to do, said the *Richmond Whig*, was the war prosperity which enabled them to pay off all their debts. With money in the bank and currency declining in value, they now found it better to withhold their commodities than to sell.[5]

Planters were also accused of driving their cattle into areas where they would be free from government impressment and of refusing to take Confederate currency for their goods. A "Virginia Soldier" said that the planters' "infernal lust for property, this hellish greed for gold," was ruining the poorer people and urged that a blacklist be published of all persons who refused to take current paper money. Reluctance to accept Confederate currency was more common in areas near positions held by the North. It was not only farmers who spurned the rapidly depreciating currency. A planter's wife told of bartering pork, lard, and tallow with merchants who would not take currency, exchanging these items for cloth, yarn, and unbleached calico (one pound of lard for one yard of cloth). At Christmas she gave relatives meal,

---

[5] Jones: *Diary*, II, 277, 281; L. A. Kibler: *Benjamin F. Perry. South Carolina Unionist* (Durham, N.C., 1946), p. 370; *Memphis Appeal*, Oct. 22, 1863; *Tuscaloosa Observer* in *Huntsville Confederate* (Chattanooga), Aug. 14, 1863; *Richmond Whig*, Jan. 22, Mar. 25, 1864; *Yorkville Enquirer*, Mar. 13, 1862.

peas, bacon, butter, lard, eggs, sausage, soap, rope, and string. In many places barter was replacing the money economy.[6]

Complaints against farmers for hoarding did not go unanswered. *The Countryman* of Turnwold, Putnam County, Georgia, declared: "There are more lying and hypocrisy about extortion and speculation than about anything else. Everybody in Atlanta and out of it, gets all he can for everything he has to sell, but abuses everybody else for doing the same. Supply, demand, and a redundant currency regulate all this. And yet certain tinkerers think legislation can remedy it all. They will only make matters worse." Another Georgian held that the critics of farmers were responsible for inflating the currency and for impressing the horses and mules needed for farming, thereby crippling production and raising costs. He claimed that the critics now wanted to limit the prices of agricultural products while enjoying the benefits of high prices for other goods.[7]

Defenders of planters and farmers pointed out that the prices they had to pay for nails, wire, shoes, clothes, tea, coffee, leather, and sugar had all advanced far more than the price of the items they raised. Thus, a Virginia farmer declared that leather was up to $2, coffee $2.25, and tea $10, but corn was priced by the government at $1.30 a bushel. A Georgia planter complained that nails, iron, osnaburgs, shoes, and hats for his many slaves had gone up twenty times their previous price, that 400 bushels of wheat had previously bought goods which now cost 1,600 bushels, and that a bushel of wheat once bought two bushels of salt but it now took 12 bushels of wheat to buy one. Others charged that they had to pay 2,000 per cent more for farming implements, clothing, shoes, salt, and hardware and that railroad rates had gone up by 600 per cent, while farmers were required to sell at prices only 200 or 300 per cent greater than before the war. Even newspaper prices were up more than farm prices, said "Justice" in the Raleigh *Daily Confederate,* pointing

[6] *Savannah Republican*, Oct. 22, 1863; *Memphis Appeal*, Dec. 1, 1863; *Huntsville Confederate* (Marietta, Ga.), Nov. 13, 1863; *Southern Literary Messenger*, XXXVIII (June 1864), 383; A. R. Childs (ed.): *The Private Journal of Henry William Ravenel, 1859–1887* (Columbia, S.C., 1947), pp. 193 ff.

[7] *The Countryman*, Nov. 17, 1862; *Memphis Appeal*, Nov. 6, 1863.

out that the yearly cost of the *Confederate* had risen to $30. He said that farmers could not combine to assure that their produce would sell at good prices, whereas manufacturers could easily unite to push prices to high levels.[8]

To free themselves from some of the odium cast upon them, farmers and planters formed Confederate Societies in which they publicly resolved that most of their produce above their needs was to go to the government and that they would sell the balance at modest prices to the families of soldiers. They also tried to induce the merchants to lower their prices and be satisfied with smaller profits.[9]

The high prices were blamed chiefly on the "wretched" speculators whose "unprincipled, heartless, reckless demands embarrassed every measure of the Government, enfeebled every movement of the army, convulsed the masses with anxiety about their supplies of bread." Jefferson Davis declared: "The passion of speculation has become a gigantic evil. It has seemed to take possession of the whole country, and has seduced citizens of all classes from a determined prosecution of the war to a sordid effort to amass money. It destroys enthusiasm and weakens public confidence." Price control did not work; taxation of the speculators brought in some revenue but did not eliminate extortion. It was the plunderers that needed to be eliminated or regulated. But how? asked the *Memphis Appeal*.[1]

Other critics charged the Commissary Department with causing the high prices because of its inefficiency and corruption, the inadequacy of transportation, and the fact that farmers' shipments were frequently displaced for military needs. Other factors which were blamed for inflation were the lack of sacks, plows, plow points, hoes, scythes, axes and spades; the poor

---

[8] *Richmond Enquirer*, July 28, 1862; Augusta *Chronicle & Sentinel*, Nov. 22, 1864; *Memphis Appeal*, Nov. 6, 1863; *Richmond Whig*, Aug. 18, 1863; Raleigh *Daily Conservative*, Oct. 12, 1864; Raleigh *Daily Confederate*, Sept. 30, Oct. 1, 1864.
[9] *Richmond Enquirer*, Sept. 18, 1863; *Mobile Advertiser and Register*, Sept. 23, 1863.

[1] Augusta *Chronicle & Sentinel*, June 27, 1863; *Mobile Register* in *Richmond Enquirer*, Mar. 31, 1863; *Mobile Tribune*, Sept. 13, 1863; *O.R.*, ser. 4, III, 810; T. C. DeLeon: *Four Years in Rebel Capitals: An Inside View of Life in the Southern Confederacy from Birth to Death* (Mobile, Ala., 1890), pp. 235 ff.; *Memphis Appeal*, Oct. 7, 1863.

supervision of hands on the plantations; impressment of slaves and their flight to freedom; the detruction caused by straggling bands of deserters and by union raids; and wasteful gathering of the crops.[2]

Farmers might have argued that it was the continued issue of paper currency which sent prices skyward. As a later writer said, the point was not that the speculators ruined the currency but that the "currency made the speculators."

Though much had been done to gear the Confederate states to a war machine, the prolongation of the war, the failure to win support abroad and to carry the border states and perhaps the upper Mississippi Valley, together with the military and naval successes of the North, presented Southern leaders with dark prospects. To win the war or to stave off defeat until the North declared for peace called for more drastic controls over agriculture, extensive relief campaigns in areas of greatest suffering, and more efficient use of the farmland and the railroads. The South, which had ably resisted efforts to centralize authority and enlarge the role of the Federal government in political and economic matters, was itself forced to move far toward centralization. The result was to create powerful divisive forces within the Confederacy that were to threaten it seriously.

---

[2] *Savannah Republican*, Dec. 31, 1863; *Richmond Whig*, Jan. 18, Apr. 1, 1864.

3

Impressment and Tithing

N<small>O WARTIME POLICY</small> affected farmers and planters more directly than government impressment of commodities and the related price controls. Almost from the onset of the war the Confederates had found it necessary to resort to impressment of horses, forage, grain, slaves, and many other commodities and items. The army used impressment reluctantly, but when the usual procurement procedures were too slow it turned to impressment as an emergency method, basing its authority to do so on war powers. Hoarders and speculators resented impressment, for it interfered with their plans for profits and farmers disliked to surrender supplies they might need in the event of a poor crop in the future. Governor Brown, ever watchful for encroachment upon state powers, disliked the Confederate government's use of impressment. In Cherokee County, Georgia, where the crop was short in 1862 owing to drought, impressment officers took corn needed for distribution among the poor. Brown feared that rebellion would occur and desertion from the army would follow unless the practice was quickly halted.[1]

Impressment was bad enough, but to make matters worse persons were posing as officers, impressing without authority

---

[1] J. E. Brown, Feb. 18, 1863, to Jefferson Davis, in A. D. Candler (ed.): *The Confederate Records of* the State of Georgia (6 vols., Atlanta, 1909–11), III, 328.

and disposing of the goods for the higher prices the government was not willing to pay. Standardization of practices, the establishment of a satisfactory method of determining prices, and the elimination of imposters were necessary.

James A. Seddon, the dedicated Secretary of War, against whom the complaints of all who had goods to sell were directed, later declared that a clear and explicit statement defining the powers and procedures of the impressment officers had become necessary because of grave questions which were threatening the very security of the Confederacy:

> The inflation of the currency and the insatiable thirst for gain and speculation induced by it have caused inordinate enhancement of the prices of all products, and a yet continuing advance, stimulated in part by the increasing volume of the currency and in part by the sordid calculation of large gains from hoarding by holders or speculators. To this has likewise contributed some distrust, not of the cause of the Confederacy, but of its future ability . . . to preserve its credit and good faith, to redeem the large issues which such enhancements of price rendered inevitable. The consequences have been an almost universal repugnance on the part of producers and holders to sell at any price, except under compulsion.[2]

After much vacillation and deliberation, pressing necessity finally brought the Confederate Congress in March 1863 to adopt an act to regulate impressment and determine prices to be paid for goods thus taken. Two methods were provided. The first, perhaps originally intended to favor farmers and planters, authorized the appointment of two appraisers from the immediate area to determine fair value, one to be named by the owner of the goods and the other by the agent. If they could not agree, the two could select an umpire whose decision was to be final. This proved cumbersome, awkward, and slow, and the second procedure was more commonly used. It called for two appraisers, one appointed by the president and the other by the governor of the state. They were to determine prices of all goods such as forage, grain, horses, vegetables, bacon, beef, hay, molasses, and whiskey and to publish lists at least bimonthly for wide

---

[2] O.R., ser. 4, II, 1008–9.

distribution. Where there was disagreement, a third person selected by the two appraisers, as in the first process, was to make
the final decision. Congress hoped that publication of prices and
names of agents would bring the operations of impressment
agents and of the appraisers out in the open and stop the criticism
that had been so destructive of morale.[3]

The impressment act was badly needed. If the war had
progressed more favorably for the South and if the food crisis
had eased, this law might have contributed to quiet the complaints that were pouring into Richmond. But the food crisis did
not ease, the area supplying the Confederate army continued to
shrink, other territory was badly ravaged, and criticism mounted.
A major complaint was that impressment prices were well below
the prices that goods were bringing in the open market. For example, flour by the hundred pounds sold for $100 in Alexandria,
Louisiana, in November 1863, but the impressment price was
$12. A little later corn was selling for $3 a barrel, while the
impressment commissioners paid only half that amount. Seddon
had hoped to wring the element of speculation out of the price
structure, but he failed to consider that farmers and planters
were having to pay equally outrageous prices for nails, hammers,
plow points, twine, leather, and cotton goods, if they could get
them.[4]

Governor John Milton of Florida protested to Seddon about
the "unnecessary abuse" of planters' rights and the "lawless and
wicked conduct" of impressment agents which had produced
serious dissatisfaction and the "desertion of large numbers of
troops." He said that 52 men had deserted from one company
because of the heartless treatment of their families. His views
coincided with those of Governor Brown about the arbitrary actions of the agents. Brown found it easy to disagree with most

---

[3] Act of Mar. 26, 1863, *Statutes-at-Large of the Confederate States* (Richmond, 1863), p. 102; W. B. Yearns: *The Confederate Congress* (Athens, Ga., 1960), p. 116.
[4] J. D. Bragg: *Louisiana in the Confederacy* (Baton Rouge, La., 1941), p. 261; *Richmond Enquirer,* July 28, 1862; *Richmond Whig,* Aug. 28, Sept. 29, 1863, Jan. 19, 1864; *Memphis Appeal,* Nov. 6, 1863. For schedules of impress-ment prices for individual states at different times see *O.R.,* ser. 1, XXIV, part 2, 811; ser. 4, II, 559, 652, 794, 836, 843, 1049; and ser. 4, III, 54, 262, 271, 391, 704, 982, 1051, 1171.

steps taken in Richmond but his philippic against impressment is telling:

> There have been so many outrages committed in this State under the guise of making impressments for the Army by unauthorized persons, who have resorted to it as a convenient mode of stealing and robbing from peaceful and unoffending and in many cases unsuspecting citizens, and so many irregularities and acts of partiality, injustice, and oppression committed by some of those who are authorized to make impressments, stripping some of nearly all their provisions and stock. . . .

The excesses of impressment were leading to disloyalty, he warned. Not to be outdone in making complaints against the activities of impressment officers, Governor Thomas H. Watts of Alabama objected to the "utterly illegal" impressment of salt belonging to the state, spoke of the indiscreet, heartless, and harassing action of agents who were taking 10,000,000 pounds of meat from Alabama through the collection of the tithe and impressment, and urged that if half of the Confederate quartermasters were dismissed from office and put into the ranks such illegal actions would probably cease.[5]

The legislature of South Carolina complained that impressment officers stripped some farmers of supplies without leaving them enough for their own needs, while others more remote from transportation routes were not troubled. Similar complaints were made by the legislatures of Georgia and North Carolina. There were arbitrary and at times questionable practices such as the impressment of farmers' last milk cows, of every beef steer two years or over, and of all but one hog.[6]

Perhaps the most extreme denunciation of impressment, linked with a bitter attack on Jefferson Davis, appeared in the *Memphis Appeal* published in Atlanta December 26, 1863. After

---

[5] Brown to Seddon, Nov. 9, 1863, *O.R.*, ser. 4, II, 943; Milton to Seddon, Jan. 26, 1864, *O.R.*, ser. 4, III, 45; Brown to Davis, Feb. 18, 1863; Candler: *Confederate Records of Georgia*, III, 328; T. H. Watts, Jan. 5, 22, Apr. 12, 1864, to Seddon, Governors' Letter Books, Alabama Archives.

[6] *O.R.*, ser. 4, II, 863, 988, 1066, and III, 47; *Richmond Whig*, Nov. 6, 1863; Bragg: *Louisiana in the Confederacy*, pp. 261 ff.

criticizing many military blunders, the mouldy corn meal in army rations, and the lack of shoes for the troops when hides were rotting in storehouses, the writer attacked the officers and men in the Quartermaster and Subsistence Departments who were of draft age and who had amassed fortunes by their thieving assessments at the expense of hungry stomachs and naked bodies. "These harpies," he wrote, "as foul as birds of prey as ever spring from the debris of revolution—are clad in linen and purple, and live in palatial residences" while the soldiers eke out their miserable existence on a daily ration of three quarters of a pound of wretched beef, including the bone, a little meal and potatoes. He urged Davis to "clean out the Augean stables."

A notable case of outright resistance to impressment officers is that of the former governor and United States senator, James H. Hammond, whose great plantations with their hundreds of slaves made him one of the richest men in the South. Hammond had not liked the drafting of his slaves for work on fortifications in unhealthy areas, but his chief grievance seems to have been the impressment of 2,400 bushels of his corn, for which he insisted he should have at least an approximation of the market price of $15. Hammond was willing to take $10, the appraisal figure that a local board of three had agreed upon, but was allowed only $5.[7]

The testimony of Richard Taylor, Major General in charge of Confederate operations in western Louisiana, is particularly pertinent in any appraisal of impressment. He found that the discrepancy between the price the government paid for impressed goods and current quotations in the open market was so great as not only to discourage people from selling to the army but also to provoke them to hide corn, drive cattle beyond the reach of officers, and reduce output. Impressment alienates the people and debauches the troops, said Taylor, and he deplored the effort to force a depreciated currency upon an unwilling people. Meager supplies compelled him to impress all the beef

---

[7] Elizabeth Merritt: *James Henry Hammond (Johns Hopkins University Studies in Historical and* Political Science, Baltimore, 1923, ser. XLI, no. 4), p. 144.

cattle he could find, much to the discontent of the people, who, he learned, were actually driving their remaining stock to the Federals to avoid impressment by him.[8]

An even more serious picture of the effect of impressment comes from Richmond where, it was said, butchers were closing their stalls, farmers were preparing to plant only so much corn as would meet their own needs, and everywhere surpluses were being withheld and secreted. "The army will be starved, and famine will ensue," unless the government will pay the market price for food, Robert Kean said.[9]

In Georgia, where farmers were accused of preferring to withhold and hide two years' supplies of corn rather than to sell at the government price, the weevil did so much damage to the old stored grain that it was no longer fit for human consumption and could only be used by distilleries. An officer of the Commissary Department thought the weevil had proved "our best friend" in forcing farmers to send in their corn. In Alabama and Louisiana planters threatened to stop raising corn and to let their fodder rot on the fields rather than sell at impressment prices.[1]

Impressment and procurement of supplies were made more difficult by the extensive issues of paper currency, amounting to an estimated two and a quarter billion dollars, which rapidly depreciated and made farmers prefer to hold onto their produce or, if they were near the Union lines, to demand greenbacks. Inflation and the failure to raise the allowance of soldiers and stipends of government clerks in proportion to the rise in prices worked untold hardships and brought many to destitution. The unfairness is seen in a letter from Clay County, North Carolina, written in August 1863, which complained that although soldiers were paid in currency and impressment agents paid for goods only in currency, creditors and those who sell provisions "refuse to take it." A volunteer's wife was told that on the debt the family

---

[8] R. Taylor, Jan. 21, 1864, to General Boggs, *O.R.*, ser. 1, XXXIV, part 2, 902–3.
[9] Edward Younger (ed.): *The Diary of Robert Garlick Hill Kean* (New York, 1957), p. 41.
[1] J. F. Cummings, Feb. 13, 1864, to L. B. Northrop, Candler: *Confederate Records of Georgia*, III, 467; *Mobile Advertiser and Register*, Nov. 6, 1863; *Louisiana Democrat* in Austin, Tex., *State Gazette*, Mar. 3, 1864.

owed, only silver would be accepted, and that it would take $9 in Confederate currency to equal $2 in silver. So rapidly was Confederate currency depreciating in November 1864 that farmers in northeastern Mississippi were refusing to accept it for their corn. When the new currency bill was enacted in 1864 providing for the refunding of Confederate obligations and exchange of $4 of old currency for $3 in the new, it became almost impossible for government officers to buy or even impress goods, so confused were the people by the partial repudiation that was unhinging the machinery of trade.[2]

Dealings with both sides in the war were described by John Houston Bills, who had four plantations near Holly Springs, northern Mississippi, which was not far from the Federal lines in 1862. Never enthusiastic for the Confederacy, Bills found himself in a position to sell to both the Union and Confederate forces, but he was content with neither side. The Federals bought his cotton but took his mules, horses, and other goods, and seduced his Negroes. The upshot was that he estimated he lost $100,000 in the transactions with them. On the other hand, the Confederates paid for the goods they took from him in their currency, which was almost worthless to him.[3]

The upsetting effect which continued issues of currency were having on the South is best shown by the rapidly shrinking value of Confederate notes in gold.[4]

Every effort was made to play down the growing dissatisfaction with the currency and to appeal to the loyalty of the people to accept it. Yet incidents continued to occur which broke into the papers despite the voluntary censorship of harmful news. When a local judge refused to take currency in payment of a debt due his father and disparaged the currency in a public statement,

---

[2] Michael Bollinger, Mar. 14, 1863, and J. M. Galloway, Aug. 21, 1863, to Gov. Vance, Gov. Corr., N.C. Arch.; J. Whitaker, Feb. 26, 1864, to Gov. Brown, and J. J. Howard, Feb. 27, 1864, to Whitaker, Commissary Files, Ga. Arch.; *Huntsville Confederate* (Marietta, Ga.), Nov. 13, 1863; R. C. Todd: *Confederate Finance* (Athens, Ga., 1954), *passim.*

[3] Diary of J. H. Bills, Mar. 21, July 31, 1862, University of North Carolina Library, courtesy of Allan Nevins.

[4] Compare DeLeon's quotations with those of J. B. Jones in A *Rebel War Clerk's Diary at the Confederate States Capital* (2 vols., Philadelphia, 1866), *passim,* and R. C. Todd; *Confederate Finance,* p. 198.

DISCOUNT VALUE OF CONFEDERATE CURRENCY IN GOLD

1861			*1863*		
January 1 to May 1	5%		February 1	3	for 1
May 1 to October 1	10%		March 1	3.25	for 1
October 15	12%		March 15	5	for 1
November 15	15%		May 15	6	for 1
December 1	20%		June 15	7.50	for 1
			July 15	10	for 1
1862			August 15	15	for 1
January 1	20%		November 15	15	for 1
February 1	25%		December 15	21	for 1
February 15	40%				
March 1	50%		*1864*		
March 15	65%		March 1	26	for 1
April 1	75%		April 1	19	for 1
April 15	80%		August 15	21	for 1
May 1	90%		September 15	23	for 1
May 15	95%		October 15	25	for 1
June 15	2	for 1	November 15	28	for 1
August 1	2.20	for 1	December 1	32	for 1
September 1	2.50	for 1			

1865		
January 1	60 for 1	
February 1	50 for 1	
April 1	70 for 1	
April 15	80 for 1	
April 20	100 for 1	

SOURCE: T. C. DeLeon: *Four Years in Rebel Capitals: An Inside View of Life in the Southern Confederacy from Birth to Death* (Mobile, Ala., 1890), p. 375.

a jury denounced his action and refused to serve under him. A little later a grand jury in Alabama declared that "A refusal to take Confederate currency strikes a death blow at our glorious cause, and should be prevented by all means which a free people can command. The man who refused to take this money is doing more damage to our cause, more injury to our soldiers and their families than if he were in the ranks of the enemy fighting us. . . ."[5] In Shreveport, Louisiana, citizens "demoralized by speculation and the love of gain, persistently refused to

[5] Augusta *Chronicle & Sentinel,* Sept. 25, 1863.

receive Confederate money in the sales of supplies and in payment of Debts." An assistant adjutant general declared that Richmond authorities regarded such action as treasonable and maintained that any person so acting could be pronounced an alien enemy, his property would be open to confiscation, and he could be expelled.[6]

Specie being practically unavailable, greenbacks were preferred to Confederate currency, particularly in areas fairly close to the Union lines. Once farmers had received some and noted their relative stability in comparison with Confederate notes, they wanted nothing else. Where it was not offered they tried to hold back their goods and even to hide them from impressment officers. Distressed by the amount of trading with the enemy in the Vicksburg area, the refusal of merchants to accept Confederate currency, and the exorbitant prices they charged, General Van Dorn issued his famous order declaring martial law and stating that "Speculation and extortion upon soldiers and citizens will not be tolerated. . . ." Persons found guilty of such acts were to be subject to fine, imprisonment, and confiscation of their property. The order was widely denounced and soon countermanded from Richmond.[7]

With the currency's purchasing power shrinking rapidly and prices rising to undreamed-of heights, it was natural that the Confederacy should contemplate price control. One form of control was the establishment of prices the government would pay for goods and services it impressed. Unfortunately, the Confederacy was competing with hunger, with state (and in Alabama, with county) relief officers who were also given impressment powers, with procurement officials of state militias, and with Federal buying; and its prices did little or nothing but discourage sales.[8]

Colonel Northrop and James Seddon attempted to meet

---

[6] *O.R.*, ser. 1, XXVI, part 2, 580.
[7] A. R. Childs (ed.): *The Private Journal of Henry William Ravenel, 1859–1887* (Columbia, S.C., 1947), p. 193; *O.R.*, ser. 1, XV, 772; P. F. Walker: *Vicksburg. A People at War, 1860–1865* (Chapel Hill, N.C., 1960), p. 111.

[8] *Richmond Whig* in *Daily Southern Crisis* (Jackson), Feb. 5, 1863; *Richmond Examiner* in *North Carolina Standard*, Mar. 10, 1863; *Southwestern Baptist* in *Democratic Watchtower* (Talladega, Ala.), Aug. 30, 1863; Act of Aug. 29, 1863, *Laws of Alabama*, 1863, p. 26.

criticism of impressment officers by forbidding them to take brood mares or stallions, or the property of officers and soldiers absent in the service (though it is difficult to see how this exemption could be justified). Horses used for carrying mail were exempt from impressment, as was one horse for each physician. Also, officers were not to resort to impressment until they had failed to negotiate a purchase. The charge was made that when an offer was rejected and impressment followed, the price paid was substantially lower than had been originally offered. Additional regulations directed that agents impressing meat should "not reduce the supplies of any person below one-half of the quantity usually allowed for the support" of himself and his family for the year, and it was required that articles should be paid for at the time of impressment. Finally, almost at the end of the war, it was made unlawful to impress "any sheep, milch cows, brood mares, stallions, jacks, bulls, breeding hogs, or other stock kept or necessary for raising sheep, hogs, horses, mules or cattle." This act also tried to assure farmers a closer approximation of the current market price.[9]

A resolution of the Alabama legislature of November 26, 1864, declaring that the schedule of prices was "arbitrary, unequal and unjust," and urging that the rates be based on fair market value, showed the dissatisfaction still prevailing with impressment. Despite these attempts at reform, complaints continued. At Pascagoula on the Gulf, when impressment officers were rounding up all cattle fit for beef and offering less than half the market price, the grand jury called their action cow stealing. The spoilage of badly needed supplies continued, impressments were stimulated by vindictive and malicious neighbors, some families had most of the bacon and corn they possessed seized, cattle and hogs died for want of food, and even officers were accused of selling at high profits the supplies they had impressed. "Under our villainous impressment system the people have been robbed and driven into the arms of the Federals

---

[9] Notice of Quartermaster Office, Natchez, in *Natchez Daily Courier*, June 23, 1863; R. L. Abernethy, Feb. 25, 1863, and Calvin Cowles, Apr. 4, 1864, to Gov. Vance, Gov. Corr., N.C. Arch.; *O.R.*, ser. 4, III, 249, 1170; Abington *Virginian* in Petersburg *Daily Express*, Apr. 11, 1864; Greensboro *Alabama Beacon*, Apr. 22, 1864.

to avoid starvation," said a distressed critic of Harrisonburg, Louisiana. "Thousands" of otherwise loyal Confederates had defected to the North because of the wrongs of impressment. A Mobile woman charged that a Confederate officer lay in wait at a big society wedding and impressed "nearly all of the mules and carriage horses" after permitting "the owners to ride home." In Texas, farmers were reluctant to haul their wheat and flour to market for fear they would lose their teams. The Austin, Texas, *Weekly State Gazette* of March 16, 1864, summarizing the wrongs of impressment in Texas, asked: "Have we any civil rights left?"[1]

All efforts to improve impressment did not silence criticism, which toward the end of the war reached a crescendo of angry denunciation and personal villification of the officers in charge. Stories of gross frauds circulated. Officers were accused of drawing full rations, giving their men half rations, and selling the balance. It was said that inspecting officers and post commissary officers conspired to condemn fresh meat as tainted and then disposed of it to their advantage. Widespread suspicion existed among the common soldiers that their rations were smaller than they might have been. The frequency with which such charges were made against the officials of the Commissary Department led to an investigation which brought out nothing more damaging than that substantial losses of provisions had occurred through spoilage. A careful scholar has concluded that many of the charges levied against the Subsistence Department and its head, Colonel L. B. Northrop, were made out of malice and without any real basis in fact. One may agree with Bell I. Wiley that it was less corruption than inefficiency which was responsible for short, moldy, and rancid rations but may disagree that the inefficiency was largely the fault of the Commissary General and the Secretary of War. Major blunders were committed by Jefferson Davis, by army officers, and by subordinate officials of the

---

[1] *Laws of Alabama*, 1864, p. 188; Kate Cumming: *A Journal of Hospital Life in the Confederate Army of Tennessee* (Louisville, Ky., 1866), p. 127; A. E. Lewis, Apr. 21, 1863, to Gov. Pettus, Gov. Corr., Miss. Arch.; Petersburg *Register* in *North Carolina Standard*, Dec. 4, 11, 1863; W. P. Bynum, May 7, 1864, to Gov. Vance, Gov. Corr., N.C. Arch.; *Houston Telegraph*, Feb. 9, 1864; Austin *Weekly State Gazette*, Mar. 16, 1864.

Commissary Department who had to make decisions without consulting the high command. And undoubtedly, private greed was a factor.[2]

Many of the faults of the impressment system may be attributed to the speed with which it had to operate, the numerous emergencies it had to meet, the political character of the appointees, the breakdown of transportation and communication facilities, and the unfavorable climate of opinion in which it had to work. Some of the complaints being channeled to Richmond through Governors Bonham, Milton, Vance, and Brown came from people who were not friendly to the continued prosecution of the war, from speculators hoping to make a killing, and from farmers and livestock men operating on an extensive scale.[3]

As deficiencies and weaknesses of impressment became apparent, the commissioners for enforcement in Alabama, Mississippi, and Georgia met to draft plans for improving their operations. They had found that other agents of the Confederacy and of the states were offering "exorbitant" prices for grain for distilleries. Rather than suffer such competition from other public agencies and from speculators and nonproducers who bid up prices beyond those the impressment officers could offer, they recommended that all surplus grain, fodder, meat, and lard be held by the producers subject to the orders of the Confederate government and be paid for at the commissioners' scheduled rates. One can imagine the anguished cries that would have been made by the Atlantic governors if such a proposal had been given serious attention.[4]

Impressment of the planters' food and forage was bad enough but impressment of their horses, mules, oxen, slaves, and tools was worse. The death rate among the animals of the cavalry, artillery, and commissary departments was high

---

[2] O.R., ser. 4, II, 391; T. R. Hay: "Lucius B. Northrop: Commissary General of the Confederacy," *Civil War History*, IX (March 1963), 5 ff.; William Watson: *Life in the Confederate Army* (New York, 1888), pp. 163 ff.; B. I. Wiley: *The Life of Johnny Reb, the Common Soldier of the Confederacy* (Indianapolis, 1943), p. 96.

[3] O.R., ser. 4, III, 402–515. For the political and states' rights position on impressment see F. L. Owsley: *State Rights in the Confederacy* (Chicago, 1925).

[4] O.R., ser. 4, III, 603.

because of careless attention, hard usage, and low rations. Such surplus stock as existed at first was soon depleted and new supplies were not forthcoming. Town residents disliked giving up their carriage horses. Farmers were even more reluctant to part with their work animals and for a more important reason: the sacrifice of any of them would force a proportionate curtailment of their farming operations. Few farmers had surplus work animals; they were consequently reluctant to sell and were most unhappy at impressment. The government attempted to ease impressment of horses for a time by ordering that mules should be employed wherever possible, but this only tended to make mules scarce. The Impressment Act allowed for the renting of horses, mules, and oxen, but planters feared their animals, like their slaves, would be abused and perhaps lost to them for good.

Competition for draft animals pushed costs up, but the prices paid for impressed animals were well below the going level. When, therefore, orders were issued to impress all the oxen in a part of Alabama for beef, there was consternation and angry opposition. The *Montgomery Advertiser* called the order scarcely credible. "It is the climax of all that is objectionable in the system of impressment," a wanton injury to the country. In the same area the appearance of six successive horse-impressing detachments within four months threatened to strip it of essential animals. In other areas impressment officers had called on the planters only once or twice. Some planters had been forced to give up one fifth of their mules while others had had to surrender one twelfth or one twentieth. Unfortunately, equality of sacrifice was impossible to ensure. For example, when Longstreet's army moved through an area just east of the Blue Ridge in North Carolina it consumed nearly all the grain, impressed the oxen, and left the region in such bad straits that prisoners in the guardhouse had to depend on charity for their food. One farmer complained that he had lost his steers, his fat milk cows, and forty-nine bushels of corn, and was left with a balky and useless horse and insufficient corn for his needs. Rural folk were certain they were harder hit than town residents and believed that the officers made no efforts to equalize the burden. Everywhere the same angry feelings swelled up against the officiousness, the unfairness, even the plundering of the officers and the disastrous effects of impressment.[5]

Yet, as was said, if the animals were not taken by the Confederates when they were needed, they would probably be confiscated by Union raiders if these appeared in the neighborhood. When the raiders first came to a community they took the best horses, generally leaving their worn-out and crippled nags in exchange. Later, they took or killed all draft animals, leaving the farmers nothing with which to carry on their plowing and planting, unless they had been successful in hiding some of them. In the last year of the war it was frequently said that the plundering of Union raiders was little worse than impressments and pillaging by Confederate officers and troops.[6]

It was in the mountain counties that conscription and impressment were most fiercely resisted, for in the last year and a half of the war many residents of that area were close to starvation. Had the unfeeling bureaucrats read the letters telling of the deplorable conditions prevailing there, they might not have recommended the use of troops to compel impressment. In these western counties of North Carolina most of the people were small farmers living at near-subsistence levels. They had no slaves and few provisions to spare, and impressment worked great hardships on them.[7]

With the white labor force withdrawn from much of the South by the army, the War Department had no reservoir of unskilled labor except slaves and a small number of free Negroes to work on defense construction, ordnance plants, or hospitals. It was unavoidable, therefore, that the planters would be called upon for a portion of their hands for such projects, particularly in view of the Southern position that certain kinds of labor should be performed only by Negroes. But all such

---

[5] *Montgomery Advertiser*, Feb. 12, Mar. 9, 1864; Greensboro *Alabama Beacon*, May 6, 1864; *Natchez Daily Courier*, June 23, 1863.
[6] O.R., ser. 4, II, 552, 616, 719, 836, 1051; *Vicksburg Daily Whig*, Jan. 23, May 10, 1863, the latter quoting the *Richmond Whig*; S. J. Ghol-

son, Apr. 16, 1864, to Gov. Clark, Gov. Corr., Miss. Arch.
[7] T. S. Barton, Mar. 23, 1864, to Col. L. B. Northrop, Confederate War Dept. Files, National Archives; petition with numerous signatures from Jackson County, April 1863, to Gov. Vance, Gov. Corr., N.C. Arch.

requests met intense resistance. The planter's economy was built around the field hands and to let a portion of them go would mean contraction of farming operations. Slaves were the most valuable property the planters owned and were treated accordingly. They were expected to do a good day's work, but the owner and slave had come to an understanding about what that good day's work was and no boss or overseer on a construction force would have the same understanding. Construction work under unknown persons might prove dangerous, the hands would never receive the same attention to their ills that they were given on the plantation, and they were more likely to be exposed to disease in congested areas than at home. A Charleston factor refused to take charge of hiring out Negroes on government jobs partly on the ground that he had no time to protect them when they were abused. Who would watch over their housing, food, and health as did the owner? Any task that took the slaves away from the plantation where their families resided and all their social relations were centered would tend to demoralize them. The risks involved in permitting slaves to be employed off the plantation were too high to be compensated by any payment that might be made.[8]

When emergencies arose, planters offered their slaves for a limited time—willingly at first, then grudgingly, then not at all. All the owners' fears proved justified. When the limited periods expired, the owners had great difficulty in recovering their slaves. Emergency seemed to pile on emergency. The men were treated brutally, were poorly housed, fed, and clothed, and were given little medical attention. In the event of a slave's accident, sickness, or death it was most difficult to recover damages or even get compensation for the time he had worked. These facts explain why there was increasing disinclination to offer hands when emergencies arose. But most important was the fact that the planter needed the slaves to put in the crops and to keep the plantation operating, particularly as the Confederacy was asking him to pay a tithe of all he produced, to pay other fairly heavy taxes, and to sell his surplus corn, wheat, pork, and beef at substantially less than the market price. Only

---

[8] J. H. Easterby (ed.): *The South Carolina Rice Plantation as Re-* *vealed in the Papers of Robert F. W. Allston* (Chicago, 1945), p. 428.

with the most efficient use of their labor force could farmers and planters meet all these obligations. True, there were slack times on plantations which had turned largely to corn growing and hog raising, as there had not been on cotton or tobacco plantations, but if the hands were not available at planting and harvesting time, part of the crop would be lost.

Voluntarism failing to procure Negroes for essential service, the government resorted to impressment. At first the practice rested on the general powers of government; later, on specific legislation which tried to limit and systematize it so as to protect both slave and slave owner. As early as January 3, 1863, Mississippi authorized impressment of slaves and required the same monthly payment to the owners, and the same rations and clothing or commutation money, as were allowed privates in the army. The risks to slave owners were too great for such a modest return and higher compensation had to be paid. Alabama in 1863 was paying double the $11 a month which privates received, and the slaves were better fed, said Governor John Gill Shorter, who was trying to convince owners there was little to the stories that slaves at work on the fortifications were abused. A year later the Confederacy was paying $175 a year for male slaves, $75 a year for female slaves, and $300 and more for men hired to work in the salt fatcories and iron foundries. In 1864, Alabama was paying $30 a month for work on fortifications at Mobile.[9]

Defense work at Wilmington, Charleston, Savannah, Mobile, Vicksburg, and other vital centers required many thousands of hands for tasks soldiers were not asked to do, and many calls were made on impressment officers. Farmers with one to three hands complained that they were obliged to give up a third or half of their labor force while the larger planters were asked for a much smaller proportion. Impressment was especially burdensome in the vicinity of cities needing hands for defense work, while the more remote plantations were more likely to escape it altogether. When fever infested Wilmington

---

[9] *Laws of Mississippi*, 1861–2, p. 83; Greensboro *Alabama Beacon*, Mar. 27, 1863, Jan. 8, 1864; F. S. Blair, Jan. 24, 1864, to J. Cowden, Gov. Corr., Miss. Arch. Blair promised medical care and transportation for the 1,500 Negroes he hoped to secure.

all classes suffered, but especially the Negroes, who were given slight attention. A Lewisburg, North Carolina, planter, writing in October 1863, said that seven of his hands had been impressed in the spring, as a result of which his farming operations had fallen behind and he had a short crop. After the tithe was taken, he would be deficient in wheat and oats. He said that he could not spare another man, that he had no blankets, and that his Negroes did not have enough clothes, but that he was still willing to send additional men if they were required.

Most complaints about impressment related to the cruel and abusive manner in which conscripted slaves were treated. They longed to return to their plantation or else they were inclined to flee to the Federal armies. In protest against this brutality and neglect, the assembly of North Carolina requested Governor Vance to complain to Jefferson Davis, which he seemed only too glad to do. Governor Brown even suggested that it might be better to hire the troops to do the work by giving them an additional $30 a month. It would be cheaper than using slaves, and the men certainly could use the additional money. Instead, Southern commanders had to depend on impressment, knowing that many planters sent their "most worthless negroes to work on fortifications."[1]

The correspondence of the governors of Virginia, North Carolina, Mississippi, Alabama, and Georgia contains numerous letters from planters urging the release of hands who had been kept long after the agreed period of service, complaining that the work of planting and harvesting could not be accomplished without them, and declaring that consequently the amount of food the plantation could produce would be small. It cannot be doubted that impressment of slaves had its part in reducing the amount of food available in the South.[2]

A final blow was dealt planters when the scarcity of tools made it necessary for impressment officers to take needed im-

---

[1] Ellis Malone, Oct. 22, 1863, to Gov. Vance, Gov. Corr., N.C. Arch.
[2] Letters of J. J. Whitaker, Commissary General of Georgia, to various persons, Letter Book, III–IV, Feb. 21, Mar. 22, 1862, May 30, July 13, Sept. 10, 1863, June 1, 1864, Ga. Arch.; T. C. Roberts, July 27, 1863, to Gov. Vance, Gov. Corr., N.C. Arch.

plements such as axes, shovels, picks, saws, and harnesses away from the plantations. The patience and loyalty of planters was stretched to the breaking point when their supplies of food were taken, their slaves required to saw out timber on the plantations or work on defense jobs elsewhere, and their remaining tools were impressed.[3]

Relative failure of the Confederacy's tax program and the unparalleled inflation that resulted from its issue of paper currency made the procurement of supplies so difficult and the cost so excessive that the government was driven to include in its revenue act of April 24, 1863, a tithing tax which is reminiscent of a similar tax required of all Mormons. Among the provisions of this measure which applied to farmers was the 8 per cent levy on the value of tobacco, cotton, wool, sugar, molasses, syrup, rice, "and other agricultural productions" which were on hand on July 1, 1863, and were not necessary for family consumption or for planting. This requirement was expected to provide information about hoarding which, since the records would be available to impressment officers, might encourage sale of the produce. Because they were subject to a tithe on their produce, farmers were exempted from the progressive income tax of 1 to 15 per cent of net incomes on their income from the land. They were, however, to pay regular income tax rates on the profits from the sale of beef cattle and 1 per cent on the value of all neat cattle, horses, and mules not used in cultivation.

Section 11 of the revenue act imposed a tithing tax on produce. It allowed farmers and planters a reserve for home consumption to which the tax did not apply, including 50 bushels each of sweet and Irish potatoes, 100 bushels of corn or 50 bushels of wheat, and 20 bushels of peas or beans. A tax of 10 per cent was to be paid in kind on all produce from the land after setting aside the reserve supply. Items listed included wheat, corn, oats, rye, buckwheat or rice, peas and beans, potatoes, cured hay and fodder, sugar, molasses, wool, cotton ginned and packed, and tobacco packed in boxes. Depots for deposit of the tithes were to be established within eight miles of the place of production.

---

[3] W. T. Jordan: *Hugh Davis and His Alabama Plantation* (University, Ala., 1948), p. 156.

Farmers having to carry goods farther were to be paid a fair transportation rate for the excess mileage. The government was to provide sacks for tithing grain and pay the cost of barrels for molasses. The production of beef was to be taxed through the income levy on net profits, as has been seen, but the tithe was to be levied on all pork commuted to bacon at the rate of 60 pounds to 100 pounds of pork. Somewhat the same time- and labor-consuming procedure that was used in appraising impressment was to be followed in determining the liabilities of the producer. Before the tax measure was finally adopted, a provision was added that exempted from the 8 per cent tax flour, wool, cotton, tobacco, and other agricultural products which were produced prior to 1863, thereby weakening the effect of the bill on hoarding. Another modification allowed the substitution of the money value for the tithe in places where it would be impracticable to collect goods.[4]

On June 4, 1863, the Quartermaster-General's office submitted its list of counties and districts where the tithing tax was and where it was not to be paid in kind. In only two states—Georgia and South Carolina—was it possible to report that, in at least part of all counties and parishes, the goods could be collected in kind. In North Carolina it was "impracticable" to do so in 31 out of 84 counties; in Alabama in 14 out of 52; in Arkansas in 24 out of 75; in Louisiana in 28 out of 48; in Tennessee in 56 out of 83; and in Mississippi in 31 out of 59. Large parts of Virginia and much of Florida were thus classified. It was wholly impracticable to tithe Texas in kind because of the lack of transportation and want of information.[5]

Seven months after the Revenue Act of 1863 was adopted, all that Jefferson Davis could say in favor of it was that it "has been as yet but measurably operative." Farmers, fearing impressment and not desiring to sell, were reluctant to offer information concerning their crops as the law required. At farmers' meetings the tithing tax was declared unjust, discrimi-

---

[4] *O.R.*, ser. 4, II, 513–24; Yearns: *Confederate Congress*, pp. 197 ff.; Todd: *Confederate Finance*, pp. 141 ff.
[5] Larkin Smith, June 4, 1863, to A. C. Myers, *O.R.*, ser. 4, II, 575; Larkin Smith: *Instructions to Be Observed by Officers and Agents Receiving the Tax in Kind*, Mar. 29, 1864, contains 14 detailed forms to be used by officers in making reports on collections.

natory, tyrannical, a relic of barbarism, practiced only by the worst despotisms. The *North Carolina Standard* declared that to enforce it in North Carolina would require a thousand officers, all of whom would be selected from the loyal supporters of Jefferson Davis and would swarm throughout the country like the locusts of Egypt, gathering the tithes. Combined with impressment, the tax in kind seemed to constitute a gross interference in the private business of individuals. As such it was certain to be attacked by the vitriolic pens of Governors Vance, Bonham, Brown, and Milton, who took every opportunity to express their views to Jefferson Davis.[6]

Like impressment, the collection of the tithing tax made necessary the employment of what Governor Bonham called a "great number of strong and able-bodied men" whom he accused of spending much of their time in buying goods for themselves. They should be in the army, he declared, and their places taken by men not of draft age. Governor Brown surpassed Bonham in flaying the "almost countless swarm of young, able-bodied officers, who are to be seen on all our railroad trains and in all our hotels . . . in brass buttons and gold lace," idling about. These throngs of men acting as clerks, purchasing agents, and impressment officials could go far in filling up the depleted ranks of the army. Governor Vance waxed most choleric in denouncing the "stealing, pilfering, burning, and sometimes murderous conduct" of officers which had become an unbearable grievance.[7]

> If God Almighty had yet in store another plague worse than all others which he intended to have let loose on the Egyptians in case Pharaoh still hardened his heart, I am sure it must have been a regiment or so of half-armed, half-disciplined Confederate cavalry. Had they been turned loose among Pharaoh's subjects, with or without an impressment law, he would have become so sensible of the anger of God that he never would have allowed the children of Israel to the Red Sea! . . . Cannot a few men be shot for perpetrating these outrages, as an example? Unless something can be done I shall be compelled to call out my militia and levy actual war against them.

---

[6] *O.R.*, ser. 4, II, 1011–12; *North Carolina Standard*, Apr. 22, 1863.
[7] *O.R.*, ser. 4, II, 709, 1061; III, 16, 63.

Governor Milton of Florida likewise deplored the number of officers of the Quartermaster and Commissary Departments to be found in almost every town and village who appeared to have no work to do.[8]

Colonel L. B. Northrop had a tremendous task to set up tithing procedures in some 400 counties and establish warehouses in which goods could be properly maintained. Whether there were facilities for storage or not, the tithes had to be collected and in turn transported to the various armies. Impressment officers and other procurement agents were instructed to house the tithing goods being collected in their districts wherever it was possible. But whereas impressment officers tended to concentrate their buying in the most likely regions, the tithing collectors were compelled to operate generally. In 1863, when manpower was being drained away into the army, construction of depots was impossible. Waste and destruction resulted from exposure to the weather, from pillage, from the very miscellaneous character of the goods, and from the fact that producers wanted to deliver their tithes at their convenience regardless whether there were officers and facilities to receive them. In Florida, hundreds, perhaps thousands, of bales of much-needed fodder were ruined by improper handling. In Richmond, Virginia, the same happened to quantities of hay and corn fodder.

Hay was particularly difficult for the farmers to transport to depots and for the agents to receive, as balers or presses were scarce and expensive. The *Richmond Whig* on August 14, 1863, urged the government to erect hay presses and thereby save the tithing hay, which was badly needed since the oat and wheat crops of that year were short and the corn crop uncertain. Farmers near Richmond who brought their surplus hay into the city for sale only to have it impressed by the Commissary Department at less than the market price then found themselves still owing commutation money for their tithe. They were angry at thus being hit twice and unfairly by the same department. A writer in the *Whig* asked why so many people in the city had to maintain riding horses "which consumed much grain and

---

[8] *Macon Telegraph* in *Savannah Republican*, Sept. 30, 1863; *Richmond Whig*, Aug. 14, Sept. 29, Oct. 3, 1863, Apr. 12, 1864; *O.R.*, ser. 4, III, 15.

forage" and urged that all horses not used for carriages, hacks, omnibuses, and drags should be taken for essential government work.[9]

Serious losses of corn through the bursting of rotten sacks, exposure of huge piles of grain-filled casks to the weather, wastage in hauling, shortages of boxes, sacks, and other containers when they were most needed, and the spoiling of great quantities of meat held twenty days in boxcars were reported and were blamed on the mismanagement and inefficiency of the Commissary Department. Actually, the very size of the task of handling the mountains of provisions and fodder is as likely to have been the cause. It may well have been true that large quantities of bacon were spoiled in North Carolina in 1862 and that thousands of bushels of corn rotted at Port Hudson in early 1863 for want of dry cover. It may also have been the case that an experiment in moving large numbers of hogs from parts of the South to the southern and southwestern counties of Georgia, where the corn crop was good, was accompanied by great waste of the precious corn, and that when the hogs were fattened, dressed, and packed and the bacon cured, the hides were not used, the tallow was not saved, and spoilage was not prevented. A representative of the Subsistence Bureau admitted that in the confusion of the time there had been considerable waste.

The state governments as well as the Confederacy were guilty of wasting food. As early as February 1862 Georgia's Commissary General was urging L. B. Northrop to relieve him of a large supply of pickled beef which the state held and which he feared would spoil with the coming of hot weather. Commissary supplies continued to spoil and deteriorate, and complaints against the rations being served led to the recall of all unfit bacon and to orders that joints of meat should be used first, since they rotted earlier than other portions. By the summer of 1863 both the Confederacy and the state of Georgia were losing great amounts of meat which spoiled as a result of being insufficiently

---

[9] *Richmond Whig*, Apr. 26, 1864; *Mobile Advertiser and Register* in *Memphis Appeal*, June 18, 1864; *Charleston Courier*, May 18, 1864; *Huntsville Confederate* (Chattanooga, Tenn.), July 31, 1863; J. D. Allen, Apr. 3, 1863, to the Secretary of War, Confederate War Records, National Archives; J. L. Lock in *Savannah Republican*, Sept. 4, 1863.

salted. Badly tainted meat was sold for soap making. Georgia's loss from spoilage included 5,000 pounds of bacon, a number of barrels of flour, and quantities of corn meal, rice, lard, and beef.[1]

A major evasion of the tithing tax occurred in Virginia. Bonded tobacco in warehouses could not be taxed because the state's law provided that when it was sold, the full amount given in the warehouse receipt should be delivered to the purchaser. True, the tobacco could not alleviate the food shortage but it might have provided additional revenue for the government and eased the problem of issuing tobacco rations.[2]

The tithing tax returns on hogs in the Hancock district of east central Georgia show that the tax did not bear heavily on larger planters. In this district in 1863, 10,897 hogs were slaughtered, producing 1,569,750 pounds of pork. Since the amount of bacon due the government was 6 pounds for every 100 pounds of pork, the amount assessed was 94,185 pounds. Two of the largest payers of the bacon tithe were Daniel Dickson, famous as an agricultural experimenter and successful user of fertilizer on his cotton and grain land, and T. G. Dickson. From their 400 and 280 hogs, 58,400 and 45,400 pounds of pork were dressed and payments of 3,564 and 2,700 pounds of bacon were made. From their large surpluses they could easily meet the tithe, but the small farmer who produced barely enough for his needs was hard hit by it.[3]

Both impressment and the tithing tax were highly unpopular throughout the South but nowhere more so than in areas having few slaves. Letters poured into the governors of North Carolina and Alabama complaining that in the mountain counties the poor crops, the quartering of troops, the impressment of supplies, and the low returns from labor on poor land made it impossible for the residents to pay the tithe. In recognition of this fact, a

---

[1] Letters of J. J. Whitaker, Commissary General of Georgia, to various persons, Ga. Commissary General Letter Book, III–IV, Feb. 21, Mar. 22, 1863, May 30, July 13, Sept. 10, 1863, June 1, 1864, Ga. Arch.; T. C. Roberts, July 27, 1863, to Gov. Vance, Gov. Corr., N.C. Arch.

[2] J. C. Robert: *The Story of Tobacco in America* (New York, 1949), p. 117.
[3] "Returns and Assessments of the Confederate War Tax Levied in Kind on Hogs Slaughtered for Pork," Hancock County, Ga. Arch.

resolution of the Alabama legislature petitioned the Congress of the Confederacy to exempt from payment of the tithe the families of all soldiers whose support was derived from the proceeds of white labor.[4]

A summary of the tithes collected during the first year of operation of the law estimates their value at close to $150,000,-000. From the same source we have a partial table of actual receipts of produce:

In terms of rations, it was estimated that these tithes would provide 29,000,000 rations of flour and 49,000,000 rations of corn meal, which at one pound to the ration would supply bread for 200,000 men for a year. The tithe of bacon at one-third pound to the ration would supply 160,000 men for a year. The balance of the tithe corn and the tithe oats would provide rations for 130,374 animals for a year, and the tithe hay and fodder would feed 35,992 animals for a year. Accompanying these figures was the comforting but questionable statement that farmers had cheerfully complied with the law.[5]

Before this optimistic statement was made, Congress, on the recommendation of the Commissioner of Taxes, Thompson Allan, who felt the burden of the tithing tax was too heavy for the small man, had introduced modifying features to the Revenue Act which slightly alleviated criticism of the tithing tax but made it less productive. Allan felt the tithing tax was unnecessarily involved, requiring great amounts of paper work by both producers and collectors to no good effect. He believed that small farmers should be exempted from its provisions, but that the same exemption on a portion of their produce should not apply to the large planters. He also agreed with critics that farmers who fed their corn to hogs were taxed doubly. Seven weeks after the adoption of the tithing tax, some of the criticisms later made by governors Vance, Bonham, Brown, and Milton were anticipated by a

---

[4] Resolution of Nov. 28, 1863, *Laws of Alabama*, 1863, p. 217.
[5] C. O. Cathey has evidence that the returns in bacon from North Carolina to June 1, 1864 were 2,800,000 pounds, in "The Impact of the Civil War on Agriculture in North Carolina," *The James Sprunt Studies in History and Political Science*, XXXIX (Chapel Hill, N.C., 1957), 109. Also, J. L. Nichols: "The Tax-in-Kind in the Department of the Trans-Mississippi," *Civil War History* V (December 1959), 382 ff.; *O.R.*, ser. 4, III, 800; Todd: *Confederate Finance*, p. 148.

RECEIPTS OF TAX IN KIND

States	Potatoes*	Corn*	Wheat*	Oats*	Peas*	Bacon†	Pork†
Georgia (to 3/1/64)	56,150	972,000	118,000			232,000	3,000
Alabama (to 3/1/64)	40,600	1,059,000	63,000			150,000	19,000
Mississippi	14,400	595,000	11,000			5,000	250,000
Tennessee		6,000	4,000			369	6,200
North Carolina (to 4/1/64)	41,000‡	613,000	767,000‡	88,000‡	7,000‡	1,500,573	
Total						1,994,130	

* Bushels
† Pounds
‡ Collections to June 1, 1864
SOURCE: Memphis Appeal (Atlanta), May 26, 1864.

measure "to abolish supernumerary officers" in the Commissary and Quartermaster Departments, but for every office abolished, more were subsequently created. On December 28, 1863, farmers were authorized to commute the tithe on sweet potatoes to a money payment. A major revision came on February 17, 1864, when heads of families with limited incomes were declared exempt from the tithe. Also, farmers who produced no more than 250 pounds of pork were exempted from the bacon tithe, and officers and servicemen who were discharged for wounds or physical disability, or the widows of men who had served in the army, were exempted from the tax imposed on neat cattle if they did not own more than two cows and calves.[6]

In June 1864, when the Commissary Department, ably aided by the newspapers throughout the South, was attempting to induce farmers to plant every possible variety of vegetable in abundance, the Congress freed all such produce that was intended for domestic consumption from the tithe. At the same time Congress provided for some further commutation of the tithe, which made the work of the Commissary Department more distasteful by forcing it back on impressment.[7]

To correct the widely held view that government service, particularly in the unpopular Quartermaster and Commissary Departments, was a sanctuary for men wishing to avoid military service, Congress struck hard at these departments. In a measure of February 17, 1864, it provided that only "artisans, mechanics, or persons of scientific skill to perform indispensable duties" between the ages of eighteen and forty-five in the Quartermaster and Commissary Departments should be exempt from required military service. The Adjutant and Inspector General interpreted the act to mean that the only persons who could be employed in these departments between the ages of eighteen and forty-five were those unable to perform active duty in the field, together with such others as were truly indispensable. There followed

---

[6] Allan recommended that no tax should be levied on pork produced in amounts less than 250 pounds, on fodder in amounts less than 100 pounds, on wool less than 5 pounds, and on ginned cotton less than 50 or 100 pounds. Report of Thomas Allan, Commissioner of Taxes, in *Documents Accompanying Report of Secretary of the Treasury* (Richmond, Va., November 1863), pp. 7–11.

[7] *O.R.*, ser. 4, III, 479.

no considerable flow of civilians to the army from these previously exempt positions, and prompt investigations were ordered to determine the cause of the failure. The much-harassed Commissary General, L. B. Northrop, replied that all able-bodied clerks in his own office had been discharged and their places filled with disabled soldiers and that throughout his department 293 men had been returned to the army. He might have added that the law worked a severe hardship on him, for men of skill and experience who were not quite "indispensable" had to be let go for untrained and incompetent persons who further aggravated his problems.[8]

Seddon and Northrop were quite aware that the supplies they worked so hard to accumulate were wastefully, indeed extravagantly, dissipated, but they would have been horrified to hear that while Bragg's army was being provisioned with mouldy cow peas and half-putrid salted beef, there were great mounds of supplies nearby, among them barrels of flour, pork, and beef broken open and scattered about, rotting in the sun and rain. Such maldistribution was not unique. Supplies were husbanded carefully and rations were reduced when they became tight, but when Nashville, Memphis, New Orleans, Atlanta, and Savannah fell, the amount of foodstuffs and material of war taken astonished the captors.[9]

---

[8] *O.R.*, ser. 4, III, 179, 524, 628.
[9] Watson: *Life in the Confederate Army*, p. 372.

4

Tightening of the Screws

IN NO MODERN WAR save World War I has a country been so successfully blockaded by sea and surrounded by land as the South in the Civil War. In no modern war has a country had great parts of its territory torn from it by the enemy, other portions ravaged by raiders, stragglers, and jayhawkers, its labor force reduced, much of its fertile land lying idle, its supply of food continually diminishing, its army rations cut to the bone and many of its people living in fear of actual starvation—and yet continued fighting, and fighting well, as the South did for four long years. Blow after blow fell upon the South. Its barns, granaries, hayricks, houses, and fences were burned, its levees breached, and its growing crops destroyed. Its unrivaled reserve (in numbers) of beef cattle in Texas was lost some time after the capture of Vicksburg and Port Hudson and the closing of the Mississippi to its ships. Its major corn, wheat, and pork producing counties in Tennessee, Virginia, Mississipi, Alabama, and Georgia passed under enemy control, and Missouri and Kentucky, with their huge reservoirs of food, failed to join the Confederacy. Furthermore, its railroads, so vital in military operations, were slowly falling apart and toward the end of the war were not able to move food from surplus-producing areas to the battlefields where it was most needed.

The shift, hastened by state legislation, from cotton, sugar cane, and tobacco to corn, wheat, and vegetables, and the adoption of impressment and tithing measures to secure food for the army without the government's having to pay speculators' prices, brought about great changes in Southern agriculture. These may be best seen in a negative way, first in the reduction of the amount of cotton produced: from 4,491,000 bales in 1861 to 1,597,000 in 1862, 449,000 in 1863, and 299,000 in 1864.[1] The reduced cotton crops resulted in part from Union control of sections of Louisiana, Tennessee, Alabama, Arkansas, and Mississippi and the demoralization that followed, but more from the changeover from staples to provisions. Except for a small quantity of foodstuffs that came through the blockade, the South was feeding itself in 1862 and 1863, but with little margin. It was clear that should the war be prolonged, the future was not bright.

Outstanding among the causes which defeated the South, said the perceptive Robert G. Kean, Chief of the Bureau of War, was the manpower shortage.[2] All able-bodied men between the ages of eighteen and forty-five were required for military service by the act of September 27, 1862, and men between forty-five and fifty by the act of February 17, 1864. Of all parts of the economy it was agriculture which was the hardest hit by these demands. Exemptions for farmers, as has been seen, were the least generous, and the twenty-Negro provision created more resentment than any other feature of conscription. It did, however, assure effective use of slaves on the plantations, as perhaps the exemption of one person for every 500 cattle or sheep or 250 horses or mules did also. But only planters of substantial resources owned as much livestock. The small farmer, whether mudsill, cracker, Cajun, sandhill tackey, piney-woods man, or yeoman, had no ground for exemption.

By no means all small farmers produced surpluses for sale

---

[1] *Historical Statistics* (Washington, 1957), p. 302.

[2] Others were a bankrupt treasury (with related evils of high prices, discontent and desertion, and decay of transportation facilities), scarcity of food, incompetence of military leaders, want of horses, difficulties of supply and recruiting, and slavery. Edward Younger (ed.): *The Diary of Robert Garlick Hill Kean* (New York, 1957), p. 214. The *Mobile Register and Advertiser*, Mar. 15, 1863, mentioned the four major crises or panics of the war to that time as lack of powder, deficiency of manpower, salt famine, and the food crisis.

but doubtless most did, and their total production, says Frank Owsley, could have supplied the South's entire needs of beef and pork. Since they constituted the great bulk of Southern white population, to exempt them would have made it impossible to create a powerful army. The withdrawal of these yeoman farmers, first by enlistment, then by conscription, meant that the necessary food could not be produced for the army and the civilian population. Wives, sisters, older children, elderly men beyond fifty, and paroled and wounded or maimed soldiers could aid in planting crops and caring for stock, but never as successfully as could the men who were drawn into the service. On the small family farms food crops were increasingly stressed and cotton and tobacco, which had supplied small amounts of cash, were abandoned. The families needed no admonition concerning the importance of corn, for it had always been their major crop and, when fed to hogs, their major dependence.[3]

After the men had been absent for a few months, the burden on those remaining in the home became ever heavier. The fuel supply for cooking and heating needed replenishing—not an easy task, as it called for the labor of able-bodied men to cut, split, and haul the wood, sometimes from a considerable distance. Plowing, harrowing, planting, and cultivating the corn, and, later, harvesting, shucking and shelling it, butchering the hogs and salting or smoking the hams and bacon, and maintaining the fences were not child's labor. Crops were planted more slowly and less care could be taken in preparing the soil, cultivating the land, and attending to the livestock. In harvesting the South Carolina wheat crop, which had been anticipated so anxiously, the cradling was done by the few males at home, the servants, and the invalid and furloughed soldiers, but the binding and stacking was done in great part by the "brave and faithful women who are worthy to be sisters of the soldiers of our army." Everywhere on the small farms the women were obliged to work in the field, to care for the livestock, and to attend to marketing duties. Wartime taxes, the fear of impressment of one's horses, mules, grain and pork, the payment of the tithe,

---

[3] E. M. Coulter: *The Confederate States of America* (Baton Rouge, La., 1950), pp. 314 ff.; F. L. Owsley: *Plain Folk of the Old South* (Baton Rouge, La., 1949), p. 135.

and illness and accidents—all contributed to the worries of the women and children who had to struggle with these burdens without assistance.[4]

Another blow at self-sufficiency on the small farms was struck when enrollment officers were compelled to conscript men from forty-five to fifty and boys of seventeen. Thus the older boys who might have carried on for their absent fathers were taken away from the farms.[5]

Few families were able to continue production beyond the first year at their prewar rate, and many with young children and no men to carry on the heavier work had to contract all outside operations drastically. Some could not even produce enough for their own needs. Letters came to soldiers telling of illness at home, poor crops, losses of livestock, or the fear of starvation. "How can our soldiers fight when they know their wives and children are destitute of even a piece of bread?" asked a North Carolina county clerk. The wife of a deserter, pleading for her husband's life, spoke of the death of her daughter and the illness of her son, the scarcity of food, the lack of fuel and of anyone to cut it, and the family's sufferings from "the chills" brought on by the cold and miserable conditions in which they lived. Bell I. Wiley wrote that "the greater burden of war was borne not by the ragged followers of Lee and Johnston, but by the poor wives and mothers at home who strove valiantly to provide a livelihood for their dependents."[6]

Had military needs permitted, it doubtless would have been a wise step for the army to have acted upon the urgent suggestion of the *Charleston Courier* of October 22, 1863, that a furlough be granted to every man in the state troops of South Carolina, most of whom were farmers desperately needed at their homes to gather the corn crop, sow wheat, and prepare the households for the winter months. Commanders on both sides

[4] *Charleston Courier*, June 22, 1863.
[5] C. P. Spencer: *The Last Ninety Days of the War* (New York, 1866), p. 242.
[6] B. A. Williams (ed.): *A Diary from Dixie by Mary Boykin Chesnut* (Boston, 1949), p. 413; Ella Lonn: *Desertion during the Civil War* (New York, 1928), *passim*;

B. I. Wiley: *Plain People of the Confederacy* (Baton Rouge, La., 1943), pp. 43, 68; G. C. Eggleston: *A Rebel's Recollections* (Bloomington, Ind., 1959), p. 89; F. B. Simkins and J. W. Patton: *Women of the Confederacy* (Richmond, Va., 1936), pp. 111 ff.

understood that men deserted because their families were suffering, and on both sides proclamations were issued allowing soldiers absent without leave to return without punishment.[7]

The routine of plantation activity was not so seriously affected, at least for some time, as that of the yeoman farmer. Planters and overseers were generally exempted from army service under the twenty-Negro law and their hands were not in demand for fortifications at the outset. True, planters who had trained their hands to work on cotton or tobacco disliked shifting them over completely to corn, but most gradually made the change. With the extra time available because corn cultivation was less demanding, it was always possible to set the Negroes to clearing new land, of which most planters had an abundance, and preparing it for cotton when the war was over.

But the plantations were not to escape the ravages of war. Their well-stocked cribs, smokehouses, barns, sheds, ginhouses, and wine cellars were sought out early by raiders and impressment officers and pillaged of their corn, wheat, forage, pork, bacon, beef, and cotton. Fences were burned by soldiers of both sides looking for dry and easily accessible wood to cook with. By 1863 and 1864 raiders and marching armies were capturing or shooting the cattle, hogs, horses, and mules found on plantations in Alabama, Mississippi, Georgia, Florida, Arkansas, North Carolina, and Virginia. They probably destroyed as much as they consumed.

Early in 1864 it was said that the largest farmers of the Piedmont counties of southwestern Virginia had furnished substitutes for the army, had devoted themselves to the production of meat, breadstuffs, vegetables, and forage, had hired out their field hands to railroads and manufacturing companies or sent them to the cities, and now were themselves being called into the service, which would prevent them from raising further crops. A Charleston resident thought the coastal planters had suffered the most, having been "driven from home by a ruthless foe" to suffer as refugees in the interior where the local people were "never so rich."[8]

---

[7] *Nashville Union*, Mar. 13, 1863.
[8] *Richmond Enquirer* in *National Intelligencer*, Jan. 28, 1864; R. H. Shryock: "Letters of Richard D. Arnold, M.D., 1808–1876," *Historical Papers of the Trinity College Historical Society*, XVIII–XIX (Durham, N.C., 1929), 110.

More serious than the impressment of plantation slaves was the seduction or capture of the slaves by the advancing Union armies. Though in the more romantic accounts of slavery the loyalty of the Negroes is stressed, and doubtless many were loyal, more were not and fled when the opportunity came. Throughout the South, in the later days of the war, slaves were slipping away, making the work of the plantations ever more difficult to carry on. A Union volunteer in Tennessee recorded in his diary that General David S. Stanley brought back from a raid to Huntsville a thousand Negroes, which "is a blow at the enemy in the right place. Deprived of slave labor, the whites will be compelled to send home, or leave at home, white men enough to cultivate the land and keep their families from starving."[9]

Military experts have frequently commented on the great benefits the Southern commanders gained from fighting the war on their own territory, with the shorter interior lines of communication, more mobile forces, and intimate knowledge of the terrain; but the other side to the question is the destruction inflicted upon the South. As the war progressed, the invaders moved from impressment, to seizure without redress or compensation, to foraging, pillaging, and outright destruction. The pilfering of fencing may not seem at first glance to be especially harmful to the Southern cause, but it was one of the most damaging blows the South received. Farmers had devoted years to splitting rails and posts and erecting their chestnut or oak worm fences, which the combination of livestock and field-crop economy made essential. The dry rails ignited easily and made admirable fuel for troops, who were delighted with the abundance of firewood. Marching armies in the Shenandoah Valley had destroyed the fences for miles around as early as May 1862. A year later the fence rails between Murfreesboro and Chattanooga in Tennessee were said to have been mostly burned, leaving numberless fields of growing corn unprotected. A Yankee soldier wrote of the importance of fence rails in making the life of the invading soldier in North Carolina more comfortable:

---

[9] H. S. Ford (ed.): *Memoirs of a Volunteer, 1861–1865,* by John Beatty (New York, 1946), p. 224.

The rail gathering is the life. You can imagine how much we are indebted to the rail fences of Secessia. They give us comfortable fires, hot coffee, and sometimes shelter itself. I can hardly conceive how we could live without them. Perhaps we are equally indebted to the pigs and potatoes of the country, for soldiers certainly never could march ten days upon hard tack and coffee alone.[1]

The other side of the story is shown in a letter of a Confederate soldier, written from near Fredericksburg, Virginia, April 13, 1863, while on the march that was to end at Gettysburg:

It begins to look like Spring, but I dont think the Farmers can do much on their farms here for their fenses are all burnt and the timber is all burnt til they can get nothing to fense there farms with You can have no idea how the Army weads out things where they go.

On a plantation near Spotsylvania where 80,000 rails were burned, the owner said that the troops of both sides had shared in the destruction. Planters near Vicksburg deplored the pilfering of their fences, saying there was no use in planting for as soon as the fences were rebuilt they were destroyed. They urged the authorities to take immediate action or there would be no crop raised in the neighborhood.[2]

Unfortunately Southern farmers suffered not only from the destruction inflicted by the invading forces but also from their own people. Captains of steamboats on the Ouachita River in Louisiana used Negroes to tear fences down and carry the rails on board their vessels for fuel. Soldiers at training camps and on the march sought out fence rails for firewood wherever they stopped. By December 1862, the plunder of rails by Southern troops had gone so far that the Adjutant and Inspector General issued an order condemning the "reckless destruction of fencing, wood and other property." He instructed commanders to use strict discipline to halt the destruction. "Fencing ought

---

[1] *The Index* (London), May 29, 1862; Ford: *Memoirs of a Volunteer*, p. 217; Z. T. Haines: *Letters from the Forty-fourth Regiment, MVM* (Boston, 1863), p. 59.
[2] Leonidas Torrence to his mother, in Haskell Monroe (ed.): "The Diary and Letters of Leonidas Torrence of the Gaston Guards," *North Carolina Historical Review*, XXXVI (1959), 504; Vicksburg *Daily Whig*, Feb. 27, 1863.

not to be disturbed where it can possibly be avoided," he declared. Because the destruction of fences was endangering the army's food supplies, President Davis himself had special instructions prepared warning against the pillage. All such instructions were useless, however. Well before the war's end, rail fences in great areas were almost entirely obliterated and farmers were compelled to resort to herding to keep cattle out of their cornfields.[3]

Efficiency of labor on the plantations and farms was reduced by scarcity of many items that were essential for good nutrition and good management. Salt, thanks to Ella Lonn, is the item about which we have the most information concerning the effects of its scarcity and the efforts to produce it. Heavily dependent in the past upon salt from the Northern states and from abroad, the South was ill-prepared to provide for its own needs. Scarcity of salt caused hoof and mouth disease among the cavalry horses of Lee's army, and left the horses of a division in the Shenandoah Valley in a deplorable condition. Large amounts of pork, beef, and hides spoiled, saltless butter would not keep sweet, and cattle deprived of their ration of salt suffered intensely and were unable to put on weight normally. Farmers in need of salt for the preservation of their pork and beef went to great lengths to find supplies of salt, and its price soon went sky high. A number of states and the Confederacy went into the manufacturing and distribution of salt—experiments in state socialism that were hardly compatible with their notions of governmental powers. In the midst of the salt famine, an Atlanta firm offered to exchange 1 bushel of salt for 4 bushels of corn or 2 of wheat, 100 pounds of salt for 100 pounds of pork, and 1,200 pounds of salt for 100 pounds of shoe leather. Destruction of the many saltworks that were speedily created to meet the emergency constituted one of the important tasks of the Union army and navy. The salt famine continued to be a major problem in the South throughout the war, ranking along with the lack of powder, the deficiency in manpower, and the growing food shortages.[4]

---

[3] O.R., ser. 4, II, 235; B. I. Wiley: *The Life of Johnny Reb, the Common Soldier of the Confederacy* (Indianapolis, 1943), p. 43; *Richmond Whig*, Aug. 28, 1863.

[4] Atlanta *Southern Confederacy*, Jan. 29, 1864; Ella Lonn: *Salt as a Factor in the Confederacy* (New York, 1933), *passim*; *Mobile Register and Advertiser*, June 15, 1863.

Leather for shoes, harnesses, and machine belts became scarce early in the war. When the supply of cowhides, horsehides, calfskins, and deerskins was depleted, the South resorted to dogskins, but supplies were soon exhausted. Wood, bark, cloth, and other substitutes were experimented with, though without much success. It was a common sight to see Confederate troops marching with no shoes and trying to get shoes from prisoners or dead Northern soldiers left on the field of battle. Slaves, accustomed to working barefoot, may not have suffered, but doubtless the small farmer was troubled and his ability to work somewhat affected by the scarcity of leather goods.[5]

It was the South's misfortune that it had not given more serious consideration to Henry J. Randall's *Sheep Industry in the South,* published in 1848. Though the book went through numerous printings and had a marked effect in promoting the raising of sheep in Texas, it seems not to have had much influence elsewhere. In three states the number of sheep sharply declined in the fifties; only in Texas was there a large increase. Furthermore, the million and more Texas sheep and their wool were available for only part of the war. Like the North, the South had been heavily dependent upon foreign supplies of wool and had relied largely upon Northern-made cloth. Woolen blankets and clothes quickly became scarce items and during the winter months their absence caused much suffering and misery. When the army's supply of blankets was exhausted, people were urged to cut up their rugs and give them to the soldiers. Some progress was made in establishing cotton and woolen mills but the lack of machines, cards, and other essentials forced people to resort to the domestic arts of knitting, carding, spinning, and weaving. Farmers were urged to take the best possible care of their sheep and severe penalties were proposed against the owners of dogs which killed sheep. A report of the comptroller general of Georgia shows that 7 per cent of the sheep of that state were destroyed annually by dogs.[6]

---

[5] *Richmond Enquirer,* Sept. 2, 1861, Apr. 28, 1862; M. E. Massey: *Ersatz in the Confederacy* (Columbia, S.C., 1952), pp. 79 ff.; Coulter: *Confederate States,* pp. 210 ff.

[6] J. M. McCue, Sept. 26, 1863, to Gov. Vance, Gov. Corr., N.C. Arch.; Massey: *Ersatz,* pp. 85 ff.; Comptroller General of Georgia: *Report,* 1864, part 2, p. 44.

Notwithstanding the inroads that coal had made in the fuel market, wood was still the principal fuel used in most homes, on locomotives and steamboats, and for public buildings. It was estimated that in 1860 the railroads of the United States alone used three million cords of wood. Some lines in Pennsylavania and New Jersey were using coal, but every Southern locomotive burned wood. One line, the Virginia and Tennessee, kept 30,000 cords spaced along its route. The business of supplying fuel wood—pine, oak, beech, ash, and chestnut—took the time of many woodcutters, with whom contracts were made by railroad and steamship agents. Much of the actual cutting was done by small farmers, who could make a little cash that way whether they were working on their own land or elsewhere, and by slaves in the few weeks when other plantation duties did not absorb their time.[7] Conscription of the small farmers and impressment or assignment of slaves to more remunerative tasks than wood cutting reduced the supplies of fuel wood for railroads and contributed greatly to their difficulties. As fuel became scarce, supplies were impressed for the army, and at the same time the railroads were giving priority to transporting other goods which paid higher freight rates. Even on the farms where there was an abundance of growing timber, the families of absent soldiers were short of fuel because there was no labor to cut the wood. They were also pinched for want of the income they had previously made from wood cutting.

The scarcity of fuel was felt early in the war in Richmond, Raleigh, Charleston, New Orleans, and other cities, and the poorer classes suffered severely from the cold. Scarcity and bureaucratic tensions between the Quartermaster Department and the Surgeon General were responsible for insufficient quantities of fuel wood being provided Chimborazo and Winder hospitals, thereby causing intense suffering. By 1865 the demand for wood had driven prices to absurd levels—five dollars a stick in Rich-

---

[7] *Railroad Record* in *Hunt's Merchants Magazine*, XLIV (January 1861), 117; R. G. Black: *The Railroads of the Confederacy* (Chapel Hill, N.C., 1952), pp. 21 ff.; A. J. Johnston: *Virginia Railroads in the* *Civil War* (Chapel Hill, N.C., 1961), pp. 12, 124; L. C. Hunter: *Steamboats on the Western Rivers* (Cambridge, Mass., 1949), pp. 264 ff.; *National Intelligencer*, Oct. 29, 1863.

mond—and led to pilfering from railroad woodyards. In the trenches nothing but green pine was available for warming the men. As early as October 1862 the *Charleston Mercury* was declaring that, next to food, the greatest problem the city faced was that of maintaining supplies of fuel which were not prohibitively priced. In January 1863, a salt manufacturer in Wilmington said: "We are about to freeze too as well as starve." "Wood extortioners" were condemned for the high prices they charged and the ingenious ways by which their jags of wood were made to appear larger than they actually were. In Mobile and Vicksburg city authorities took over the entire wood supply to assure equitable distribution.[8]

Memphis, Nashville, Vicksburg, and other cities captured by the Federals needed fuel as much after capture as before, and though coal could now be brought in by steamboat, fuel wood remained scarce. Partly for the government and partly for relief, the Federal Depot Quartermaster in Nashville called for bids for 35,000 cords of merchantable hardwood but stated that only bids from loyal persons would be considered.

While city residents and small farm families alike suffered hardships from the want of fuel, residents of the piney woods of southern Alabama and Mississippi and of the English parishes of Louisiana were hard hit by the blockade. It halted their customary trade with New Orleans, Mobile, and Pensacola, where cordwood, charcoal, lightwood, lumber, tar, rosin, and turpentine were exchanged for grain and flour. In addition they suffered heavy losses of livestock from cholera and anthrax, and in 1862 their corn and potato crops were drastically reduced by a severe drought. This series of catastrophies brought them to the verge

---

[8] *Richmond Enquirer*, Sept. 18, 1863; J. B. Jones: *A Rebel War Clerk's Diary at the Confederate States Capital* (2 vols., Philadelphia, 1866), II, 400; J. G. de Roulhac Hamilton (ed.): *The Correspondence of Jonathan Worth, Publications of the North Carolina Historical Commission* (2 vols., Raleigh, N.C., 1909), I, 227; Raleigh *North Carolina Standard*, Oct. 17, Dec. 2, 1862; Mrs. M. H. Williams, Feb. 15, 1863, to Vance, Gov. Corr., N.C. Arch.; Jackson *Daily Southern Crisis*, Feb. 7, 1863; *New Orleans Picayune*, Nov. 13, 1863; *Mobile Advertiser and Register*, Oct. 29, Nov. 1, 1863, Jan. 13, Feb. 7, 1864; Augusta *Chronicle & Sentinel*, Sept. 11, 1863, Jan. 12, 1864; *Charleston Mercury*, Oct. 30, 1862.

of starvation, or as an alternative, to desertion of the Southern cause. Heroic relief measures had to be instituted to prevent starvation and disloyalty.[9]

Aside from the casualties of war, the destruction of homes, and the flight or emancipation of their slaves, little that happened to planters distressed them more than the burning of their cotton. It was to the proceeds from the sale of their crop of 1860 and the new crop of 1861 that they looked to meet the interest and principal payments on their debts, provide for their needs for the next year, and take care of their taxes and all other calls that might be made upon them. Suddenly, with the blockade, cotton became unsalable. Under the Produce Loan Acts of 1861 planters could exchange for Confederate 8 per cent bonds a portion of their cotton, rice, tobacco, sugar, molasses, or wheat, which was to be stored in warehouses and sold on or before a fixed date. Since, despite the variety of stay laws the states adopted, these bonds brought no cash to the planters, who were hard pressed for funds, the cry went up for the Confederate government to buy the cotton, or at least to make advances on the crop. Believing the Confederacy had no power to make such purchases or loans, the authorities declined to move, but a number of states did inaugurate loans on cotton. In 1862 the Confederacy enlarged its produce loans of the previous year. Altogether, 500,000 bales of cotton and smaller amounts of other produce were thus subscribed and were subsequently used as a basis for securing credit for the purchase of supplies abroad. Unfortunately for the planters, all such devices brought them little cash. The cotton was piled up in warehouses or ginhouses, a major invitation to fire.[1]

As Federal troops advanced into the South, capturing coastal areas and important sea and river ports such as New Orleans, Baton Rouge, Nashville, Memphis, and Natchez, patriotism dictated the burning of cotton before it fell into their hands. Where patriotism failed, the army commanded destruction. General Samuel G. French ran into strong opposition, however, when he

[9] Jackson *Weekly Mississippian,* Dec. 19, 1861; *Nashville Daily Union,* Aug. 27, 1863; G. L. Gaines, Oct. 14, 1862, and A. E. Lewis, Jan. 18, 1863, to Gov. Pettus, Gov. Corr., Miss. Arch.; C. W. Ramsdell: *Behind the Lines in the Southern Confederacy* (Baton Rouge, La., 1944), pp. 27 ff.

[1] R. C. Todd: *Confederate Finance* (Athens, Ga., 1954), pp. 31 ff.

ordered the burning of all cotton in eastern North Carolina not removed by December 15, 1862. The legislature of North Carolina adopted a resolution declaring the order unjust, impolitic, and unnecessarily destructive, since the people themselves would burn cotton if it were likely to fall into the hands of the enemy.[2]

Southern newspapers printed accounts of the widespread destruction of cotton before the advancing Federals. "Planters are piling up their cotton . . . ready for the fagot" the moment the enemy arrived, said the Confederate-financed *Index*, which claimed that half a million bales along the banks of the Mississippi had been destroyed by June of 1862. It was said that in Arkansas alone 300,000 bales had been burned. After the capture of Memphis, cotton was rapidly destroyed as a result of raids into Alabama and Mississippi and Sherman's march through Georgia and South Carolina. Where Northern raiders saw no opportunity of removing captured cotton, they likewise burned it. Professor Coulter estimates that altogether, 2,500,000 bales were destroyed. Thus was lost the South's greatest cashable resource, which at the conclusion of the war might have aided in the restoration of the economy. "If our cotton had been saved, we would be in comparatively easy circumstances," wailed the wife of a South Carolina planter in May 1865.

On the other hand, Northern newspapers claimed that the Federals had found cotton which had not been burned. The *National Intelligencer*, for example, quoted dispatches showing the quantities of cotton that had survived Confederate fire and Northern destruction. Some planters had hidden cotton away in parlors, lofts, cellars and swamps; some had even buried it. Then they brought it out when Union forces were near and traded through the lines.[3]

Meantime, the area controlled by the Confederacy and producing crops for its army and for civilians was shrinking

---

[2] Resolution of Dec. 9, 1862, *Laws of North Carolina*, 1862–3, p. 53.
[3] *Senate Ex. Doc.*, 40 Cong., 2 Sess., 1868, I, no. 22, and II, no. 56; *The Index*, May 1, 15, June 19, 1862; *National Intelligencer*, Aug. 23, 1862, quoting the *New York Journal of Commerce;* Coulter: *Confederate States*, p. 242; J. G. Fletcher: *Arkansas* (Chapel Hill, N.C., 1947) p. 157; Williams: *Diary by Mary B. Chesnut*, p. 529; A. T. Richardson: *The Secret Service, the Field, the Dungeon and the Escape* (Hartford, Conn., 1865), p. 264.

dangerously. Even nature seemed unkindly disposed to the Confederates. The weather during the war years may not have been unusual, but the succession of droughts, devastating rains, and floods seemed so to people painfully aware of the necessity for maintaining and expanding the food supplies of the region. In 1862 a widespread drought sharply reduced the corn crop throughout the South, except for southern and southwestern Georgia. In northern Georgia, especially in Cherokee County, farmers did not harvest enough corn to provide for their own needs and were said to be suffering from want of provisions. Earlier that year the warm and rainy weather in Georgia had caused rust to develop on wheat, lowering output to one sixth of the expected crop. Elsewhere in Virginia, eastern Tennessee, and the lower South, wheat was badly damaged by rust or ruined by drought. The Montgomery *Advertiser* even declared that wheat was almost a complete failure throughout the South. Yet in Mississippi the highest flood on the Mississippi River to that time breached the levees in the Delta and did great damage to growing crops.[4]

Again, in 1863 both droughts and too much rain plagued Virginia, a severe summer frost did damage in Tennessee, extraordinarily heavy and long-continued rains in Georgia held back the corn and spoiled much of the promising wheat crop. In 1864 excessive spring rains were followed in Georgia by another destructive drought. In the early part of the growing season of 1864, sections of Virginia had a drought of six to eight weeks, which materially shortened the corn crop. However, the dryness contributed to the early maturity of the wheat, making it available for harvesting before the normal time. In Texas, the harsh winter of 1863–4 was reported to have killed from one half to nine tenths of the cattle on many farms. Elsewhere the cold winter killed many farm animals, cut fruit production heavily, injured gardens, and damaged the wheat crop. Drought also parched the growing crops in Alabama and Mississippi, further reducing output. In

[4] *Savannah Republican*, Feb. 19, Sept. 4, 1863; J. L. Robertson, Jr.: *The Diary of Dolly Lunt Burge* (Athens, Ga., 1962), p. 80; Ramsdell: *Behind the Lines*, pp. 43–4; D. C. James: "Mississippi Agriculture 1861–1865," *Journal of Mississippi History*, XXIV (1962), 135.

the closing days of the war a freshet in North Carolina, combined with two destructive fires in Charlotte and Salisbury, ruined vast quantities of food.[5]

The destitute condition of many families whose head had enlisted or been conscripted and whose meager allowance was insufficient led to relief movements being organized. State legislatures appropriated generous sums for the aid of the indigent, counties developed relief programs of their own, and private charitable groups collected and distributed large amounts of money and food. The Georgia legislature asked the railroads to ship corn to distressed areas at half rates and provided for the purchase of 97,500 bushels of corn for distribution among suffering families.[6]

North Carolina was the most generous in providing relief for soldiers' families: its total expenditures, including those of the counties, amounted to $26,000,000. In addition to direct financial relief distributed through the counties, the state purchased corn, pork, medicines, and clothing, partly for resale at cost and partly for free distribution to needy cases. It also operated saltworks to keep the speculators' profits out of the manufacture of this much-needed item. Counties granted from $4 to $20 a month to needy wives and from $1 to $10 for dependent children. Next in liberal support of its soldiers' dependents was Georgia, which contributed to 83,628 widows, mothers, and orphans of soldiers a total of $22,000,000. It also attempted to keep food costs down by arranging free transportation for food intended for the poor, and aided in the removal of the indigent from areas threatened by Federal troops.[7]

Alabama began its relief work for the indigent families of

[5] Augusta *Chronicle & Sentinel,* July 25, 30, 1863, Nov. 10, 1864; *Nashville Union,* Dec. 4, 1863; *Nashville Dispatch,* Sept. 1, 1863; Spencer: *The Last Ninety Days,* p. 29.
[6] Resolution of the Georgia legislature, Dec. 4, 1862, *Laws of Georgia,* 1862, p. 107; *Laws of Georgia,* 1863-4, p. 67; *Laws of Georgia,* 1864-5, p. 34; J. E. Brown to Jefferson Davis, A. D. Candler (ed.): *The Confederate Records of the State of Georgia* (6 vols., Atlanta, 1909-11), III, 328.
[7] Comptroller General of Georgia: *Annual Report,* 1863, p. 21; W. F. Entrekin: "Poor Relief in North Carolina in the Confederacy," master's thesis, Duke University, 1947, *passim;* Ramsdell: *Behind the Lines,* p. 62; Coulter: *Confederate States,* p. 426; T. C. Bryan: *Confederate Georgia* (Athens, Ga., 1953), p. 62.

soldiers by levying a special tax of 25 per cent on the amount already imposed on all taxable property. The tax could be paid in provisions or material for clothing valued at a fair market price. In five subsequent measures the legislature appropriated $11,500,000 for this purpose in addition to $500,000 it authorized for aid to persons rendered destitute by enemy action. When these funds proved insufficient to meet all needs, the counties were permitted to levy taxes for relief and to impress goods where necessary. At the outset Alabama denied relief to families of substitutes, and then to families of substitutes who had received more than $1,500 for taking the place of a drafted person, but finally relief was extended to all needy families of soldiers.[8]

Louisiana appropriated $5,000,000 for aid to families of soldiers but had much trouble in distributing these funds because of the inroads of the Federal armies. Mississippi appropriated $1,500,000 for relief to families of volunteers, granted county police boards power to impress supplies as they were needed, and adopted a 2 per cent tax on agricultural and manufactured goods to provide additional aid. Texas and South Carolina also appropriated funds for relief, but Virginia left it mostly to private charity and local governmental bodies.[9]

Private charity working through relief associations supplemented the state relief activities in towns and cities. A list of contributions to the Georgia Relief and Hospital Association shows that openhearted and grieving people were giving whatever they could share from their own table to aid the sick and wounded. Included in this list were vegetables, peaches, buttermilk, baked fowls, soap, potatoes, blackberries, bread, onions, chewing and smoking tobacco, a jar of pickles, and a bundle of rags. The Union Benevolent Society of Richmond, aided by the city government, was regularly feeding 4,500 people by the close of the war.[1]

Elsewhere public stores were maintained at which food was sold for cash, and free markets were organized to which people brought their surpluses for the indigent. At Mobile $30,645 and

---

[8] Acts of Nov. 11, 1861, Nov. 12, 1862, Aug. 29 and Dec. 8, 1863, and Oct. 7 and Dec. 13, 1864.
[9] J. D. Bragg: *Louisiana in the Confederacy* (Baton Rouge, La.,

1941), p. 238; James: "Mississippi Agriculture," p. 137; Coulter: *Confederate States*, p. 426.
[1] Augusta *Chronicle & Sentinel*, July 2, 1863.

6,000 bushels of corn for the needy were contributed by March 1863. In Natchez two free markets were open two mornings a week, one for the families of soldiers and the other for the poor who were not entitled to draw goods at the first. Through the *Natchez Daily Courier* appeals were made for vegetables, buttermilk, corn meal, and other food. The local paper tells of Mrs. E. Surget, the grande dame of Natchez, bringing in four half-barrels of buttermilk, one barrel of lady peas, carrots, leeks, onions, cabbage, salsify, and other goods. One of the first and most extensive of the free markets was that of New Orleans, where in December 1861 an average of 1,850 families were supplied with provisions for each of the ten days it was open. In March 1862 the cash and dollar value of goods contributed came to $16,249. Included were codfish, beef, flour, potatoes, vegetables, bread, rice, salt, eggs, and a gold watch. Two thousand loaves of bread were baked for distribution in a single day. It was rumored that some people secured relief goods and later sold them, which tended to put a damper on the flow of goods.[2]

In Texas relief was needed on a much larger scale, if the *Weekly Texas State Gazette* of Austin did not exaggerate in reporting that aid should be provided for 74,000 indigents and dependents of soldiers. Among the proposals it suggested to handle this great burden were a tax in kind, treasury warrants with a tax to retire them, land scrip, a tax on real property, and a tax on distilling of liquor. Houston, which was not in a farming region, found it difficult to supply its needy with food, though the railroads offered to bring in grain and fuel free and the county was ready to provide sacks of grain.[3]

Aid from these various sources eased the misery of families whose husbands and sons were in the army; but the total effect of both state appropriations and private charity was small and, as the complaints coming in to the governors showed, inadequate.

In a region where pork products constituted a large part of the diet of both free and slave, any threat to the supply of pork

---

[2] *Mobile Advertiser and Register,* Mar. 1, 1863; *Natchez Daily Courier,* May 22, 23, June 3, 27, 1863; *New Orleans Picayune,* Nov. 14, 20, Dec. 7, 1861, Jan. 3, Mar. 30, 1862.

[3] Austin *Weekly Texas State Gazette,* Oct. 26, 1864; *Houston Daily Telegraph,* Sept. 16, 1864.

was a serious matter. With the exception of yellow fever, no disease hurt the Confederacy more than hog cholera. This major affliction caused losses planters and farmers could ill afford. Although the disease was not confined to the South, its effects were more disastrous there. It attacked hundreds of thousands of swine and caused losses amounting to millions of dollars before its cause—a virus—and its remedy—immunization with a serum—were discovered. The disease first became serious in the Middle West in 1856 and 1857. It quickly spread to Kentucky, Tennessee, and Arkansas. In Kentucky hogs were dying so fast in 1860 that the Kentucky legislature offered an award of one thousand dollars for a successful cure or remedy. By late 1861 the disease had done such damage among the hogs in Mississippi as to lead some farmers to cease raising them. Martin W. Philips, one of the best-known Southern agricultural writers, who had argued for diversification and livestock raising before the war, lost a hundred hogs in 1862 and turned his attention to Morgan horses to recoup his losses.[4]

There are no reliable figures of losses from hog cholera during the war but the evidence showing how widespread the disease was is abundant. The summer of 1862 was marked by three months of drought and hot weather in most of the South, a condition which some persons thought contributed to the spread of the disease. Mississippi was very hard hit in that the corn crop was ruined and thousands of hogs died from cholera. The next year the *Richmond Whig* reported heavy losses from cholera in all areas bordering the Blue Ridge from Harrisonburg and Culpeper to Fincastle and Lynchburg, while a writer in the Mobile *Advertiser and Register* commented on the widespread ravages of the disease in Alabama. Cholera drastically curtailed the number of hogs the Confederate Commissary Department could count on from Georgia and contributed to an extremely pessimistic report on the available supplies of meat for the army in late 1863. Hog cholera appeared again in 1864. In Alabama and Florida

---

[4] "Hog Cholera," Commissioner of Patents, *Annual Report, Agriculture,* 1861, pp. 147 ff.; E. D. Ross: *Iowa Agriculture* (Iowa City, 1951), p. 132; *Cultivator,* VIII (February 1860), 69; *Ohio Culti-* *vator,* XVI (May 15, 1860), 151; *Southern Cultivator,* XXI (March–April 1863), 4; *New Orleans True Delta,* Nov. 25, 1861; Milledgeville *Southern Recorder,* Jan. 21, 1862; *O.R.,* ser. 4, I, 873.

planters reported losing as many as 100 to 140 animals, and in North Carolina some farmers lost their entire stock. Again, in 1865 mortality from "that dreadful disease, the cholera," was reported very extensive.[5]

The disease raged throughout the war, taking its toll almost everywhere. It was a major factor in reducing the army's rations of bacon and the supply of meat on farms and plantations. Letters came to the tithing and impressment officers and to the governors enumerating the heavy losses and stating that planters were having to buy hogs because their own supplies were insufficient for their needs. The planters declared they were unable to contribute a tithe of their pork and begged that the impressment officers would not touch their meager stock. The losses from hog cholera and the poor crops of corn may also have contributed to the movement for allowing the tithe to be commuted to cash payments.[6]

Science was not to discover a cure for hog cholera for many years, but a variety of remedies were tried which worked wonders, according to their advocates. Among the cures or preventatives were a teaspoon of arsenic in meal for twenty hogs; garlic boiled with corn; a mixture of lime, copperas, or sulphur; drenching followed by feeding corn well smeared with tar; peanut oil, or spirits of turpentine; a mixture of raw rosin, copperas, and sulphur; and a brew of antimony, saltpeter, and sulphur.[7]

Factors other than cholera contributed to the decline in the number of hogs and the amount of pork and bacon in the South. An estimated 400,000 hogs were driven from areas threatened by the Federals. The succession of short grain crops—and their almost complete failure in some regions—cut the number of pigs

[5] *Hinds County Gazette* (Raymond, Miss.), Sept. 3, 1862; *Memphis Appeal* (Atlanta), Feb. 20, 1864; *Montgomery Daily Mail*, Sept. 20, 1864; *Charleston Courier*, Mar. 29, 1864; *Clarke County Democrat*, Sept. 18, 1862; J. G. de Roulhac Hamilton (ed.): *The Papers of Thomas Ruffin, Publications of the North Carolina Historical Commission* (3 vols., Raleigh, N.C., 1918–1920), III, 350, 401, 427.

[6] A. J. Fordham, Mar. 24, 1864, to Vance, Gov. Corr., N.C., Arch.; Augusta *Chronicle & Sentinel*, Nov. 28, 1864; W. T. Jordan: *Hugh Davis and His Alabama Plantation* (University, Ala., 1948), p. 158.
[7] *Southern Recorder* in *Raleigh Daily Confederate*, May 3, Aug. 19, 1864; Augusta *Constitutionalist*, Apr. 10, 1865; *The Countryman* (Turnwold, Ga.), July 5, 1864; *The Morning Mississippian* (Selma), Apr. 19, 1864.

in the new crop and the amount of pork on the hogs that were dressed. Also, the capture and shooting of livestock by raiders and the destruction when army units evacuated territory added up to heavy losses. As the Mobile *Advertiser and Register* of November 1, 1863, said, there was a "palpable, real scarcity" of hogs and pork products, and no legislative device to reduce prices would have any effect on them.

Charbon or anthrax was another disease which brought death to many hogs as well as to large numbers of horses, mules, cattle, and sheep in Mississippi and Alabama during the war. It was serious enough in 1860, and disastrous in the summer of 1861. Since it was becoming increasingly difficult to bring in mules from Kentucky, Ohio and Missouri, the losses—25 out of 90 on one plantation—were a matter of deep concern. Losses of cattle in St. Mary and Plaquemines parishes in Louisiana were extensive. Remedies included drenching with whiskey and brandy.[8]

To weaken the South and bring the Confederacy to surrender, the Northern military command was doing its best to strike at Southern food supplies. Accounts of the smashing of plows, McCormick reapers, threshing machines, and other farm implements, the killing of livestock which could not be run off, the cutting down of fruit trees, the burning of shops, foundries, granaries, barns, gristmills, warehouses, fences, tanneries, hayricks, and wheat stacks, the destruction of sluice gates, and the breaching of levees are to be found in the newspapers, the official documents, and in numerous soldiers' diaries.[9]

Grenville Dodge's raid into Alabama in 1863 captured 1,000 horses and mules as well as quantities of grain, cattle, sheep, and hogs, and destroyed 1,500,000 bushels of corn, 500,000 pounds of bacon, 3 tanyards, 5 mills, and 60 flatboats. "It has rendered desolate one of the best granaries of the South, prevented them from raising another crop this year and taken away some 1,500 negroes," said one who suffered. Professor J. K. Bettersworth has

---

[8] *New Orleans Picayune,* June 14, July 14, 1861; Ramsdell: *Behind the Lines,* p. 27; C. P. Roland: *Louisiana Sugar Plantations during the American Civil War* (Leiden, 1957), p. 29.
[9] *Richmond Whig,* June 9, 12, 19, July 17, 1863; Augusta *Chronicle & Sentinel,* Nov. 18, 1864.

shown that "siege, surrender, and devastation prostrated" Mississippi by 1863.[1]

Two raids in North Carolina by only a few troops destroyed 350,000 pounds of bacon along with other supplies. Raiders on the Combahee destroyed great amounts of rice, corn, and cotton, broke sluice gates, flooded the fields, killed the growing crops, and brought away 800 contrabands. Sheridan destroyed all grain, flour, fodder, hay, livestock, barns, and mills—even the garden crops and corn in the field. Grant's instructions that "nothing should be left to invite the enemy to return," and that troops should "carry off stock of all descriptions and negroes, so as to prevent further planting" show the extent to which the Federals were prepared to go to compel surrender. Familiar to readers of American history is the enumeration by General Philip Sheridan of the capture or destruction carried out by his forces in the Shenandoah in 1864. It included 880 barns, 57 grain mills, 4 sawmills, 1,910,000 bushels of wheat, 500 barrels of flour, 1,347 cattle, 1,231 sheep, 725 hogs, and hundreds of tons of straw and fodder.[2]

The devastation inflicted upon Georgia by Sherman's army may best be epitomized in an account of the damage done to a plantation belonging to W. D. Tyrell in Putnam County. The ginhouse and packing screw were burned, the wheat thresher and fan were broken, his carriage was hacked and broken, the harness was carried off along with all the mules and horses but two, all the cows and sheep were driven off, the shoats, sows, and pigs were shot, meal and flour was taken, all oats, corn, and fodder were trampled down by the horses, fowls were destroyed, heads of syrup barrels were stove in, and six negroes were taken. Small wonder that the owner was in despair when he returned in February 1865.[3]

Earlier in the war the Confederate forces had been obliged to burn 169,000 pounds of meat and to give 200,000 pounds to people at Manassas because it could not be removed in time, but

---

[1] O.R., ser 1, XXIII, part 1, 249. J. K. Bettersworth: *Confederate Mississippi. The People and Policies of a Cotton State in Wartime* (Baton Rouge, La., 1943), p. 263.
[2] *Harper's Weekly*, VII (July 4,

1863), 427; *Richmond Whig*, Mar. 7, 1864; *National Intelligencer*, Oct. 15, Nov. 19, 1864; O.R., ser. 1, XLIII, part 1, 59, 917.
[3] *The Countryman* (Turnwold, Ga.), Feb. 21, 1865.

these losses were more than compensated by the subsequent capture of Union supply trains. As late as 1864 the capture by Wade Hampton of 2,466 beeves estimated at 800 pounds of meat each gave temporary encouragement to the Confederates. But by 1863 and 1864 Union troops were making a clean sweep of wheat, corn, hogs, sheep, and poultry from Murfreesboro to Chattanooga, Hood had to give away much of the 500,000 pounds of meal on hand when he surrendered Atlanta, and Sherman was able to leave Atlanta with 1,760 wagonloads of corn, 436 loads of sweet potatoes, and quantities of meat which his foraging parties had assembled. These losses, which constitute only a small part of the total, counteracted many of the sacrifices that had been made to meet the provision and forage requirements of the army and dependent civilian population.[4]

The pillaging and burning by Northern raiders was bad enough but the civil war within a Civil War fought by Southern Unionists on one side and loyal Confederates on the other was even more bitter. Unionists in east Tennessee, portions of North Carolina, and Alabama, who were dubbed Tories by their enemies, were joined by stragglers, skulkers, and deserters, and in small bands they raided Confederate centers, plundered and burned homes, and destroyed crops. The *Nashville Union* urged the Unionists to destroy all stores and crops they could not use. "To spare them is to leave them for the rebels. We must burn out treason with fire and then drown its embers in blood," it declared. In retaliation Confederate officers permitted their men to forage upon the Tories, run off their horses and mules, take their pigs and corn, and burn their homes. If Tories or deserters were caught, they were likely to be hung or shot. Marauding and pillaging went on until whole areas were laid waste, with all horses, mules, hogs, and cattle taken or killed, and sons and fathers shot, hung, hunted down with dogs, starved, and poisoned. In east Tennessee it was said in 1864 that not a farmer would be able to start a single plow.[5]

[4] *O.R.*, ser. 4, I, 1038 ff.; Ford: *Memoirs* by Beatty, p. 217; *Mobile Advertiser and Register*, Sept. 18, Dec. 10, 1864; Columbia *South Carolinian*, Sept. 24, 1864.

[5] *Nashville Union*, May 23, 1863, Jan. 22, 1864; *Mobile Tribune*, Oct. 17, 1863; *Southern Confederacy*, Apr. 29, 1864; Augusta *Chronicle & Sentinel*, Dec. 2, 7, 22, 1864.

The hourly widening of the belt of desolation, the wearing out and destruction of the railroads, and the demoralization of railroad employees all called for the most vigorous action if even the reduced rations for the army were to be obtained and the civilian population fed. Governmental powers could be used to meet this emergency only in a limited way because of the Confederacy's constitutional straitjacket and because disillusionment and disinclination to take more stringent measures was growing in the states. Farmers doubtless shared this disillusionment, for they had been subjected to bitter criticism for prices over which they had little control while at the same time they were being exhorted to produce more food on grounds of patriotism.[6]

Plantations and farms were becoming less and less productive because farm implements had worn out or been destroyed and could not be replaced. Two petitions to Governor Vance of North Carolina in July 1863, signed by twenty-six and twenty-eight men respectively, stated that there was only one thresher in their neighborhood and that to get their wheat out they must have two skilled operators released from army duty. Although farm implements were irreplaceable for most people, John D. Gray and Co. of Columbus, Georgia, was advertising in March 1864 that he was prepared to exchange plow and scooter bar iron, horseshoes, nailrods, shovels, spades, frying pans, potware, kettles, and sugar mills obtained from the ironworks and rolling mill in Alabama for lard, syrup, potatoes, tallow, butter, wheat, or flour.[7]

Military strategy was seriously hampered by the growing food crisis, particularly in Virginia. Robert E. Lee could not bring himself to use military impressment powers as rigorously as he was told by Colonel Northrop, the Commissary General, that the law allowed. To use military impressment, instead of impressment by the civil authority in the War Department, would penal-

---

[6] J. H. Easterby (ed.): *The South Carolina Rice Plantation As Revealed in the Papers of Robert F. W. Allston* (Chicago, 1945), p. 430; Black: *Railroads of the Confederacy, passim.*
[7] Thos. Simons and 25 others, July 17, 1863, Daniel Reap and 28 others, July 17, 1863, and J. E. Goodwin, July 7, 1864, to Gov. Vance, Gov. Corr., N.C., Arch.; *Montgomery Weekly Advertiser,* Feb. 26, 1864; *Montgomery Daily Mail,* Mar. 24, 1864; *Richmond Whig,* Mar. 3, 1864, *Columbus Times,* Mar. 5, 1864.

ize farmers in Virginia compared with farmers of other parts of the South where there was more food and where military impressment was unnecessary. Lee was aware that the armies of Johnston and of other commanders were getting more generous rations but he held to his opinions.

Forage and grain for the starving horses and meat and bread for the troops had to be obtained, however, and since the Commissary General was not able to provide these essentials in sufficient amounts, time and again Lee had to divert troops from his command to reopen and maintain supply lines and to make food and forage sweeps into eastern North Carolina and southwestern Virginia. At the very end of the Confederacy, just before Appomattox, when the expected rations did not reach him and men and horses were exhausted and almost overcome by hunger, Lee had to order wagons out on foraging expeditions; but with little success this time. The breakdown of supply lines, Douglas Freeman has shown, had a major bearing upon the crackup of Lee's army and its final surrender.[8]

World War I was not the first time that people who advocated restricting the liquor traffic bolstered their moral position with the argument that restriction was necessary to save grain. In the Civil War also, these groups tried to ban the manufacture and sale of alcohol other than for medical purposes. Many of them, of course, were concerned about the scarcity of food and the plight of the poor.

The privations of camp life—short rations, rain, cold, inadequate clothing, and lack of blankets—made both men and officers prone to resort to whiskey when it could be bought and they had the price. Dram shops sprang up around the camps; liquor stores were clustered around hospitals to tempt the sick and wounded. "Multitudes of drinking shops whose poisonous whiskey is sold to soldiers" were located in Richmond, leading to disgraceful scenes of intoxication, said the *Richmond Enquirer*. The writer regretted that there was no power to halt the traffic.[9]

Efforts to ban the distillation of liquor from grain were defeated in the Confederate Congress and the matter was left,

---

[8] D. S. Freeman: *R. E. Lee* (4 vols., New York, 1934–5), II, 492, and III, 246; J. G. Barrett: *The* *Civil War in North Carolina* (Chapel Hill, N.C., 1963), p. 149.
[9] *Richmond Enquirer*, July 8, 1863.

more appropriately, it was thought, to the states. Virginia first took action on March 12, 1862, by banning the manufacture of whiskey or other spirituous or malt liquors from corn, wheat, rye, or other grain and providing heavy penalties for violation of the law. It was soon seen that banning all distilling went too far and an act of October 1, 1862, authorized the manufacture of alcohol for medical, hospital, chemical, and manufacturing purposes. Other states rapidly adopted similar measures, with local variations. Alabama authorized the seizure of stills in operation and prohibited the use of peas, potatoes, molasses, and sugar, as well as grain in distilleries, but permitted any whiskey making consistent with the common defense and general welfare. Later it sanctioned the use of grain, other than corn or wheat, and molasses and fruits for distilling, but levied heavy license and production taxes. In counties where there was a surplus of grain Alabama sanctioned small distilleries provided they sold the whiskey at a moderate profit. The law allowed physicians to charge only 50 per cent above cost and druggists 25 per cent, and required part of the profits to be used to provide medicines for the poor. Mississippi provided stiff penalties for distilling from grain but, like the other states, failed to set up a rigorous enforcement agency to ferret out and punish violators. South Carolina allowed the use of fruit but North Carolina did not; Louisiana banned the use of cane sugar in the manufacture of liquor.[1]

Governor Joseph E. Brown of Georgia carried his opposition to the manufacture and sale of liquor the farthest. His first action was a proclamation of February 28, 1862, commanding all distillers to cease operating on March 15 until the next meeting of the legislature, when he hoped to get a law adopted that would ban their operations. He also forbade the railroads to haul whiskey, and demanded that the army's regulations concerning drunkenness should be strictly enforced. On November 22 he signed a law which banned all distilling except for medicinal,

[1] *Laws of Virginia*, 1861–2, p. 101; *Laws of Virginia*, 1862, p. 17; Acts of Dec. 2, 1862, Aug. 27 and 29, 1863, and letter of Gov. T. H. Watts, Dec. 19, 1864, to J. J. Walker, Watts, June 10, 1864, to T. J. Portis, and J. G. Shorter, Oct. 21, 1862, to C. G. Memminger, Gov. Corr., Ala. Arch.; J. G. Haman, Oct. 1, 1863, to Gov. J. J. Pettus, Gov. Corr., Miss. Arch.; *Southern Cultivator*, XX (July–August 1862), 137.

hospital, and industrial purposes, but which authorized him to grant licenses to contractors of the Confederate government for the distillation of one million gallons of whiskey. The distilleries, however, had to be located more than twenty miles from any railroad, so that grain near the railroads would not be used for this purpose.[2]

Large quantities of whiskey were required by the army and the hospitals—two million gallons were budgeted for the army alone in 1864. In its effort to meet these needs the Confederacy was in conflict with the states, which were attempting to ban liquor drinking and the use of grain for distilling purposes. As over conscription, angry clashes occurred with Governors Brown and Vance and even with officials of Virginia and South Carolina. In one instance Georgia ordered several hundred barrels of liquor destroyed. Within forty-eight hours an agent of the Confederacy arrived to purchase five hundred gallons of whiskey and had to pay a much higher price because of its scarcity. Lacking a supreme court to decide questions concerning the overlapping rights of the states and the Confederacy, the Attorney General of the Confederacy had to try to decide such thorny questions as the right of South Carolina, Georgia, and Virginia to prevent the Confederacy from distilling whiskey from grain. The legal subtleties to which he resorted in an effort to uphold central authority without unduly jeopardizing the South's position on states' rights are amusing.[3]

A large Confederate distillery at Salisbury, North Carolina, caused Governor Vance endless trouble. The poor complained that the distillery paid high prices for grain and used huge quantities of it, making it difficult for them to buy their most necessary item of food. In December 1863, it was said that many people in the state would be faced with starvation if the distillery continued to operate. Since the tithe grain collected in the vicinity was turned over to the distillery, people refused to pay their tithes because

---

[2] Act of Nov. 22, 1862, *Laws of Georgia,* 1862, p. 26; *Southern Cultivator,* XX (March–April 1862), 66.

[3] *Documents Accompanying Report of Secretary of the Treasury,* November 1863, p. 37; *Charleston Courier,* Sept. 4, 1862; O.R., ser. 4, III, 24, 875, 879; R. W. Patrick: *The Opinions of the Confederate Attorneys General, 1861–1865* (Buffalo, N.Y., 1950), pp. 334, 358, 392, 528.

the grain was not used for military purposes. Vance passed these complaints on to the much-harried Secretary of War, James A. Seddon, who upheld the right of the Confederacy to run its own distillery for the benefit of sick and wounded soldiers. He declared that the government controlled quality better in its own distillery than it could if it had to buy from private contractors and that it kept the whiskey solely for medical purposes. Only 30,000 bushels of grain were used at Salisbury in the course of a year, he told Vance. The Confederate Surgeon General later maintained that "a large portion of the grain" used in the distilleries at Salisbury, North Carolina, and Columbia, South Carolina, was damaged.[4]

Despite the restrictive legislation in the states, threats of state officials to destroy or confiscate stills, and the desperate need for the grain, the liquor trade continued and prospered. The profits, said the *Memphis Appeal*, were fabulous, with a bushel of corn costing $7.50 producing two gallons of whiskey which sold at the still for $30 to $35 a gallon. Others claimed that a bushel of wheat or barley might make as much as four or five gallons of whiskey and leave mush for hog fattening that was almost as nutritional as the grain itself. Small wonder that people turned to "stilling" on a large or small scale.[5]

Protests poured into Governor Vance about the large number of distilleries still in operation and using up the sorely needed grain. In Moore County there were 4, in Rutherford 13, in Davie 6, in Wake 20, in Wilson 3, and in Pitt 14. Stills were also reported in 6 mountain counties. The *North Carolina Standard* declared that an insane disposition to distill all the grain into whiskey, sometimes to save it from invading Yankees, was destroying the people's food and corrupting the moral fiber of the army. One hundred thousand Yankee troops, it maintained, would do less damage than the whiskey distillers. The *Standard*, one of

---

[4] Letters of P. S. Rogers, Dec. 15, 1863, J. A. Seddon, Jan. 12, 1864, J. Jarratt, Oct. 12, 1864, to Gov. Vance, and petition with numerous signatures from Burke County, Feb. 4, 1865, Gov. Corr., N.C. Arch.; *O.R.*, ser. 4, III, 1074.
[5] *Hillsborough Recorder*, Apr. 30, 1862; *Memphis Appeal*, Jan. 24, 1864; Augusta *Chronicle & Sentinel*, Mar. 18, 1864; Raleigh *Daily Confederate*, Apr. 29, 1864; J. F. Pickett to S. R. Moore, Confederate Secretary of War Files, National Archives.

the few unfettered newspapers in the South, asked whether there would be "famine as well as drunkenness," urged that the distilling industry be compelled to move to Florida or South Georgia, where there was an abundance of grain, and demanded tighter laws against distilling and a rigorous enforcement of them.[6]

In Mississippi enforcement of the anti-distilling laws was made difficult not only because of the weakness of administrative officers but also because the courts by 1863 were virtually closed as a result of the destruction of the armies and the flight of officials. Criminal justice was administered laxly if at all, continuance and change of venue were easily obtained, trials were held infrequently, and the fines which once seemed huge had become small through inflation. There was so little respect for the law that in one county eleven stills were operating openly and were paying any price for grain, in competition with the impressment officers of the state and the Confederacy.[7]

Union forces were also troubled by the scarcity of corn, particularly in Kentucky and Tennessee. In November of 1863 the commander of the Ninth New Hampshire Volunteers ordered all corn owned by distillers on the line of the Kentucky Central Railroad to be brought to the quartermaster's post, where a fair price would be paid for it. No more grain was to be sold to distillers. Later, distilling of grain in the two states was ordered ended, and it was suggested that because of the great damage the late August frost had done to the corn crop, it might be necessary to extend the order to Ohio and Illinois.[8]

Governors Brown and Vance were the most vigorous in using state powers to curb speculators, protect consumers, and aid the indigent and distressed. On November 30, 1861, Governor Brown barred the shipment of salt from Atlanta by speculators and authorized its confiscation when held for more than five dollars a bushel. Governor Vance placed an embargo on the export of salt, bacon, pork, beef, corn, meal, flour, and potatoes from North

---

[6] Letters of C. Dowd, Jan. 7, M. W. Simmons, Apr. 18, E. S. Morris, Apr. 23, A. J. Battle, May 31, 1864, and James Sloan, Jan. 17, 1865, to Gov. Vance, Gov. Corr., N.C. Arch.; *North Carolina Standard,* Nov. 11, 25, 1862.

[7] M. M. Johnson, Mar. 18, 1863, to Gov. Pettus, Gov. Corr., Miss. Arch.; *Natchez Courier,* Apr. 10, 11, 1863.

[8] *Nashville Dispatch,* Nov. 11, 1863; *Frankfort Tri-Weekly Commonwealth,* Dec. 17, 1863.

Carolina for a limited period. In a more rigorously drafted proclamation of 1863, in which the evils of speculation and the fear of starvation were stressed, the order was made permanent, although some exceptions were permitted. As corn became an increasingly important food both for the army and for civilians, particularly the poor, the Alabama legislature tried to require a license for dealing in corn, to limit price advances to 20 per cent over cost, and to prevent sale of the grain out of the county in which it was produced. Later the legislature prohibited the sale of beef from Washington County without the approval of five respectable stock raisers of the county.[9]

The army also had occasion to interfere with the normal flow of provisions. General Kirby-Smith in 1862 barred the withdrawal of forage from east Tennessee until his command had been furnished with five months' supplies. One may wonder why the War Department did not prohibit the use of wheat as food for horses sooner than July 21, 1864.[1]

Corn was wanted above everything else save meat for the army. But a diet of much corn, little meat, and few or no vegetables, combined with the hardships of camp life, was not good for the men; they "make it necessary that anti-scorbutics be collected" and given them. Troops exposed to yellow fever should have vegetables, especially sweet potatoes and pumpkins, said commanding officers. General Joseph E. Johnston's order of June 1864 calling upon Georgians to bring forward their vegetables for the army doubtless contributed to the movement for more extensive cultivation of potatoes, onions, tomatoes, squashes, turnips, carrots, and green vegetables. Townsmen as well as farmers were exhorted to plant vegetables in every little spot of unused ground they could find. Plant vegetables and you may save the army from scurvy, said the *Memphis Appeal*. The army has suffered more from lack of vegetables than of clothing, shoes, or medicine, said the Jackson *Southern Crisis*. "We have never seen any portion of the habitable globe so afflicted for the want of vegetable

[9] *Southern Confederacy*, Dec. 5, 18, 1861; *Hillsborough Recorder*, Dec. 10, 1862; *Richmond Enquirer*, Apr. 28, 1863; O.R., ser. 4, II, 214; *Laws of Alabama*, 1862, p. 45; *Laws of Alabama*, 1864, p. 159.

[1] A. C. Myers, Apr. 26, 1862, to G. W. Randolph, Letters Sent to the Secretary of War, 1861–4, National Archives; O.R., ser. 4, III, 548.

supplies as the States of the Southwest. . . . We have not seen five gardens that could have supplied two men and three turkeys for ten days with vegetable matter." It pleaded for cabbage, kale, lettuce, mustard, beets, radishes, potatoes, and turnips.[2]

Although vegetables, with some exceptions, were not subject to the tithing tax, they had not been extensively planted. Unfortunately vegetable gardens, like fruit orchards, invited foraging by stragglers, who usually left little for the owners. Scarcity of garden seeds was also partly responsible for the failure to plant vegetables. To ease the situation the Ordnance Bureau brought in considerable quantities of seeds from England. The high prices in the inflated currency that vegetables brought soon placed these scarce foods beyond the reach of the ordinary family. In Richmond tomatoes at $20 a dozen, onions $1 each, cucumbers at $5 to $8 a dozen, and early apples at $5 a quart caused farmers to be accused of extortion.[3]

Farmers were exhorted to take great care in the management of their livestock, particularly their hogs, because of the shrinking supplies. Use only the best animals for breeding, farrow in the spring, cook the corn and place it in troughs to assure its most complete use, they were told. It was suggested that the usual meat ration of three and a half pounds a week for slaves could be sharply reduced by substituting squash, collards, and tomatoes and by increasing the proportion of sorghum molasses. Colman's *European Agriculture and Rural Economy* was cited to show that an abundance of oatmeal, bread, milk, and beer would allow the elimination of most of the meat ration. Meat eating is "purely a luxury and a habit"; "bread is the staff of life," readers were reminded. Some planters who reduced the meat ration to a quarter of a pound a week, and others who allowed none, observed no ill effects in their slaves or in the slaves' capacity for work.[4]

---

[2] *Southern Confederacy*, Jan. 29, June 21, July 5, 1864; *Houston Daily Telegraph*, Oct. 3, 1864; *Memphis Appeal*, Apr. 1, 1864, *Montgomery Advertiser*, Apr. 3, 1864; Shryock: "Letters of Richard D. Arnold," p. 111; *Mobile Evening News*, Jan. 15, 1865; *Jackson Daily Southern Crisis*, Feb. 10, 1863.

[3] *Montgomery Daily Mail*, Apr. 12, 1864; *Charleston Courier*, July 8, 1864; *Richmond Whig*, July 2, 1864.

[4] Augusta *Chronicle & Sentinel*, Nov. 22, 1863; *Southern Field and Fireside*, Jan. 9, 1864; *Nashville Union*, Nov. 20, 1862; *Mobile Advertiser and Register*, Jan. 17, 1864; *Richmond Whig*, Feb. 20,

Generally favorable weather in the sugar-producing parishes of Louisiana in 1861 led to expectations of a large crop of cane with a yield of sugar that might surpass the 414,000,000-pound output of 1858. Since none would be sold in the North, there was no need or demand for such a large output and planters were admonished to feed the cane to their hogs, thereby saving corn. Two years later, with the sugar parishes either overrun by Union troops or subject to raids by forces of both sides, and with much of the plantation country abandoned by its owners, the yield was expected to be no more than 57,000,000 pounds and perhaps as little as 28,000,000 pounds. Both North and South were to suffer for the want of sugar and both turned to the production of sorghum and the use of sorghum syrup and molasses. Every farmer ought to cultivate sorghum cane, said the Raleigh *Daily Conservative*, the Richmond *Dispatch*, and the Augusta *Chronicle & Sentinel*. The fodder from the sorghum was excellent for cattle and the mashed cane for hogs. Planters were assured that there was more money to be made in raising sorghum and making syrup than in cultivating cotton. When meat supplies were low or nonexistent it was found that grumbling could be reduced both in the army and among work gangs by offering a cup of sorghum molasses, which helped to get down otherwise unpalatable food.[5]

Spurred on by their leaders, the pressure of the times, and their own faith in the righteousness of their cause, Southern farmers and planters accomplished an amazing change in Southern agriculture by shifting large acreages from tobacco, cotton, rice, and sugar cane to corn, wheat, potatoes, and other food crops and in providing food for their army and civilian population despite the contracting area under Southern control. A table showing the increase in the number of acres in wheat, corn, and potatoes for 1862, 1863, and 1864 and the approximate production of these crops is suggestive, though admittedly little more; and indeed, these figures may be partly the result of wishful thinking. The shrinking area in Southern control should be kept

23, 1864; *Mobile Tribune*, Feb. 7, 1864; *Charleston Courier*, Mar. 22, 1862.

[5] *New Orleans True Delta*, Sept. 6, 1861; *National Intelligencer*, Oct. 29, 1863; *Nashville Dispatch*, Oct. 1, 1863; Augusta *Chronicle & Sentinel*, Apr. 23, 1863, Feb. 6, Apr. 8, 18, 1864; Atlanta *Southern Confederacy*, May 30, 1864; *Mobile Advertiser and Register*, Sept. 13, 1864.

in mind in relation to this table.[6] Increasing production of food-stuffs could not, however, make up for the fact that the transportation system was falling apart. Food could not be transported to areas where it was most needed.

ACRES IN THE CONFEDERACY IN WHEAT, CORN, AND POTATOES				
STATES	1860	1861	1862	1863
Alabama	1,000,000	1,300,000	1,500,000	1,800,000
Florida	100,000	150,000	200,000	250,000
Georgia	3,000,000	3,000,000	4,000,000	5,000,000
Louisiana	500,000	500,000	500,000	500,000
Mississippi	1,000,000	1,500,000	2,000,000	2,500,000
North Carolina	2,000,000	2,500,000	3,000,000	3,500,000
South Carolina	1,000,000	1,500,000	2,000,000	2,500,000
Virginia	3,000,000	3,500,000	4,000,000	4,500,000
Total	10,600,000	13,950,000	17,200,000	20,550,000

PRODUCTION OF THREE STAPLES IN THE EIGHT STATES *(in bushels)*				
STAPLES	1860	1861	1862	1863
Wheat	24,000,000	45,000,000	35,000,000	55,000,000
Corn	196,000,000	330,000,000	300,000,000	350,000,000
Potatoes	36,000,000	50,000,000	40,000,000	60,000,000

SOURCE: *Memphis Appeal* (Atlanta), May 15, 1864, quoting the *New York World.*

As the food crisis deepened, the South resorted to blockade runners to provide additional rations for the army.[7] Earlier, the government had permitted them to bring in high-profit luxuries

[6] Willard Range in *A Century of Georgia Agriculture, 1850–1950* (Athens, Ga., 1954), p. 40, (citing the *Annual Report* of the Comptroller-General of Georgia for 1862, pp. 23–5), accepted the figure of "over 5,000,000 acres" in grain in 1862 and the following war years. In view of statistics showing an alarming decline in production of corn in South Carolina from 15 bushels an acre in 1861 to 6 in 1864 or 1865, one may question whether the corn yield in these tables is not too high. See J. T. Trowbridge: *The South: A Tour of Its Battlefields and Ruined Cities* (Hartford, Conn., 1866), p. 566.

[7] How differently historians react to events may be seen in F. L. Owsley: *King Cotton Diplomacy* (Chicago, 1959), chap. VII, "The Ineffectiveness of the Blockade," and Massey: *Ersatz in the Confederacy*, p. 12, where she speaks of "the stranglehold" of the blockade.

(for which it was subjected to much criticism), in addition to guns, powder, iron, salt, and clothing, all of which were obtained by exchanging cotton. We have seen that a supply of European seeds for the garden and the farm was secured in 1864. North Carolina, which ran its own blockade runners, brought in 10,000 scythes, 200 barrels of bluestone for wheat growers, leather and shoes amounting to 250,000 pairs, and 100,000 pounds of bacon, in addition to quantities of woolen goods, rifles, drugs, coffee, and oil. In the last two months of 1864 ships carrying 8,632,000 pounds of bacon (equal to twice as many rations) successfully evaded the naval craft at the mouth of Cape Fear River and landed at Wilmington. The tightening of the blockade, however, permitted only the most essential items to be brought in, and with the capture of Wilmington, the last port to fall, early in 1865, the once flourishing and highly profitable business was ended.[8]

The South's policy toward cotton changed from prohibiting its export to shipping as much as possible through the blockade, and from burning it when it was endangered by the approach of the Yankees to trading it across the battle lines in order to get scarce goods. Restrictions on the sale of cotton were further relaxed when officers of the Mississippi Central Railroad were permitted to trade it through the lines for such items as were needed for repair of the road and equipment, provided that the cotton was shipped to neutral, but not necessarily European, ports. By May 1863 J. A. Seddon, Secretary of War, was aware that a good deal of the cotton carried by blockade runners went indirectly to the North, but he saw no way to prevent this. In 1864 the request of an official of the Mississippi Central Railroad to exchange cotton through the lines for essential supplies was granted. Soon cotton was being shipped through the lines by way of Memphis, Nashville, Vicksburg, and New Orleans almost daily, and high officers on both sides were taking part in the scramble for profits. It now came out that planters had not altogether

---

[8] *Charleston Courier*, July 5, 1864; O.R., ser. 4, III, 899, 900; F. B. C. Bradley: *Blockade Running during the Civil War* (Salem, Mass., 1925), pp. 59, 317; J. M. Merrill: "Notes on the Yankee Blockade of the South Atlantic Seaboard, 1861–1865," *Civil War History*, IV (December 1958), 387; H. T. Lefler and A. R. Newsome: *North Carolina* (Chapel Hill, N.C., 1954), p. 436; T. C. DeLeon: *Four Years in Rebel Capitals* (Mobile, Ala., 1890), p. 279.

followed the orders of General Beauregard to burn their sugar and cotton as the Union forces advanced but instead had hidden large quantities. These caches now brought them high profits.[9]

Learning the extent of the trade in cotton, Secretary Seddon attempted to re-establish control over it and limit it to properly licensed arrangements. He found, however, that the trade had become so common, the regulations so extensively evaded, the goods thus received so desperately needed, and the profits so great as to make control impossible. By February 1865 the Confederate War Department was sanctioning exchanges of cotton with Yankees for woolen and flannel cloth, blankets, and shoes. Some idea of the amount of trade through the lines may be realized from the fact that of the 900,000 bales of cotton imported into Boston and New York during the war, 400,000 were brought through the lines, 350,000 were captured at New Orleans, Savannah, Memphis, and the Sea Islands, and the balance came from England. Robert E. Lee was greatly distressed at this trade, as was Grant. Lee feared it was not bringing adequate returns to the Confederacy.[1]

Though the South was desperately in need of wool for clothing and blankets for the army, Texas wool was being exported. Protests were made against this undercover trade, and the Secretary of War was urged to take action to prevent further loss of wool. But Texas, the major producer, was too remote for the Confederate government to exercise control over its wool supply.[2]

There is abundant information available concerning the flow of cotton to the North, but much less concerning the nature and

---

[9] *O.R.*, ser. 4, II, 306, III, 388, 476, 478, 547–8, 646; *Harper's Weekly*, VII (June 13, 1863), 375; E. M. Coulter: "Commercial Intercourse with the Confederacy in the Mississippi Valley, 1861–1865," *Mississippi Valley Historical Review*, V (March 1919), 377 ff. A former brigadier general of Mississippi, James L. Alcorn, made large profits from the sale of cotton to Yankees. *Journal of Southern History*, III (May 1937), 201 ff. For J. F. H. Claiborne's trading through the lines see H. H. Lang: "J. F. H. Claiborne at 'Laurel Wood' Plantation, 1853–1870," *Journal of Mississippi History*, XVIII (January 1956), 15.

[1] *O.R.*, ser. 4, III, 286, 689, 718, 789, 1078; T. H. O'Connor: "Lincoln and the Cotton Trade," *Civil War History*, VII (March 1961), 32.

[2] A. C. Myers, Mar. 25, 1863, to Seddon, Quartermaster Dept., Letters Sent to the Secretary of War, 1861–4, National Archives.

quantity of goods the South received in return. A congressional investigation of trade through the North Carolina ports controlled by the Federals brought out that sixty plows, castings for plows, trace chains, rope, twine, seeds, nails, hoes, axes, shovels, spades, coffee, salt, drugs, bacon, pork, groceries, shoes, and candles all passed through to Confederate territory and that cotton was exchanged, pound for pound, for meat. All these items were scarce and desperately needed.[3]

The nature of exchanges through the lines in Louisiana and Mississippi is not altogether clear, a fact which leads to the suspicion that the trade was more for the benefit of the officers and others participating than it was for the Confederacy. On the other hand, when Lee found early in 1864 that the army's supplies of meat were inadequate to sustain vigorous operations, he was quite willing to sanction trade through secret channels that would bring in pork, bacon, and beef. In this instance, however, it was only desperate necessity which led him to initiate and sanction the trade.[4]

Even before the war was over, the high price of cotton in the North had proved irresistible to planters who had revived production of the staple. Lee surrendered on April 9 and Johnston on the 26th, but long before that many planters in the Deep South had turned from food crops to cotton, as the table of production suggests. Many millions of acres which had been in food crops in 1864 were planted in cotton, mostly before the war had actually been concluded.

WHOLESALE COTTON PRICES AND PRODUCTION, 1861–5

YEAR	PRICE	NUMBER OF BALES
1861	$ .13	4,491,000
1862	.31	1,597,000
1863	.67	449,000
1864	1.01	299,000
1865	.83	2,094,000

SOURCE: *Historical Statistics* (Washington, 1957), pp. 124, 302.

---

[3] "Trade with Rebellious States," *House Reports*, 38 Cong., 2 Sess., no. 24, pp. 11, 48–9, 147–8, and elsewhere.

[4] *O.R.*, ser. 1, XXXIII, 1112.

By 1865 Southern agriculture had gone through tremendous stresses and strains from which it was to take years to recover. Indeed, it was to fall into worse conditions before it improved. Destruction of the fences, houses, barns, and gin and rice houses; neglect and abandonment for years of fields which once had been planted to staples; the losses in horses, mules, oxen, cattle, and hogs; the wearing out and destruction of farm equipment, which forced the substitution of more primitive methods of farming; and the disappearance of credit facilities left many planters and farmers unable to meet their taxes or other debts and therefore threatened with the loss of their farms. Emancipation of their slaves meant a capital and credit loss to the planters and left them dependent on free labor, to which they could not easily reconcile themselves. Repudiation of the debt of the Confederacy and the loss of more than a half-billion dollars owed for goods impressed for the Confederate forces, as well as the destruction or capture of the planters' cotton, all weakened the position of the agricultural class and made it exceedingly difficult for both planters and farmers to begin the work of restoration.[5]

---

[5] F. L. Owsley: *State Rights in the Confederacy* (Chicago, 1925), p. 227; F. A. Shannon: *The Farmer's Last Frontier* (New York, 1945), pp. 76 ff.

5

The Belt of Desolation

AFTER THE FALL of Vicksburg and Lee's defeat at Gettysburg, the South grimly settled down to make the best of its narrowing area, concentrate even more on the production of food and munitions, and give the greatest possible mobility to its armies. It had suffered grievously, large areas had been torn away, other portions had been sacked and gutted by swift-moving invaders who burned, destroyed, and retreated. The South learned to use its interior lines of rail and water to draw supplies and transport troops where needed. The army granted furloughs in quieter times so that troops could return to their homes and plant the crops or harvest them. All but a tiny fragment of the land formerly in cotton was now in corn or wheat, the production of which was amazing, taking into consideration the shortage of manpower. A section which had carried on little manufacturing before 1860, the South had done wonders in making guns, powder, and clothing, in constructing ships, and in keeping its railroads operating under great adversity.

But time was running out for the Confederacy. Its manpower could not be further stretched. Calling up boys of seventeen and eighteen and elderly men in home guards and militia cut into farm work seriously. The cultivated land was losing fertility and was producing smaller crops. Impressment may have been unavoidable, but it created as many issues as it decided. Since the Confederacy lacked the kind of educational propaganda that George Creel and Herbert Hoover utilized so effectively in 1917 and 1918, the conflicts arising from impressment added seriously to the burdens of the government and to the resentment and ill feeling that was breaking down the will to win.

Despite the remarkable achievements of the South on battlefields, in factories, and in grain fields, Confederate troops were not getting sufficient rations, and civilians, especially residents of cities and small family farms, were feeling the pinch of hunger. There was growing talk of a "food crisis," "great suffering," destitution, and the possibility of starvation, though newspapers were trying to keep out of their columns anything that would shake the confidence of the people in the Southern cause. How important and how well based was this fear? "Are provisions as scarce as represented?" asked the *Huntsville Confederate* on May 20, 1863. With some hesitation the editor answered in the negative, but thereafter doubts grew. For example, on April 1, 1863, the *Charlotte Democrat* estimated that in late March there were 900,000 barrels of flour in the unoccupied portion of the Confederacy, which it deemed sufficient to last until the next harvest, *unless* the crop failed. On April 3, Governor Vance declared that the "failure of our provisions is our greatest danger" and thought that, if there was enough food, there was none to spare. "Starvation is imminent" in six counties, said a measure of the Alabama legislature in 1864, by reason of the waste, destruction, and seizure of the subsistence of the people by the armies of both sides. To counteract the depressing effect of such stories, newspapers began to play on the theme which has been followed by some historians—that there was an abundance of food but the gradual breakdown of the railroads made it difficult to get it where it was most needed.[1]

---

[1] *Hillsborough Recorder*, Apr. 1, 1863; Raleigh *North Carolina Standard*, Apr. 3, 1863; *Richmond Examiner* in *Nashville Dispatch*, May 5, 1863; W. G. Stevenson: *Thirteen Months in the Rebel Army* (New York, 1862), pp. 135–7; B. I. Wiley: *The Life of Johhny Reb, the Common Soldier of the Confederacy* (Indianapolis, 1943), p. 96; E. M. Coulter: "The Movement for Agricultural Reorganization in the Cotton South during the Civil War," *Agricultural History*, I (January 1927), 16.

The South could survive the blockade and Federal control of the Mississippi, but the spread of the belt of desolation by marauding raiders, Sherman's bummers, stragglers, Southern Unionists, and even by Lee's own troops sapped its capacity to resist, aroused fears, and drove many to despair. Nowhere is this better expressed than in the *Richmond Whig* on June 9, 1863: "Day by day the track of the destroyer becomes broader." Two thirds of Virginia and Tennessee, the coasts of North and South Carolina, part of Georgia, nearly all of Florida, northern Mississippi, western and southern Louisiana, and large parts of Arkansas and Missouri "have been laid waste and every hour brings tidings of fresh destruction." This was before the fall of Chattanooga, Knoxville, Vicksburg, Port Hudson, Atlanta, and Savannah, and before Sheridan's destruction in the Shenandoah Valley and the loss of adjacent territory. Fifteen months later, after the fall of Atlanta but before Sherman had begun his march to Savannah, the Confederacy could still count on three fourths of Georgia and Virginia, five sixths of South Carolina, and seven eighths of North Carolina for support in taxes and tithes. Or so said a professor at the University of North Carolina, though he disregarded the portions of these states which were too badly plundered and sacked to be able to contribute.[2]

For example, a portion of the Piedmont of North Carolina, on which Lee had to depend for much of his provisions in the later days of the war, was so exhausted by raids, by the quartering of several hundred horses belonging to a contingent of Virginia cavalry, and by the impressments, foraging, and burning of fences that one half of the farms previously cultivated were lying idle, growing up to weeds and briars. Of the farms still in cultivation, many would make only half a crop because of the scarcity of farm implements and the absence of the men in the army. This area tried to have its conscripts released to get in the crops, for provisions were extremely short. If the men's help was not made available, said one urgent appeal, the people would soon be in "a state of absolute starvation." A petition signed by 522 women of Guilford County declared the suffering was so general over the state that "unless the Governor . . . takes the necessary

---

[2] D. L. Swain, Sept. 26, 1864, to Gov. Vance, Gov. Corr., N.C. Arch.

steps for the relief of the poor, there will be many a life lost for want of bread." From Polk County a woman with five sons in the army wrote that she and her other children had not had a piece of bread for three days and were faced with starvation. Others had nothing but bread. From Charlotte came an appeal from a woman with five children who had not a mouthful to eat and "God only knows where I will get something." Another person wrote that "Starving is already in the Dwelling of not a few and none has anything to spare." None had starved to death yet, but there were many cases where families had eaten neither bread nor meat for three or four days.[3] Governor Vance was sympathetic to the appeals from this region and, knowing that there was not enough grain to meet local needs, ordered that none should be shipped elsewhere. He threatened to call out the militia to eject the cavalry horses if they were not soon removed.[4]

Meantime, the capture of Hatteras and Roanoke Islands opened up eastern North Carolina to destructive raids deep into the interior and led to the overrunning of about twenty counties, some of which were heavy producers of corn, wheat, and hogs. Stripped of its slaves, who fled, were captured, or were taken to safer regions by their owners; with its towns sacked and burned, its ports and rivers, except for Wilmington and the Cape Fear River, lost to the invaders; and with its horses, mules, oxen, and wagons impressed and not paid for, this "splendid grain growing region" was "hopelessly ruined," said a local eidtor.[5]

Governor Vance tried to remove the grain and bacon from the eastern counties before the Federals arrived. As a result of this

---

[3] Petition of 522 women of Guilford County, Oct. 9, 1863, accompanying letter of D. E. Mendenhall, Oct. 9, 1863, and letters of M. E. Love, May 10, 1863, J. C. Mills, Apr. 29, 1864, "A poor woman and children," Jan. 10, 1865, and J. C. Keener, Apr. 18, 1864, to Vance, Gov. Corr., N.C. Arch.

[4] *North Carolina Standard*, Dec. 5, 1862, Mar. 17, 1863; Governor's Letter Book, 1862–3, p. 231, N.C. Arch., for texts of orders forbidding exports; R. F. Hackett, Jan. 13, 1863, and A. C. Merriman, Apr. 4, 1863, to Vance, and petition of Mar. 18, 1864, to Vance, Gov. Corr., N.C. Arch.

[5] *North Carolina Standard*, Oct. 10, 1862. Statistics of taxable land in farms within the Confederate lines in North Carolina are incomplete but suggestive. In 1860 the acreage included was 26,123,-723, for 1862 it was 23,557,821, and for 1863 it was 23,478,121. Compiled from North Carolina Comptroller of Public Accounts, *Reports*, 1860, 1863.

action and of the destructive raids which followed, whole areas were stripped bare. Many families could not pay tithes on what they had raised but lost and became dependent on outside aid. At this time North Carolina, which was a major source of food for Lee's army, was being anxiously urged by Lee's quartermaster general to free such state supplies as were under the Governor's control and to provide transportation for them to Virginia, where rations for the army were almost exhausted.[6]

North Carolina soldiers with Lee's army voiced the anxieties of thousands of yeoman farmer-soldiers in a plaintive communication of January 24, 1865. They stated that their wives were not able to keep up their small farms, were producing little, and were not getting the necessaries of life for themselves and their children. The soldiers said that they suffered much themselves from insufficient food and clothing and that when they were sick in the hospital, they were fed coarse and ill-prepared food; but that they could bear anything except the knowledge that their families were faced with destitution and famine.[7]

South Carolina and the mainland of Georgia were late to feel the scourge of invading armies. However, the capture of the Sea Islands and the resulting panic drove many planters and their slaves from the coastal region to the uplands as far inland as Spartanburg. The loss of the rice-producing area and the flight of population to the inland cities and towns created food problems that were aggravated by severe droughts in parts of north Georgia in 1862, 1863, and 1864. The plight of the people of this area was compounded in 1863 by depredations of Federals, foraging of Confederate troops, and an early frost, and in 1864 by heavy protracted rains in the spring, followed by drought in the summer. Special relief measures were needed each year to prevent starvation. As in other states, the families of enlisted men found it impossible to live on the small amount they re-

---

[6] J. A. Seddon, Feb. 10, 1863, to Vance, and C. S. Carrington, Feb. 24, 1863, to Col. A. C. Myers (copy), H. T. Clark *et al.*, Apr. 9, 1863, to Vance, and other letters of April and May 1864 from Kinston and other eastern communities, Gov. Corr., N.C. Arch. For the advance of the Federals in the eastern counties of North Carolina see J. G. Barrett: *The Civil War in North Carolina* (Chapel Hill, N.C., 1963), pp. 48 ff.

[7] Letter of North Carolina soldiers of Lee's army, Jan. 24, 1865, to Gov. Vance, and N. Rayner, Mar. 30, 1863, to E. B. Dache, Gov. Corr., N.C. Arch.

ceived from the absentees, and expensive relief programs had to be instituted. Although a great deal more food was produced in 1861 and 1862 than in previous years, the same high level of production could not be maintained when the small farmers were conscripted and supervision on the plantations became less successful.[8]

The Georgia wheat crop of 1863 was estimated at 2,500,000 bushels and there was talk about a surplus which might be available for the use of Lee's army in Virginia. This proved not to be the case, however. The 400,000 bushels needed for seed in 1864 and the heavy requirements of the forces under Johnston, Pemberton, Bragg, and Cobb left little or none for Lee. In January 1864 Governor Brown reported:

> Many of our fields now lie uncultivated, and if large additional levies of troops are to be made . . . many more must be neglected. How, then, are we to make a support for another year? I have lately been through the upper, middle and southwestern portions of the State, which are its most productive portions, and I tell you in all candor that the country is becoming so far drained of supplies that if relief cannot be had from some other source, I do not see how it is possible to supply the people and the army with bread till another crop is made, while the supply of meat is entirely inadequate.
>
> The cattle have been so generally taken for the army as to leave a still less encouraging prospect for meat for another year, and if heavy calls are to be made for troops to be taken from the agricultural pursuits the prospect for bread will indeed be gloomy.[9]

Governor Brown had good reason for alarm, for the area of land on the tax books of the Comptroller General of Georgia showed a sharp decline before Sherman began his march. It fell from 33,663,723 acres in 1861 to 25,892,769 in 1864. To ensure that the people of Georgia had the necessary provisions, Brown

[8] *Columbus Times* in *New Orleans Price Current*, Apr. 10, 1861; *Charleston Courier*, July 29, 1861; Mar. 6, 1862.
[9] *Augusta Constitutionalist* in *Mobile Advertiser & Register*, Nov. 5, 1863; J. E. Brown, Jan. 29, 1864, to J. A. Seddon in A. D. Candler: *The Confederate Records of the State of Georgia* (6 vols., Atlanta, 1909–11), III, 460–1.

resorted to embargoes on exports of grain and salt from his state. At one point, however, he was unable to purchase a quantity of corn for the relief of indigent families of soldiers in upper Georgia, where there was much suffering; and when he found a source of 50,000 bushels in Alabama, he was indignant that the supply was withheld to meet the needs of Confederate troops.[1]

After the fall of Atlanta on September 2, 1864, when Sherman began his destructive march to Savannah and then on to Columbia and Raleigh, he found quantities of provisions which had been accumulated for the winter use of planters' families and slaves and possibly some that had been hidden from impressment and tithing officers. It is easy to make too much of these quantities of food, which seemed to Sherman's men to be great surpluses but were only the supplies needed to carry the farmers and planters through the nonproductive season. Any New York or Pennsylvania farmer's premises at the same time of year would have contained haymows bursting with tons of hay and straw, bins filled with corn, oats, and wheat, cellars stocked with many bushels of potatoes, onions, turnips, and apples, and cider, and attics filled with smoked meat—all for family use. Most of the food that Sherman's bummers captured or destroyed was not surplus but simply stored supplies for winter consumption.

By Christmas of 1864, when Savannah fell to Sherman, 154,000 slaves had been set free. "In forty days," writes Willard Range, Georgia "had been reduced from a land of peace and comparative strength and plenty to a land of weakness, poverty, and turmoil." It could hardly be said thereafter that Georgia could ship corn and bacon for the army in Virginia, since whatever surplus supplies existed in some areas were needed elsewhere in the state. In the sixty-mile-wide vale of destruction from Atlanta to Savannah, later extended across South Carolina, crops were trampled or consumed, livestock was taken or slaughtered, fences, barns, factories, and warehouses were burned, and everything edible was plundered, wasted, or destroyed. Destitution and the threat of starvation were left in the wake of the army.[2]

Alabama, Mississippi, and Louisiana, which had been heavily

---

[1] Brown to Jefferson Davis, Apr. 20, 1864, Governor's Letter Book, 1861–5, Ga. Arch.

[2] Willard Range: *A Century of Georgia Agriculture, 1850–1950* (Athens, Ga., 1954), p. 66.

dependent on the states of the upper Mississippi Valley for corn, flour, beef, pork, and hay, moved rapidly from cotton to grain with the coming of the war. Unfortunately, much of the land on which they planted grain had previously been cropped to cotton for years without the addition of fertilizer and was not able to produce even fair yields. A traveler who conversed with many planters in South Carolina gives the following estimates of the declining yield of corn during the war, estimates which would be applicable to Alabama, Mississippi, and Louisiana also: 1861, 15 bushels per acre; 1862, 12; 1863, 9; and 1865, 6.[3]

The near-catastrophic drought of three months in 1862 almost eliminated wheat and sharply reduced the output of corn, as has been seen. "Hundreds of families will not make enough corn to do them and many will make none of consequence," reported the *Alabama Beacon* of Greensboro. Potatoes, peas, and all garden vegetables were "well nigh used up." While this was happening, the Federals captured Fort Donelson, which opened up the Tennessee Valley to them and enabled them to raid much of the food-producing area of northern Alabama, while their blockade of the Gulf ports prevented grain being brought in by water. Finally, the enlistment of a very large portion of the small farmers took much land out of cultivation. An early effect of this combination of events was the "starvation prices" for food which prevailed in Mobile. Corn meal sold at $4 to $5 a bushel, beef and mutton at 40¢ to 50¢ a pound, and turkeys at $7 apiece. With such prices, a soldier's income of $11 a month would not go far. Distress was widespread. The state legislature tried to prevent speculative transactions by banning the export of corn from the state or from one county to another and by setting a limit of 20 per cent to the profits in the grinding and sale of corn and corn meal.[4]

Conditions went from bad to worse well before military operations had ravaged Alabama. In March 1863 the *Montgomery Advertiser* declared that although the civilians and the army had been sustained so far, the paucity of provisions was the most

---

[3] J. T. Trowbridge: *The South: A Tour of Its Battlefields and Ruined Cities* (Hartford, Conn., 1866), p. 566.

[4] *Alabama Beacon*, July 25, Aug. 22, Sept. 5, Nov. 21, Dec. 19, 1862.

threatening danger the South, and particularly Alabama, faced. Much good farmland was already in the possession of the enemy, a larger part was lying bare and desolate, and there was no carryover of grain from the previous year. Private and public charity helped; surplus grain was bought and distributed among the indigent, but it clearly was not reaching all needy cases. As the fear of starvation reached alarming proportions, the *Selma Daily Reporter*, published in the heart of the richest agricultural section of Alabama, declared that the food crisis was not owing to the inability of the state to support itself but was caused by the enlistment of a large portion of the farming class, by military operations in the principal grain-growing counties, and by the waste accompanying government impressment that discouraged planting.[5]

Additional efforts by the legislature to relieve the shortage of food and to aid the destitute families of soldiers led to many special and general laws and resolutions during 1863 and 1864. Among them was a resolution urging the Confederacy to permit the state to have for relief all tithe corn in counties remote from railroads and other public conveyances, in return for which the state would purchase for the Confederate government a like quantity at points convenient to railroads. Another measure for the preservation of cattle in Washington County banned the sale of "butchered beef" save when approved by five respectable stock raisers of the county. The most meaningful of these measures was an act to "provide for families rendered destitute of subsistence" in certain counties, which had this preamble:

> Great suffering and destitution exists in the counties of Cherokee, De Kalb, Morgan and a portion of St. Clair, Marshall, and Blount, by reason of the seizure, waste, and destruction of the subsistence of the people of said counties by the Confederate and Federal armies, so much so as *starvation is imminent* in many families, unless immediate relief is granted. . . .[6]

---

[5] *Montgomery Advertiser* in *Natchez Courier*, Mar. 14, 1863; *Selma Daily Reporter*, Mar. 7, 1863; *Alabama Beacon*, Apr. 17, Oct. 9, 1863.

[6] *Laws of Alabama*, 1863, *passim*, and 1864, p. 131. Italics added. *Alabama Beacon*, Apr. 22, 1864, tells of the destitution in Calhoun County.

In the correspondence of Governors John J. Pettus and Charles Clark are scores of letters urging that heads of families be permitted to go home on furlough to get the crops in. One letter of March 12, 1863, reminded the governor of the great scarcity of food in Alabama and warned him that if crops were to be put in he must release the men from the militia. The writer argued that the rich could hire their work done but the poor "wool hat boys" who made up the state militia had to do their own work. Another writer declared that the militia was disorganized and was accomplishing little, and that the men would be more useful if permitted to return to their farms on furlough. A soldier's wife complained that the men in the army had not been paid for five months and that with the high cost of provisions, "we are in more or less destitute and suffering condition," imposed upon by speculators and unprovided for by the state.[7]

"Want" and "starvation" were terms increasingly used in Alabama beginning in late 1863 and continuing until the conclusion of the war. The loss of horses, mules, and Negroes to Union raiders; the raiders' destruction of farm implements, fences, and stores of grain; the impressment of wagons; the short crops; and the ravages of hog cholera—all combined to produce a serious deficiency. In Mobile "the whole topic of conversation," said Kate Cumming, "is what can be procured to eat? This pervades all classes of society, and has ceased to be a vulgarism. The greatest treat that can be given is a cup of coffee, with milk and sugar." Then came the punishing raids of the last few months of the war in which Federal troops crisscrossed the state in every direction, wreaking great destruction. The reduction in the land under cultivation may be partly determined from the figures showing the contraction of land in farms within Confederate-controlled areas of Alabama which were taxed. The acreage thus listed for 1861—20,066,858—fell to 17,351,468 in 1862, to 15,274,906 in 1863, and to 9,996,689 in 1864. Much of the area listed by the Controller as being cultivated was ill-protected from wandering livestock because the fences had been destroyed, and through neglect the fields had become weed-infested. Yields

---

[7] E. R. Hicks, Mar. 16, 1863, W. V. W. McLendon, Mar. 12, 1863, L. M. Beythe, Apr. 15, 1863, to Gov. Pettus, Gov. Corr., Ala. Arch.

diminished on a per acre basis while the total yields declined even more.[8]

Discouragement and disillusionment contributed to the Union movement in northern Alabama. Defensive and raiding bands of stragglers, deserters, and draft dodgers contributed further to the destruction which was reducing the supply of food and bringing the people of Alabama to exhaustion. Walter Fleming summarizes the destruction in Alabama at the conclusion of the war:

> All farm animals near the track of the armies had been carried away or killed by the soldiers (as at Selma), or seized after the occupation by the troops. Horses, mules, cows, and other domestic animals had almost disappeared except in the secluded districts. Many a farmer had to plough with oxen. Farm and plantation buildings had been dismantled or burned, houses ruined, fences destroyed, corn, meat, and syrup taken. The plantations in the Tennessee Valley were in a ruined condition.[9]

Mississippi began to feel the effects of the blockade in cutting off food supplies in mid-1862, when, with the Federals in control of the coast, one third of the Negroes absconded, and all commerce with New Orleans suspended, the people were reduced to "great distress." One influential person who publicly declared for the Confederacy but furtively corresponded with Union forces wrote Governor Pettus on August 4: "We are now proving our loyalty by starvation—by the tears of our women and the cries of our children for bread!" Another wrote that he had never witnessed so much suffering for want of food. Starvation was driving people to the Yankees, it was said. At the same time at Natchez in one of the richest parts of Mississippi, wheat flour was unobtainable and corn meal was high in price and coarse in quality. The same drought which had been so damaging in Alabama and Georgia ruined the Mississippi corn crop, which

[8] *Mobile Weekly Advertiser*, Jan. 6, 1864; Kate Cumming: *A Journal of Hospital Life in the Confederate Army of Tennessee* (Louisville, Ky., 1866), p. 122; Alabama Controller of Public Accounts, *Report*, 1864, *passim*.

[9] W. L. Fleming: *Civil War and Reconstruction in Alabama* (New York, 1905), pp. 256-7, especially a map showing the movement and many raids of Union troops in Alabama.

meant that hogs and cattle had to be slaughtered before they were properly fattened and that humans had to make shift with other food or go on meager rations. Catastrophies did not come singly. The year that brought Mississippi its most disastrous drought opened with the rivers at the highest level since 1815. The levees on the Mississippi, Yazoo, and Ouachita rivers were breached. Some of the most productive land in Mississippi and Louisiana was inundated and the crops destroyed. Lack of men to maintain the levees aggravated the crisis and made possible the worst crevasses ever known. The *New Orleans Picayune* reported that the small crops already planted would be greatly reduced.[1]

Destructive Federal raids and the invasions of Grant and Sherman, which left the region around Jackson "stripped and burnt to a cinder," led numerous planters to flee with their slaves to safer areas in Alabama and Georgia. Those who remained suffered the loss of their workhands, horses, and mules. Militia calls for all men capable of doing farm work left whole areas of once-productive cotton or corn land bare of anything but sedge grass and other weeds. "There is more to fear from a dearth of food than from all the Federal armies in existence," said a Jackson paper. "Who," it asked, "can fight starvation with hope of success?"[2]

Well before Vicksburg was invested, food supplies for the Confederate army were running short. Forage and grain for the horses and mules were insufficient, and the animals were so weak that it became necessary to increase the number assigned to hauling the big guns. Corn meal, given improper care in the wet weather, became musty and liberally supplied with "hairy worms" that produced debilitating diarrhea. Meat was very scarce; whole regiments went without meat rations for two weeks at a

---

[1] H. H. Lang: "'J. F. H. Claiborne at 'Laurel Wood' Plantation, 1853–1870," *Journal of Mississippi History*, XVIII (January 1956), 10; *New Orleans Picayune*, May 24, 28, June 22, 1862; *Monroe Register* in Alexandria *Louisiana Democrat*, May 14, 1862; A. E. Lewis, Jan. 18, 1863, to Gov. Pettus, Gov.

Corr., Miss. Arch.
[2] Letter signed by numerous citizens of Lafayette County, Feb. 20, 1863, to Gov. Pettus, Gov. Corr., Miss. Arch.; *Hinds County Gazette*, July 23, 1862; *Natchez Courier*, June 12, Oct. 16, 1862; *Daily Southern Crisis*, Feb. 23, 1863.

time. Even the hospitals were short of food. More than three months before the fall of Vicksburg, the soldiers were forced to forage for themselves, which further wasted resources and demoralized the people, as well as the army.[3]

Farming operations in Mississippi and the supply of provisions went from bad to worse in 1864. Federal occupation of Meridian was accompanied by the destruction of two million bushels of corn and other supplies which could not be removed in time to avoid capture, and the area in production was further narrowed. The region north of Jackson was badly plundered. One writer described it as a dreary spectacle: "The largest plantations are thinning out, grown up in weeds & pastured upon by a few scattering cattle; fences are pulled down & destroyed; houses burned; Negroes run off. A general gloom pervades everything and the people appear to be in a listless spirit, perfectly impassable, subjugated, in some instances, by prospective want and suffering, and utterly devoid of any disposition to continue longer the struggle for Independence." Twelve battles and heavy skirmishes were fought near Jackson and nearly every acre was traversed by marching armies, and in this "fearful, fiery ordeal" little in the way of livestock or forage survived. The Delta counties which were formerly capable of growing huge crops of corn either were occupied by Union forces or were producing virtually nothing. A final blow to agriculture in Mississippi came in 1865 just as the war was ending when another flood breached the levees, causing the inundation of large areas of the Delta and the destruction of the remaining livestock and crops. Veterans returning from the war and wading through miles of overflowed country could have little hope of the future in that area.[4]

---

[3] William Scott, Feb. 27, 1863, to Gov. Pettus, Gov. Corr., Miss. Arch.; *Vicksburg Whig*, Feb. 24, Mar. 7, 21, 1863; *Mississippian*, Mar. 8, 1863, in *Southern Crisis*, Mar. 7, 13, 1863.
[4] *Memphis Appeal* (Atlanta), Feb. 17, 1864; W. L. Nugent, Mar. 13, 1864, to his wife, in J. K. Bettersworth (ed.): *Mississippi in the Confederacy as They Saw It*

(Baton Rouge, La., 1961), p. 213; *Hinds County Gazette*, Oct. 7, 1865; R. W. Harrison: "Levee Building in Mississippi before the Civil War," *Journal of Mississippi History*, XII (1950), 96 ff. Six of the Delta counties showed population losses for the sixties, though the state of Mississippi had a small gain.

Louisiana, which among the plantation states was the lowest producer of swine, corn, wheat, oats, and forage, early recognized that to assure itself sufficient provisions would require the most prudent use of its land and its supplies. The *Louisiana Democrat* of Alexandria advocated sharp reduction in the meat rations of slaves and the substitution of rice, molasses, and meal. Bank's expedition brought destitution to the plantation region by seizing many slaves and capturing and destroying large numbers of horses, mules, cattle, hogs, poultry, and meat houses as well as quantities of corn, fodder, molasses, bacon, and flour. Meanwhile, conscription took off the small farmers who had previously supplied New Orleans and the planters with much of their meat and corn. New Orleans was to be provisioned by the Union forces after capture of the city, but the sugar and cotton parishes, in which bitter strife continued between Federals and Confederates, were reduced to a style of living very different from that of the antebellum period.[5]

Florida, which, except for Texas, had the most favorable ratio of cattle to humans at the outset of the war, was in a position to provide the Confederacy with considerable surpluses of cattle, beef, and fish. However, the state was slow to turn from cotton to corn, and it was not until 1863 that its land and labor were rigorously applied to meeting the food needs of the South. The state was then producing annually 25,000 head of cattle, 10,000 head of hogs, 100,000 barrels of fish, 50,000 sides of leather, and quantities of sugar and syrup. But its surplus meat, like that of Texas, became unavailable early in the war because of the distance it had to be hauled and the fact that Sherman cut all rail connections with the north. Furthermore, the Federal raids on the coast drove planters and their slaves into the interior, where as refugees they became little more than subsistence farmers.[6]

Well before Lee's surrender, the food-producing area of the Confederacy had been shorn of practically all Tennessee and Arkansas and the most productive parts of Mississippi and

---

[5] *Louisiana Democrat,* Oct. 16, 1861, May 6, 7, 8, 1863; *Baton Rouge Planter* in *New Orleans Price Current,* Feb. 22, 1862.

[6] J. E. Johns: *Florida during the Civil War* (Gainesville, Fla., 1963), pp. 69, 131, 146–7.

Louisiana. Texas, Missouri, and Kentucky, which had contributed great amounts of food earlier, were unable to help.[7] Destruction of food and the shrinking of the area from which the Confederacy could draw provisions, together with the enlargement of the zone of desolation within that area, created an ever more serious food problem. By August 1864 Secretary of War Seddon was frantically calling on the farmers and planters of South Carolina and Georgia to furnish stores, particularly corn and forage, because supplies in Virginia and North Carolina were exhausted. Two months later it was reported to Colonel Northrop, the Commissary General, that the whole Confederacy was "completely exhausted of supplies," with meat rations available for only 25 days and the new hog crop still 48 days away. Food "must come from abroad if it be got at all."[8] The South was "fearfully narrowed" by Union forces and as prices rose and demands could not be met, there was suffering in the heartland and talk of famine, starvation, and nakedness. Even mouldy bread, rotten bacon, damaged rice, and spoiled flour brought famine prices in Richmond and Petersburg. With thousands of Federal prisoners in the vicinity to be fed, the *Richmond Whig* was led to speculate whether they or the people of the capital would freeze or starve first.

Army rations, which had never been generous, were reduced from ¾ pound of pork or bacon to ⅓ pound, or from 1¼ pound of fresh or salt beef to 1 pound, and extra amounts of sorghum, molasses, tobacco, and whiskey were given to both soldiers and slaves to aid them in forgetting their hunger. This led a "Rymster" to inveigh:

---

[7] *Nashville Daily Union*, Feb. 17, 1863; *Natchez Daily Courier*, May 26, 1863; *O.R.*, ser. 1, XLVI, 1222.
[8] *O.R.*, ser. 4, III, 738. Shelby Foote: *The Civil War, Fredericksburg to Meridian* (New York, 1963), frontispiece and p. 952, has two useful maps showing roughly the areas of the Confederacy held by Federal forces as of Dec. 1, 1862, and presumably the end of 1863. In his appeal of Aug. 3, 1864, Seddon said: "The recent interruptions in rail road communications with the more Southern States, whence the supplies for the Army of Virginia must, in consequence of the great dearth of forage and bread stuffs which exists in Virginia and North Carolina, be mainly drawn, render it indispensable that extraordinary exertions and sacrifices should be made by the people of the south, who are more fortunate in the possession of such stores, to furnish them liberally to the government." Copy in Duke University Library.

Reduce our rations at all?
It was difficult, yet it was done—
We had one meal a day—it was small
Are we now, Oh ye gods! to have none?

On January 1, 1865, Josiah Gorgas noted that Lee's army was "almost without bread and quite without meat." Ten days later Lee, with only two days' supply of rations, said the "country is swept clear." But both on the 10th and the 27th, when he wrote about the high rate of desertion, which he attributed to the small rations the men were getting, he seemed to think that food could be brought in from outside the core of the Confederacy if more vigorous efforts were made. The facts lend little support to his view.[9]

Southern resistance or will to fight was reaching its breaking point, as is shown in the despairing tone of letters to the governors telling of the scarcity of food and fuel and the fear of starvation. The same kind of letters were sent to relatives in the army and in turn contributed to the alarming rate of desertion. In cities like Augusta, Atlanta, Selma, Montgomery, and Richmond, where major war industries were centered and to which thousands of whites and blacks had fled from invaded areas, enormous prices had to be paid for food and fuel. These conditions in the cities, combined with the failure of farmers to bring in food because of fear of impressment and with the refusal of stores and factories to accept Confederate currency, brought angry passions, turbulence, disorder, and lawlessness to the surface. Evidence of the breakdown of the South's will to fight was to be seen in the numerous bands of stragglers in the country and in the cities who plundered homes, stores, and warehouses; in the greater belligerence of the Southern Unionists; and in the bitter disillusionment which led many people, perhaps wrongly, to maintain that it was a rich man's war but a poor man's fight. Conscription, commutation of tithe payments, exemption of overseers and of numerous other classes of govern-

---

[9] *Richmond Examiner*, May 10, 1863, in *National Intelligencer*, Jan. 12, 1864; *Richmond Whig* in *North Carolina Standard*, Nov. 3, 1863; *O.R.*, ser. 1, XLVI, part 2, 1035, 1143, and ser. 4, III, 931.

ment employees and workers in war industries, and currency problems provided some foundation for such charges.[1]

Right up to Lee's surrender, there were stores of grain and meat in every Confederate state that remained hidden away, but their amount should not be exaggerated. They could only be brought out by the most rigorous exercise of impressment—stringently enforced during the last months of the war—or by the offer of something other than Confederate currency. (As Confederate money shrank in value, it was refused outright near the Union lines and accepted elsewhere only with reluctance.) Yet these stores were being turned up to such an extent that commissary officers continued to feel somewhat optimistic that the new crops coming in and the hogs and cattle still left would be sufficient to tide the South over until victory. As late as March 10, 1865, when Lee's army was on desperately short rations, when cavalry and artillery horses were dying by the hundreds, and when Richmond residents were close to starvation, reports were being received of as much as 26,000,000 rations of bread and 16,500,000 rations of meat that might be available if the areas where they were located were cleared of enemy troops, the transportation lines restored, and money—that is, acceptable money such as gold or greenbacks—offered, or, failing that, if planters were allowed to market their cotton through the lines.

More and more the continuance of the war seemed to depend on the ability of officers, contractors, and others to exchange cotton by way of the Mississippi, Tennessee, or even Virginia, for Northern horses, meat, drugs, and other items. Before his dismissal in 1865, Colonel L. B. Northrop, Commissary General of Subsistence, pointed this out, saying: "The army is also sustained by various contrivances to draw supplies from beyond our lines by barter and by secret arrangements with the enemy, turning on their anxiety to get cotton." As much as 10,000 pounds of bacon, as well as other essential items of food and drugs, were traveling from Union to Confederate lines daily in exchange for cotton during the last months of the war. Much of this illicit

---

[1] F. F. Corley: *Confederate City: Augusta, Georgia, 1860–1865* (Columbia, S.C., 1960), pp. 76 ff.

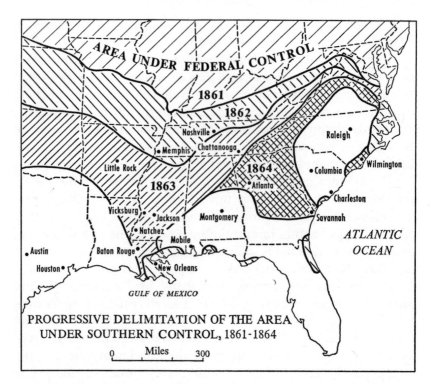

Area Under Federal Control

1861
1862
1864
1863

Nashville
Memphis
Chattanooga
Little Rock
Vicksburg
Jackson
Montgomery
Natchez
Mobile
Baton Rouge
New Orleans

Raleigh
Columbia
Wilmington
Charleston
Savannah
Atlanta

ATLANTIC
OCEAN

Austin
Houston

GULF OF MEXICO

PROGRESSIVE DELIMITATION OF THE AREA
UNDER SOUTHERN CONTROL, 1861-1864

0   Miles   300

trade was winked at by Confederate officers, who understandably were driven to desperation by the difficulty of providing rations and drugs for their troops. It was the more shameful that the trade was tolerated by the North.[2]

But the supplies brought through the lines were inadequate, and Grant finally put a halt to them. The scarcity of food, felt in all parts of the South and in the army from Virginia to Texas, desertion from and attrition in the army, and a disastrous currency combined to defeat the South.

---

[2] *O.R.*, ser. 1, XLVI, part 2, 1297; L. H. Johnson: "Contraband Trade during the Last Year of the Civil War," *Mississippi Valley Historical Review*, XLIX (March 1962), 635 ff.

II

THE NORTH

6

Diversity

ON THE EVE of the Civil War Northern agriculture was
characterized by small farm units, relatively intensively
developed with less waste and unused land than in the South,
employing about one fourth as many hired hands as the South
did slaves, and making much greater use of labor-saving machinery. Although there were bonanza farms in the North that
were as large as any plantation in the South, they were few and
atypical. The average size of farms in representative Northern
states was: New York, 106 acres; Pennsylvania, 109; and Ohio,
114. In Virginia the average size was 324 acres, in Georgia 430,
in Louisiana 536. In New York 68 per cent of the land in farms
was improved; in Pennsylvania, 62 per cent; in Ohio, 61 per cent;
in Virginia, 36 per cent; and in Georgia and Louisiana, 29 per cent.

In New York and Pennsylvania, where tenancy had once
flourished, the older tenures were being replaced by owner operation. Only on the Wadsworth estate in the Genesee Valley of
New York had a fairly extensive system of landlord-tenant relations survived. Stability of ownership over generations was not
common. It was frequently observed that every farmer had a price
for his land which he would readily accept in order to start over
elsewhere. Donald Grant Mitchell tells in his charming *My Farm
of Edgewood: A Country Book* that when he advertised for a
farm of at least one hundred acres not more than three hours

from a city and having an eastern or southern outlook, twenty acres of wood, a running stream, and a water view, he received hundreds of replies offering farms that were said to meet his ideal conditions completely. Only among the Pennsylvania Germans was there continuity of farm ownership.

Farm families were large and did most of the work themselves. Yet the census of 1860 shows there was one hired hand for 40 per cent of the farms. This is not quite as meaningful as it appears, however, for older boys of sixteen and more who were living on their parents' farm were listed as farm laborers.[1]

In the North agriculture was much more diversified than in the South, where the production of staple crops with slave labor led to a similarity of problems even though the staples were dissimilar. There was little in common among the operations of the Merino sheep breeder of Vermont, the onion or tobacco raiser of the Connecticut Valley, the fluid milk producer of Westchester County, New York, the wheat raiser of Wisconsin, or the beef cattleman of the Scioto Valley of Ohio. These farmers were becoming specialists in a small way, but most of them still pursued a diversified economy and rarely committed themselves wholly to one crop or one branch of farming.

For the most part Northeastern farmers practised a diversified near-subsistence type of farming, although they might have a little surplus from the wheat field, poultry yard, dairy, or orchard to barter or sell. Such a farmer had to count his pennies carefully and try to raise or to improvise most of what was needed in the home. In New York and New England he could make maple syrup. If not too far from town, he might "draw" for sale a few loads of wood or a few sawlogs that he cut out of his woodlot. He worked out his road tax laboring with his own team on nearby roads. The products that he bartered or sold might be used locally or might go through the hands of various middlemen, jobbers, and storekeepers before ending up on tables in Boston, Albany, or New York. Usually he employed no hired labor except to harvest his hay, his most essential crop. If the

---

[1] Donald Grant Mitchell: *My Farm of Edgewood: A Country Book* (New York, 1863), pp. 2 ff. The statistics for 1859 and 1860 are taken from the *Eighth Census of the United States, 1860, Agriculture.*

climate was right, the Northeastern farmer tried to raise corn for his livestock, but if the growing season was too short, he contented himself with oats for his horses and working oxen and gave his cattle and hogs little grain.

The diary of a farmer living near Geneva, New York, illustrates both the diversification of Northeastern agriculture and the continued enlargement and improvement farmers were making over one or even two generations in areas naturally wooded. During the war H. K. Lacy drew income from the sale of a pair of oxen, pork, a surplus horse, a heifer, hides, 34 turkeys and other poultry, 30 bushels of corn, and wood which he hauled to Geneva. He exchanged labor with neighboring farmers, hired some hands at $8 to $18 a month, and worked at pulling stumps, picking stone, clearing hedges, butchering, making some of his farm implements, drawing 230 loads of manure, plowing, reaping, threshing grain, husking corn, and cutting, hauling, splitting, and piling wood.

On the eve of the Civil War this simple picture had begun to change. The transportation revolution was bringing railroads close to many farms and making it possible for butter, fruit, vegetables, and other commodities to be shipped to distant cities. No longer was the local merchant the farmer's only market and source of credit. The coming of the railroads made it possible also for farmers to concentrate on producing the crops for which their land was best adapted. There was no swift overnight change, but farming patterns were going through many changes. Farmers were producing more for sale, were becoming increasingly dependent upon markets, were in need of more capital to purchase the machines and tools that specialization made necessary, and were losing their fear of debts and mortgages, since these made improvements possible.[2]

Pockets of specialization were emerging, spreading along the rail lines, moving away from canals and rivers which had previously been the routes by which produce flowed to market.

---

[2] P. W. Bidwell and J. I. Falconer: *History of Agriculture in the Northern United States, 1620–1860* (Washington, 1925); D. M. Ellis: *Landlords and Farmers in the Hudson-Mohawk Region, 1790–1850* (Ithaca, N.Y., 1946); N. A. McNall: *An Agricultural History of the Genesee Valley, 1790–1860* (Philadelphia, 1952).

These specialized areas appeared early close to the burgeoning cities, producing garden vegetables for them. Although the total value of garden products as tabulated by the census for 1860 was not large—$16,159,000—the concentration in urban or suburban counties was marked.[3]

Other farm items for which the cities were calling were fluid milk, hay for the many horses used with omnibuses, streetcars, hacks, and private carriages, and fuel wood, for coal had not yet displaced the millions of cords of wood burned regularly in homes, industrial establishments, railroad locomotives, and river steamboats. The coming of the railroad enlarged the area on which the cities could draw for fresh milk and enabled them to free themselves gradually from the distillery and brewery slop dairies, which turned out thin, bluish, germ-laden milk that had proved to be the carrier of deadly diseases. Farmers now could haul their whole milk to the nearby station and were no longer obliged to go through the wearying process of churning butter and manufacturing cheese in order to market their dairy products. We shall return to this subject in more detail in a later chapter.

Hay, which Hinton Rowan Helper thought more valuable to Northern farmers than cotton was to the South, but which Carl Russell Fish said was "merely compensation for a climate that made preparation of winter forage a drastic necessity," was an item of considerable market value that entered substantially into trade.[4] It was in demand in all the towns and cities throughout the country and on the plantations in the South. In an earlier period a common sight was great loads of loose hay being transported through the streets, and loose hay continued to be sold throughout the Civil War years and later. New baling techniques were being perfected, however, and baled hay had such obvious advantages and brought so much higher prices that baling be-

---

[3] The leading truck gardening counties were Middlesex, Mass., New York and Queens, N.Y., Philadelphia, Pa., and Hamilton, Ohio, of which Cincinnati was a part. The value of average gross production per farm of garden vegetables in New York County was $3,322, in Queens $360, and in Bergen County, N.J., $181. Other counties having a high value of garden produce were Burlington and Camden, N.J., Allegheny, Pa., St. Louis, Mo., and Anne Arundel and Baltimore, Md.

[4] C. R. Fish: *The American Civil War* (London, 1937), p. 157.

came widely adopted. Beater presses operated by three men and a team of horses and costing $165 could turn out a bale of 400 pounds bound with wire hoops and manila cord at a cost of $1.00 to $1.50 a bale. Other presses were advertised as baling 12 tons a day using one horse, or as pressing a bale of 400 pounds in three minutes with six men and a span of horses. Neither the cost of the balers nor the amount of horsepower required was excessive except for small farmers who had only one or two tons of surplus hay to sell. Consequently the sale of baled hay became an important source of income to many farmers who were advantageously located with respect to railroads, waterways, or urban markets.[5]

Trade in hay, like that in fuel wood, did not attract the attention of census takers, and information concerning its volume is not easy to obtain. Fragments here and there do, however, give some indication of it. The 2,010 horses employed on the Third, Sixth, and Eighth Avenue omnibus lines in New York consumed from nine to thirteen pounds or more daily, which amounts to about 4,480 tons annually. Dray horses; carriage and riding horses, both private and public (there were 188 livery stables in New York in 1864); and brewery, distillery, and express company horses (there were 86 breweries, 62 distilleries, and 146 companies and individuals in the express business) brought the total number of horses in the city to 110,000. Their hay consumption must have been not far from 250,000 tons. In addition there was the hay fed to cattle in the great distillery and brewery dairies and to the cows kept by the well-to-do families. Rye straw for bedding was also in demand. Seven of the more distant Hudson-Catskill counties, which produced 712,000 tons of hay in 1863, were estimated to have sold 100,000 tons, in addition to $100,000 worth of straw.[6]

In 1859–60 New Orleans, with about one fifth of New York's

---

[5] *Country Gentleman*, XVI (Aug. 23, 1860), 120; New York State Agricultural Society, *Journal*, XIV (1864), 94, and XV (1865), 102.
[6] *Country Gentleman*, XIX (Mar. 6, 20, 1862), 156, 192; Adams, Sampson & Co.: *New York State Business Directory*, 1864 (Albany, 1864), *passim*; New Orleans Price Current, June 8, 15, Sept. 8, 1861. The statistician of the U.S. Department of Agriculture (in its *Report*, 1871, p. 55), gives the number of cattle and horses not on farms in 1860 as 3,347,009 and 1,185,514. In 1870 the numbers were 4,273,-973 and 1,547,370.

population, drew from the upper Mississippi Valley states one half of its hay, or 21,666 tons, part of which was destined for plantations in the vicinity. All through May and well into June 1861, when both sides were rushing to war, flatboats were bringing hay, corn, and other food items to New Orleans. Indeed, as late as June 8 and 15, the *New Orleans Price Current* reported the arrival of flatboats from St. Louis bringing 1,900 bales of hay, which sold for $30 to $35 a ton. Judging by the market for hay in New York and New Orleans, we can easily conclude that the nationwide demand for hay off the farms was well over a half million tons.

Because of its bulk the price of hay varied widely according to the cost of transporting it to market. Shipment into the South more than doubled the price for which the farmer sold it. A bonanza farmer of Illinois, Michael Sullivant, owner of a great 40,000 acre farm, sold 10,000 tons of timothy hay, baled and delivered at a nearby depot, for $10 a ton in 1860. For hay delivered in Rochester, New York, farmers could expect to get from $8 to $13 a ton, depending partly on its quality and the way it was put up.[7]

Heavy buying of hay by army quartermasters sent prices up throughout the North after 1861. The purchases amounted to 289,000 tons in the fiscal year 1863, 373,219 tons in 1864, and 1,518,621 for the four years of the war. The low price was $6.00 for hay cut near army camps and the high was $97.50 for hay delivered at Fort Halleck, near Denver. Except for prairie hay bought in Kansas or Nebraska for delivery to nearby forts, hay usually sold for $25 to $35 a ton. The army's needs became so pressing by 1865 that the government ordered exports, amounting to an estimated 10,000 to 15,000 tons that year, to be halted during the emergency.[8]

Meantime, abuses had grown up in the pressing of hay that produced a demand for legislation to outlaw the cheating. Hay was being baled too soon after cutting, which lowered quality.

---

[7] *Illinois Farmer* in *Ohio Cultivator*, XVI (May 15, 1860), 149; *Rural New Yorker*, XII (Jan. 5, 1861), 11.
[8] "Contracts Made by the Quartermaster's Department," *House Ex. Doc.*, 39 Cong., 2 Sess., XIV, no. 84, *passim;* Secretary of the Treasury: *Reports*, 1863, 1864, 1865; *O.R.*, ser. 3, V, 312.

Solon Robinson's barbed pen condemned farmers for including heavy stones in the bales and binding them with as much as thirty-seven pounds of wood, for which the buyers had to pay inflated hay prices. Drovers who bought many bales of hay for the stock they were bringing by rail from the Middle West to New York were angry at the deception. In the Chicago market hay was required to be carefully marked according to the kind of grasses. Timothy baled in a roller and beater press brought the top price of $19 to $20; timothy loosely pressed brought $18 to $19; timothy loose brought $17 to $18; prairie hay, roller and beater pressed, brought $13; prairie hay loosely pressed sold for $11 to $12.[9]

Not everyone approved of the high prices hay brought and the increasing tendency of farmers to sell part of their hay. The short-sighted view was that at $10 a ton the farmer should sell rather than feed the hay, a view that was publicly supported by that strange combination of first-rate agricultural editor, impostor, and manufacturer of adulterated guano manures, James J. Mapes. Others, however, took the long-range view that continued selling of hay further impoverished land already depleted of essential minerals by constant cropping to grain. It was better to maintain first-rate stock, feed them the hay and grain, and use the manure for soil building. As one pithy commentator put it, "He that sells hay is a candidate for the poorhouse." Farmers who insisted on selling hay because they were situated close to cities should bring back manure from city stables to restore their soil, advised the *American Agriculturist*.[1]

Throughout much of the Eastern states the terrain was so irregular that many farms had some broken, steep-sloped, rocky,

---

[9] Contrast these Chicago prices with New York prices of $33 to $37 at about the same time or with prices in Washington, where, with army needs and city demands, hay was quoted at $37 to $40 a ton. Even oats and wheat straw brought from $20 to $25 a ton. *Country Gentleman*, XV (Apr. 19, 1860), 251, XIX (Mar. 27, 1862), 209, and XXV (Feb. 9, 1865), 101; *New York Weekly Tribune*, Feb. 15, Mar. 3, 1863; *Prairie Farmer*, XV (Jan. 21, 1865), 41; *National Intelligencer*, Feb. 11, 1865.
[1] American Institute of the City of New York: *Annual Report, 1861–1862*, p. 351; New York State Agricultural Society: *Transactions*, XXIII (1863), 297; C. A. Day: *Farming in Maine, 1860–1940* (*University of Maine Studies*, 2d ser., no. 78, Orono, Maine, 1963), p. 22; *American Agriculturist*, XXI (October 1862), 300.

or thin-soiled acres ill-adapted for cropping or even for pasture. These areas were left uncleared and became the source of the farmers' wood for fuel, fencing, and lumber. As population grew in neighboring towns and cities and as railroads were extended, the demand for fuel wood reached practically every portion of the country, and farmers found their woodlot a profitable source of income. One sees in country weeklies of the mid-nineteenth century frequent notices of merchants, lawyers, and newspaper proprietors offering to accept fuel wood for debts. Cutting cord-wood and hauling it to the home, the nearby village, or the rail-road woodyards which were spaced at regular intervals along the tracks was done in the winter when farmers' tasks were light. Not only fuel wood was in demand but also sawlogs cut for dimension lumber. Either the logs were hauled to the nearby sawmills, where they were sold or cut into boards for use on the farm in expanding and improving the housing or else they were sold to box mills, spool, furniture, and dowel factories, and shops making spade handles, wooden pumps, and other miscellaneous products. There were few villages in the Northeast that did not have their sawmill, shingle mill, lath mill, tannery, and other industries using wood.[2]

Though coal was beginning to replace it, fuel wood remained the major source of heat and power in homes, offices, factories, locomotives, and steamboats during the Civil War. In 1860 all the railroads save the Pennsylvania and the Central of New Jersey relied on wood for their locomotives, and all Western steamboats used wood. With the closing of the Southern ports by the blockade the normal supplies of fuel wood which had come from Virginia and North Carolina to New York City were cut off and prices rose to $8 and $10 a cord. At such levels farmers and suppliers rushed wood to the city from as far away as Maine and Maryland, as well as from New Jersey. The high prices quickly dropped, but only for a short while. In New York State farmers sold 3,721,973 cords of fuel wood in 1864 in addition to what they cut for their own use. The return to farmers from this source would, at the going prices, surely have amounted to $15,000,000 and must have made fuel wood one of their important income-producing items. The

---

[2] Day: *Farming in Maine*, p. 175.

following year 516,228 cords valued at $3,016,841 were produced in Massachusetts. For other states the demand for fuel wood was doubtless as great relative to the population.

Wartime demand pushed the average price of fuel wood from $3 to $7 a cord. Purchases for the War Department and the greatly increased volume of fuel wood needed by the railroads to carry their expanded business created a scramble for supplies that was felt in many parts of the North as well as the portions of the South in Union hands. In 1863 the War Department purchased 214,718 cords of fuel wood and 130,820 tons of coal; in 1864 it bought 355,969 cords of fuel wood but increased its coal purchases to 317,000 tons.[3]

The heaviest users of fuel wood during the war were railroads, though cost studies had shown that coal was a more economic fuel. Among the lines for which we have figures are the Illinois Central, which burned 46,576 cords in 1861, the Michigan Central, which used 43,440 cords in 1862, the New York Central, which used 140,000 cords in 1861 and 211,000 in 1862, and the Vermont railroads, which used 63,000 cords annually. Even the Reading Railroad in the heart of the anthracite region of Pennsylvania, a road which drew much of its revenue from carrying coal, used 7,738 cords in 1861.

Scarcity of labor brought the fuel supplies of the North to a perilous state, as it did those of the South. In January 1865 the New York Central sheds were empty of fuel and the railroad was forced to seek supplies in Canada. Some companies had to resort to green wood, which made very poor fuel.[4]

The advance of the woodcutter's axe and the war-created

---

[3] *Working Farmer*, XIV (Jan. 1, 1862), 4, quoting the *New York Express*. Figures for purchases of wood by the War Department are compiled from its *Reports* for 1863 and 1864. See also Thomas Weber: *The Northern Railroads in the Civil War, 1861–1865* (New York, 1952), p. 11; *Rural New Yorker*, XII (Jan. 5, 1861), 11, and XVI (May 27, 1865), 170; *Statistical Information Relating to Certain Branches of Industry in Massachusetts* (Boston, 1866), p. 759;

Census of the State of New York, 1865, p. ciii.
[4] *American Railroad Journal*, XXIV (Mar. 9, 1861), 193, and XXXV (May 24, Nov. 29, 1862), 386, 941; Michigan Central Railroad: *Annual Report*, 1863, p. 26; New York Central Railroad: *Annual Reports*, 1860–2; Railroad Commissioner of Vermont: *Third Annual Report*, 1858, *passim*; *Rural New Yorker*, XVI (Jan. 21, 1865), 23.

scarcity of fuel aroused alarm for the country's forests, and the Commissioner of Agriculture included in his report for 1865 a remarkably perceptive essay on "American Forests: Their Destruction and Preservation." Its author, Rev. Frederick Starr, Jr., of St. Louis, assembled statistics and information which showed that American forests were being cut down at an appalling rate. He predicted that the United States would be faced with the same disasters that had followed the destruction of the forests in the Old World. The railroads alone used hundreds of millions of board feet of construction timber, millions of hemlock, chestnut, and oak ties, and 6,465,000 cords of fuel annually. Enormous amounts of fuel wood were consumed every year in homes, offices, steamboats, and factories. These constant drains, together with continued clearing of timber land for agricultural purposes and the destruction of timber by the war, were exhausting supplies, raising costs (since it had become necessary to bring wood longer distances), and holding back industrial growth by imposing high costs. Starr urged careful conservation of the country's remaining supplies of timber and cautious use of farm woodlots. His major point, which was truly prophetic, was that the government should conduct experiments in reforestation and timber growth.[5]

A third small source of income for the mixed farming characteristic of Northern agriculture was maple sugar and syrup. Farmers tended to combine their fuel wood and sugar business by cutting sufficient trees to meet both needs, selling the merchantable wood for fuel, and using the poorer material, including tops and branches, in the sugarhouse. At least a full cord of wood was needed to make 100 pounds of sugar.

During the war farmers were admonished to increase their output of maple sugar and syrup where they had abundant trees and fuel, being reminded that prices in 1862 were nearly double their former level. The scarcity and cost of labor, however, tended to prevent any large increase in production. Ohio seems to have excelled in expanding output by raising its yield of sugar from 3,323,942 pounds in 1860 to 8,204,824 in 1863 and its syrup from 392,932 gallons to 542,400 gallons for the same years. New York's output, on the other hand, declined about 10 per cent

---

[5] Commissioner of Agriculture: *Report,* 1865, pp. 210–34.

between 1860 and 1865. The crop of the North as a whole was 25 per cent greater in 1863 than in 1862, but weather had much to do with the increase.[6]

Although hops, an essential item in the brewing of beer, were being raised in every state except Florida by 1860, 88 per cent of the crop of 10,991,996 pounds was raised in New York, and 88 per cent of the New York crop was grown in six counties north and south of the Mohawk River. Otsego County alone produced 3,507,069 pounds of hops. Here hop growing became a specialty. Hops were a demanding crop, taking two years from planting to harvest and requiring a fertile, well-drained soil heavily manured both before and during the growing season and protected from winds. They had to be strung on poles from twenty to thirty feet high, a small army of pickers was needed to harvest them, and they had to be carefully dried in kilns. The investment in poles, twine, fuel, sulphur, kilns, baling cloth, and labor was so costly that many farmers were prevented from experimenting with the crop. Yields varied widely from year to year, ranging from as little as 400 pounds to the acre to as much as 2,000 pounds, depending on weather and the ravages of insects. Prices also varied extensively—from 6 cents in 1860 to 52 cents in 1864.

With average yields of 888 pounds to the acre, and with prices generally well over 12 cents, the returns from hops were large. Stimulated by the influx of German immigrants and what Cochran calls the spread of German drinking habits to the rest of the population, as well as by the rapidly growing overseas demand for American hops, production mounted during the war. Exports ranged from 4,851,000 pounds in 1862 to 8,864,000 pounds in 1863, and production increased from 11,000,000 pounds in 1860 to 16,000,000 in 1862. In the absence of statistics one can only guess how much larger the crops of 1863 and 1864 were.

In the midst of the excitement generated by the high war prices for hops and by the appearance of the *Hop Grower's Journal,* farmers raised their crops on the same land year after

[6] *Rural New Yorker,* XIII (Feb. 15, 1862), 54; Clarksburg, W.Va., *National Telegraph,* Feb. 21, 1862; *Census of the State of New York, 1865,* p. viii; *Hunt's Merchant's Magazine,* L (February 1864), 159, and LII (February 1865), 122; *Eighth Census of the United States, 1860, Agriculture,* p. 187; Ohio State Board of Agriculture: *12th Annual Report,* 1862, p. xxxvii.

year. Destructive insects, particularly the hop louse or aphis, accumulated and seriously diminished output. The ravages of the aphis became progressively worse, reducing the crop in 1864 to 12,247,000 pounds. The damage was compounded by the severe winter of 1863–4, which killed many old plants. In Otsego County, where most farmers raised some hops and a few were engaged in large operations, the losses were extensive. Many hop raisers reported a crop only one fourth the average of previous years and others said their hops had failed completely. By 1869 recovery had set in and New York was producing more hops than the entire United States in 1859, but meantime hop raisers had taken a bad beating.[7]

New York State remained the Empire state, excelling in hop production as it did in the number and value of its farms, the value of its livestock, and the production of dairy products, fruit, and vegetables, but it had competition. What had been New York's loss in 1864 and 1865 was Wisconsin's gain. Hops planted on fresh land in the Badger state and given much attention when prices were most favorable brought small fortunes to some. Fabulous stories of profits created great excitement, or "hop on the brain," as the *Beaver Dam Citizen* reported.[8] In hop-picking time in late August swarms of women and girls flocked to aid in the harvest. In 1868, at the height of the craze for growing hops in Wisconsin, as many as 30,000 people would be so engaged. The excitement and romance of these occasions was described by Flavia A. Canfield in her *Hop-Picking: Girl Life in the Sixties*.

Northern agriculture was further diversified by its fruit industry. Rural America owed much to the work of great nurserymen such as Ellwanger & Barry, William R. Prince, Andrew

---

[7] Lewis Bollman: "The Hop Plant," in U.S. Commissioner of Agriculture, *Report*, 1864, pp. 97 ff.; T. C. Cochran: *The Pabst Brewing Company* (New York, 1948), p. 29; Secretary of the Treasury: *Report*, 1864, *House Ex. Doc.*, 38 Cong., 2 Sess., VII, no. 3, p. 246; P. L. Simonds: *Hops: The Cultivation, Commerce, and Uses in Various Countries* (London, 1877), p. 96; *Genesee Farmer*, XXVI (October 1865), 311; *Country Gentleman*, XXV (Apr. 27, 1865), 274, and XXVI (July 6, Aug. 10, 1865), 17, 97; *Rural New Yorker*, XV (July 23, 1864), 238.

[8] *Beaver Dam Citizen* in *Green County Advocate*, Nov. 23, 1865; Frederick Merk: *Economic History of Wisconsin during the Civil War Decade* (Madison, Wis., 1916), pp. 37 ff.

Jackson Downing, and Joseph Breck, whose raspberries and straw-
berries, and pear, apple, plum, peach, and cherry trees, were
carried into every corner of the land, along with Norway spruce,
lilacs, and other flowering shrubs. Most enterprising farmers
bought a few fruit trees to supply the family table from these
traveling salesmen. If the trees proved well adapted to the area,
the next step was to introduce more of them for commercial
purposes.

The decade of the sixties was one of marked expansion in
the fruit industry. New York, Ohio, and Pennsylvania led, with
Illinois and Michigan also showing substantial growth. Although
fruit was raised widely in all parts of these states, areas of
specialization appeared, notably in the region tempered by the
Great Lakes. Farmers specializing in fruits were learning how to
combat borers, bark lice, tent caterpillars, and codling moths, but
against other insects and diseases they had no defense.
Entomologists had done useful work in describing insects, but
preventive treatment was still in its infancy.

Commercial canning of fruits and vegetables widened the
market and made it possible for city people to enjoy them throughout the year. During the sixties the output rose from five million
to thirty million cans. At the same time home canning was
flourishing and was encouraging more extensive growing of fruits
and vegetables on farms and in town gardens. The apple market
did decline in New England, where the temperance movement,
stimulated by the war, had brought the drinking of that old
standby, cider, into disapproval. Most families, said the Amherst,
New Hampshire, *Farmer's Cabinet*, had formerly used the cider
of thirty to forty barrels of apples; now all that could be done
with such quantities of apples was to dry them for absent soldiers
or feed them to the livestock.[9]

Potatoes continued to be the most important vegetable in bulk
and value. Although the destructive blight of the forties had
forced many to abandon the crop for a time, no remedy had been

---

[9] U. P. Hedrick: *History of Horticulture in America to 1860* (New
York, 1950), *passim; Ninth Census
of the United States, 1870*, III, *Industry and Wealth*, 81; Day: *Farm-
in Maine*, pp. 107 ff.; R. O. Cummings: *The American and His
Food. A History of Food Habits in
the United States* (Chicago, 1941),
pp. 69, 85; Amherst, N.H., *Farmers' Cabinet*, Nov. 20, 1862.

discovered. Growers, however, had learned that some varieties were less troubled by the rot and that early planting and good drainage might avoid its worst effects. Half the total potato crop was raised in the Northeastern states, but its cultivation was extending into Michigan, Ohio, Illinois, and other states of the Middle West. Because of their bulk, weight, and storage costs, the wholesale price of potatoes fluctuated markedly, ranging from $1.25 to $6 and more per bushel, though farmers never received such returns. As the *Rural New Yorker* said, the high prices quoted in the spring when potatoes were becoming scarce induced heavy planting and low prices in the fall.[1]

By withdrawing from the Union and precipitating the war, the South invited, if it did not compel, the North to free itself from its former dependence on Southern tobacco, sugar, and cotton, and to make every effort to produce these items or to find satisfactory substitutes or new sources of supply. The aim of self-sufficient nationalists was expressed by the *La Crosse Republican:* "Let Northern sorghum supersede New Orleans sugar; and Northern flax take the place of Southern cotton, and Northern tobacco drive out 'Dixie's weed,' and three strong points will have been made."[2] Federal and state governments, farm journals, the state agricultural societies, and various farm organizations all joined in encouraging the production of satisfactory substitutes.

The South could ill afford to have the North expand its production of tobacco. Every Northern state was already producing some of this staple and seven produced from three to twenty-five million pounds. If the border states remained loyal, 62 per cent of the country's tobacco-producing capacity as of 1859 would be available to the North. Nevertheless, wholesale prices of tobacco, which ranged from 3 to 13 cents in the New York market from November 1860 to May 1861, began to work upward thereafter, reaching 10 to 18 cents in February 1862, falling for a short period to 7 to 18 cents, and rising to 11 to 15 cents in September 1862, to 15 to 32 cents in February 1863, and to 15 to 35 cents a year later. The rise was caused not only by the withdrawal of

---

[1] *Rural New Yorker,* XVII (Sept. 1, 1866), 277. Wholesale prices were listed regularly in the *American Agriculturist,* 1861–5.

[2] *La Crosse Republican,* Mar. 3, 1863. This reference was provided by Frederick Merk.

Southern tobacco from the market but also by the fact that in the three border states which were heavy producers of tobacco, military operations cut production from 171,624,000 pounds in 1860 to 103,959,000 pounds in 1864 and 99,317,000 in 1865. Alert Northern farmers moved quickly to fill the gap in the tobacco market and to take advantage of the flow of gold the prices assured.[3]

Tobacco is a most exacting crop in that it requires skillful labor throughout the year, from the preparation of the seedbed to the curing and packing of the leaf. It also makes heavy demands on the soil. Not all farmers who tried the crop succeeded. Those who did had already had experience with tobacco and owned land adapted to it.

In a comparatively small area of the Connecticut Valley extending from Hartford nearly to the northern boundary of Massachusetts, farmers had learned how to cultivate their land intensively to tobacco, onions, and other vegetables. They had the benefits of a favorable climate and rich alluvial soil, to which they continued to apply manure and mineral fertilizer. This combination of excellent management, rich soil, and good weather made it possible for them to out-produce farmers elsewhere, both in quantity per acre and quality. The average yield of tobacco per acre in 1864 was 1,650 pounds for the Massachusetts farms and 1,450 for the Connecticut farms. In 1865 it was 1,200 and 1,350, these being by far the highest yields in the country. Because of the premium price the Connecticut Valley tobacco brought—25 cents in 1864 and 22 and 30 cents in 1865, in contrast to 14 cents for New York, 9 cents for Pennsylvania, 12 cents for Kentucky, and 10 and 13 cents for Missouri tobacco—the gross value per acre of tobacco crops on Massachusetts and Connecticut farms was $160 and $182 in 1862, $318 and $312 in 1863, $412 and $362 in 1864, and $270 and $405 in 1865. No other crop except hops in Otsego County, New York, yielded such high returns.[4]

Elsewhere only Pennsylvania came near the production rate of the Connecticut Valley farms, with an average of 1,068 pounds

---

[3] The quotations are from the *American Agriculturist.*
[4] Commissioner of Agriculture:

Report, 1862, p. 129, and 1865, p. 63.

to the acre in 1864 and 977 in 1865. The only area where tobacco was intensely grown was the Amish and Mennonite stronghold in Lancaster County.[5] Other small areas favorable to the production of tobacco were in three central New York counties—Onondaga, Madison, and Cayuga—and in Illinois, southern Indiana, and Ohio. Expansion in tobacco production was most marked in Illinois, where the yield increased from 6,885,000 pounds in 1859 to 20,397,000 in 1863. During the war New York more than doubled its yield, as did Massachusetts, but growth elsewhere was more moderate.[6]

ESTIMATED TOBACCO PRODUCTION FOR LEADING NORTHERN STATES
(*in pounds*)

STATE	1859	1862	1863	1864	1865
Connecticut	6,000,133	7,500,166	7,500,166	9,900,218	8,167,681
Illinois	6,885,202	9,452,307	20,397,337	18,867,722	18,867,722
Indiana	7,993,318	9,057,665	10,416,314	8,767,065	8,547,889
Massachusetts	3,233,198	4,041,497	5,200,000	7,760,000	5,746,000
New York	5,764,582	7,205,727	10,088,017	12,912,662	11,836,607
Ohio	25,092,581	25,528,972	28,081,869	29,017,931	26,116,138
Pennsylvania	3,181,586	3,976,082	5,567,774	6,124,551	5,512,090
ESTIMATED YIELD OF BORDER STATES					
Delaware	9,699	12,123	15,618	14,057	7,029
Kentucky	108,126,840	—	—	56,292,968	54,108,646
Maryland	38,410,965	40,601,179	48,721,415	33,292,968	29,963,672
Missouri	25,086,196	28,609,948	26,340,505	13,697,063	15,237,982
All Loyal States		208,000,000	258,000,000		

SOURCE: *Eighth Census of the United States, 1860, Agriculture*, and Commissioner of Agriculture, *Reports*, 1862–5.

Production of tobacco in the North and in the border states, together with the quantities that were captured as the Northern troops pressed into the South, not only provided for the increased

---

[5] S. W. Fletcher: *Pennsylvania Agriculture and Country Life, 1840–1940* (Harrisburg, Pa., 1955), p. 144.

[6] The data for 1859 are the result of the tabulation of the returns of farmers made to the census takers; those for later years are estimates prepared from many reports coming in to the Commissioner of Agriculture.

demand resulting from fuller pocketbooks of soldiers and workers but also permitted continued exports. True, exports fell off from 167,000,000 pounds in 1860 to 107,000,000 in 1861, 112,000,-000 in 1863, and 110,000,000 in 1864. Not until 1865 did the gold value of tobacco exports return to the level of the more prosperous years of the previous decade.[7]

Some people in the Land of Steady Habits were distressed that the rich soil of the Connecticut Valley was being used during the war for a non-food crop which was detrimental to the health of the users. *Homestead,* one of the better farm journals, opposed the planting of tobacco during the war, because it required much labor, was an uncertain crop, did not combine well with other crops in rotation schemes, and induced neglect of other features of farm economy. Other writers in *Homestead* frankly revealed their prejudice against tobacco, arguing that the land devoted to the crop should be put in grain, beans, or potatoes. "The raising of tobacco on the best of our land is unpatriotic and illegitimate," one writer said.[8]

Tobacco could readily be grown by Northern farmers, but cotton and sugar cane were another story. There was little prospect that either crop could be raised in commercial quantities in any Northern state. Moreover, for a long war the rest of the world clearly could not meet the cotton needs of the North. Sugar production outside of the United States, however, was sufficient so that no scarcity of sugar was to be feared, though its price was certain to rise. Because of the fall of New Orleans early in the war and the increasing penetration of Northern troops into the sugar parishes, much captured sugar flowed northward, while the South had to go without the sugar it had produced. This supply rapidly dried up, however, for the sugar parishes were hard hit by bushwackers and by skirmishing between forces of both sides.

Sorghum, sugar beets, and maple sugar were the substitutes the North had for sugar cane, though, as has been seen, maple sugar and syrup were not to contribute materially to relieving the shortage because too much labor was required to produce them. The more optimistic, on the other hand, believed that sorghum

---

[7] *Historical Statistics of the United States* (Washington, 1960), p. 547.

[8] *Homestead,* VII (May 9, 30, 1861), 388, 447.

could free the North from dependence on Louisiana planters and could contribute to diversification of Northern agriculture. Sorghum caught the fancy of the populace as the silkworm craze and the "hen fever" had in the antebellum years.

Sorghum is a thick-stemmed, drought-resistant grass raised largely in the Great Plains today for silage and grain, but in the mid-nineteenth century its principal attraction was the saccharine content of its juice. Though sorghum was known and grown in America before 1853, it was probably in that year that the well-known nurseryman William Prince of Flushing, New York, began to keep a record of it. In the next few years increasing publicity was given to sorghum by nurserymen, farm journals, the agricultural branch of the Patent Office, and the state and local agricultural societies. Numerous articles optimistically predicted that the new crop was certain to become a major one in all parts of the country. To stimulate interest, the *American Agriculturist* distributed eight tons of sorghum seed to its 31,000 subscribers and the agricultural branch of the Patent Office also sent out eight tons of seed along with the other seeds it distributed. The *Sorgo Journal and Farm Machinist* was established as a monthly magazine to keep people up to date on new varieties of sorghum seed, new instructions on planting and caring for the crop, and the bewildering variety of crushing and evaporating devices to make syrup that were coming on the market. That its publisher was manufacturing these devices helps to explain the excitement the journal tried to create by exaggerated accounts of yield of syrup per acre. Books were rushed into print likewise giving optimistic claims for sorghum. Conventions of sorghum growers, doubtless aided by nurserymen and inventors and manufacturers of machines for processing the cane, were held in most Western states, and great enthusiasm was displayed at them for the possibilities of the new crop.[9]

---

[9] C. R. Ball: *History and Distribution of Sorghum*, U.S. Department of Agriculture, Bureau of Plant Industry, Bulletin no. 175 (Washington, 1910), pp. 32–3; Subhas Kumar Dhar: "Grain Sorghum and Millet," Ph.D. dissertation, 1950, Cornell University Library; Proceedings of the conventions of Ohio, Michigan, and Wisconsin may be found in *Sorgo Journal and Farm Machinist*, I–III, and the *Prairie Farmer* for 1862 and 1863; Isaac Hedges: *Sorgho or the Northern Sugar Plant* (Cincinnati, 1863); Henry S. Olcott: *Sorgho*

Stories of fabulous yields of sorghum syrup and profits from its sale appeared in the press. One widely copied story was that farmers were getting from 200 to 300 gallons of syrup, worth $60 at a low estimate, from one acre of sorghum, a crop that took no more labor in the field than corn. Other accounts stated that sorghum grew to a height of eight to sixteen feet and yielded from 80 to 320 gallons per acre. Companies were organized to produce sorghum on a large scale. One of them agreed to establish syrup manufactures at five places where farmers had contracted to put from 500 to 700 acres into sorghum. A planter in Virginia seems to have the record for size of operations, for he expected to have 150 gallons of syrup from each of his 1,100 acres in sorghum, or a total of 15,000 gallons. His case is one of the few for which the sequel was published: his syrup was reported to be poor, filled with specks and small pieces of cane too hurriedly prepared and tasting strongly of vegetable acid. Most reports, at least until 1863 and the big freeze, were favorable. Sales of sorghum syrup in Chicago in 1861 were 1,000 barrels. In 1862 they were 10,000 barrels, and in 1863 they were expected to be 100,000 to 120,000 barrels.[1]

The best year for sorghum production was 1862. In Iowa, still a young state with much of its land undeveloped, the number of acres in sorghum was 36,667 and the number of gallons of syrup produced was 3,012,396. A large proportion of Iowa farmers dependent on sorghum for family sweetening, even used it in tea and coffee, and it had become a common article of sale in stores. Elsewhere, in states like Illinois, Indiana, and Wisconsin, farmers were using sorghum syrup in place of cane sugar and molasses, but throughout the North sorghum substituted for only a small part of the sugar and molasses consumed. Late in 1862 sugar was beginning to move north from the captured plantation region of Louisiana, and larger amounts were being

---

and Imphee: The Chinese and African Sugar Canes (New York, 1858); C. F. Stansbury: *Chinese Sugar Cane as Sugar Making: Its History, Culture, and Adaptation to the Climate, Soil and Economy of the United States* (New York, 1857).

[1] *American Agriculturist*, XXII (September 1863), 270; *Cincinnati Daily Commercial*, Dec. 2, 1862; *Sorgo Journal*, II (March, August 1864), 44, 121; *Richmond Whig*, Oct. 2, 6, 1863; *Rural New Yorker*, XIV (May 30, 1863), 173.

imported from Cuba. Commercial production of sorghum had not developed very successfully, possibly owing to the opposition of the major sugar refiners. Most of the producers were farmers experimenting with a few acres and crude crushing and refining devices.[2]

Middle Western farmers experimenting with sorghum growing had a bad year in 1863, when at the end of August an extraordinarily early and severe frost swept down over Minnesota, Wisconsin, Iowa, Illinois, and states farther east. In many areas sorghum was destroyed and corn, tobacco, and other crops were badly damaged. The crop was drastically cut and the syrup output fell from an estimated 12,000,000 gallons in 1862 to no more than 5,500,000 gallons in 1863. Compared with the annual consumption of 45,000,000 gallons of molasses and of 800,000,000 pounds of sugar, this was a negligible part of the market. Furthermore, it became increasingly clear that no sugar of desirable quality could be refined from the sorghum syrup.

New York's agricultural leaders felt that their state too should raise sorghum if this new crop proved suited to their climate and soil, and they sent one of their ablest members to the West in 1863 to make a detailed study. John Stanton Gould, who was later to have charge of the work in agriculture at Cornell University, was appointed to study all the steps—and all the costs—in the production of sorghum, from the selection of the seed and the soil to the harvesting of the crop and the manufacturing of the syrup and sugar. Arriving in Chicago a month after the great frost of August, Gould found that it had so sharply reduced prospects of yield that many farmers did not expect to cut their cane. He examined many thousands of acres in cane, talked with three hundred farmers and others experienced in sorghum making, and came out with the best, most judicious, and at the time most critical, examination in print. Gould quickly became aware that most of the stories of high yield of juice and syrup to the acre were greatly exaggerated, that there was a grave question whether commercially desirable sugar could be made from the juice, that most of the syrup had a "disagreeable herbaceous taste which no

---

[2] *Rural New Yorker,* XV (Jan. 2, 1864), 6; *American Agriculturist,* XXII (September 1863), 270.

Eastern palate could tolerate as a substitute for molasses," and that the syrup had to be sent to Belcher's sugar refinery in Chicago for further processing to make it edible. He found frauds in the sale of seed of different varieties of sorghum and major book-keeping errors in determining profits and losses for the business of sorghum making. His conclusion was that the crop offered little or nothing to New York and Eastern farmers, but that in the West, notwithstanding the "overwrought statements," it had prospects if "cultivated with skill and judgment." He warned that greater attention needed to be paid to costs which seemed hidden to most promoters of the crop, and he predicted that the high cost of labor would make cultivation on a large scale un-profitable.[3]

The popularity of sorghum as a substitute for sugar cane was at an end, though farmers were to continue to produce their own sorghum syrup for years to come. Officials in the Depart-ment of Agriculture were not ready to give up, however, and arranged to send an agent to China to secure supplies of Chinese sugar cane, as one variety of sorghum was called, in the hope that American seed, which some thought was running out in this country, could be replaced by seed of better quality.[4]

Meantime, considerable interest was developing in the possibility of making sugar from beets. Beet sugar manufacturing came to the United States years after the process had been de-veloped and large-volume production begun in France and Ger-many. European beet sugar production was greatly expanded during the Civil War as a result of the high world price of sugar. The output for the Continent increased from 464,000 tons in 1863 to 693,000 tons in 1865–6. Forward-looking Americans, aware of this development, naturally asked themselves whether the beet sugar industry could not be introduced into the United States.[5]

---

[3] *New York Weekly Tribune*, Nov. 28, 1863; *American Agriculturist*, XXIII (July 1864), 202; *Prairie Farmer*, XII (Sept. 5, 1863), 153; *Davenport Daily Gazette*, Sept. 1, 1863; U.S. Department of Agricul-ture: *Monthly Report of the Con-dition of the Crops*, August–Sep-tember 1863; "Report of John Stanton Gould on Sorghum and Sugar Beet Culture," New York State Agricultural Society, *Trans-actions*, XXIII (1863), 735 ff.

[4] *Sorgo Journal*, III (March 1865), 46.

[5] Commissioner of Agriculture: *Report*, 1867, p. 33.

Experiments with sugar beets had been undertaken in the Connecticut Valley in 1838–40 by the Northhampton Beet Sugar Company, which raised a quantity of sugar beets and from them produced both brown and granulated sugar, the latter of only fair quality. Apparently the experiment was not followed up, and it was not until the war that the sugar beet again attracted attention. In 1862 Maurice Mot planted seed from France on ten acres near Newark in central Ohio and secured 95 tons of beets. Using a crude device for crushing and rendering the juice, he produced a dark but fine-grained sugar at a cost of four cents a pound. At about the same time, William H. Osborn, president of the Illinois Central Railroad, who was engaged in a nationwide advertising effort to draw immigrants to Illinois to purchase the railroad's high-priced land, joined efforts to introduce the sugar beet industry into the Prairie state. He sent copies of a treatise on sugar beets to members of the Illinois legislature, promised free transportation to factories for beets produced on his line, imported many hundred pounds of seed for distribution to farmers, induced two refinery firms in Chicago to establish plants in the midst of large blocks of Illinois Central land, and brought machines and skilled mechanics from Europe to get the plants under way.

The largest of the operations was that of the Gennert Brothers, later incorporated as the Germania Sugar Company, which was said to have bought 2,300 acres near Chatsworth, Illinois, and during the war to have raised beets with a high sugar content. Their manufacturing plans seem to have gone awry, however. In 1866 they tried again, planting 400 acres in beets from which they gathered more than 4,000 tons. But their manufacturing was still unsuccessful; green hands, equipment that continually proved faulty, including a boiler not adapted to local coal, and an insufficient supply of water combined to make the venture a commercial failure, though nine tons of sugar were manufactured. The conclusion of observers was that beet sugar could be made in the United States, but not without the best modern machinery and skilled hands to direct the process. They did nor doubt the ability of prairie soil to yield beets with high sugar content.[6]

[6] *Cincinnati Daily Commercial,* Dec. 25, 1862; *Prairie Farmer,* XII (Nov. 7, 1863), 289, and XIII (Mar. 12, 19, 1864), 165, 185;

The most important Southern crop which the North had to replace was cotton. (It is interesting to note that in 1959, California, Arizona, and Missouri produced well over half the amount of cotton which had been grown in all states a century earlier.) In 1861 not even Missouri could be counted upon to furnish cotton for the North, for its authorities and many of its people were sympathetic to the South. There was a Northern area, however, where cotton had once been grown, mostly for home consumption, and where a considerable quantity could be raised if seed could be provided. This was southern Illinois between the 37th and 38th parallels, an area where the Illinois Central Railroad still held many thousands of acres of land and an area not endowed with the high quality of soil found above the Shelbyville moraine. President Osborn of the Illinois Central saw that if cotton could be raised in quantity, this area could provide more traffic for the railroad and income from the sale of its lands.

At three different periods in southern Illinois, cotton had been experimented with: 1818, 1833, and 1840. Prices had been favorable and yields were reported as high as 1,000 to 1,600 pounds of seed cotton, most of which was used in the home. But the decline in prices, the great amount of labor required to secure a crop, and the fact that cotton goods could be bought cheaply had led to the abandonment of the staple. Now with cotton selling at between 27 and 40 cents a pound instead of the 8 to 12 cents a pound of the fifties, it was easy for some southern Illinois farmers to convince Osborn that cotton could be profitably raised on eight or ten million acres in their latitude.[7]

Osborn took the lead in a campaign to induce farmers in southern Illinois to raise cotton and to persuade Congress to assist them. By his first effort in 1862 he obtained a congressional ap-

---

E. B. Grant: *Beet Root Sugar and Cultivation of the Beet* (Boston, 1867), pp. 57 ff., 144 ff.; P. W. Gates: *The Illinois Central Railroad and Its Colonization Work* (Cambridge, Mass., 1934), p. 287; Commissioner of Agriculture: *Report*, 1867, pp. 32 ff.
[7] *Prairie Farmer*, VIII (Dec. 26, 1861), 418–19; *Chicago Tribune*, Dec. 23, 1861, Jan. 7, 1862. The

Richmond Enquirer (Dec. 28, 1861), hearing that 5,000 acres were to be planted to cotton in Illinois in 1862, said: "The Yankees will derive quite as much benefit from the culture of cotton and oranges in Illinois and Massachusetts as they will from their efforts to plant the seed of Unionism in Southern soil."

propriation of $3,000 for the procurement and distribution of cotton seed. Agents were sent to New Bern, North Carolina, and Tennessee for the seed, and 1,700 bushels were bought for distribution in Ohio, Indiana, and Illinois. Earlier efforts to bring seed from Port Royal, South Carolina, had been thought ill-advised because the cotton would not be adjusted to the colder climate of the North, as might that of North Carolina or Tennessee. Osborn had southern Illinois canvassed to determine what had been the earlier experience with cotton and secured valuable information from individuals concerning the amount they had produced.[8]

Osborn was now advertising the Illinois Central lands extensively, using his patronage of the press to secure free publicity for his efforts to promote the development of agriculture. In a large, smartly illustrated advertisement in the *Rural New Yorker* the many thousands of acres of the railroad's lands in southern Illinois were said to be "well adapted to the perfection" of cotton, which should yield "a most profitable account." He won the support of the Illinois State Agricultural Society, which offered prizes for the best essays on cotton cultivation and a prize for the first bushel of cotton seed raised in the state. One of the essays—by M. L. Dunlap, a well-known nurseryman—in effect recharted the isothermal lines, pushing them well north of their natural location, by declaring that cotton "is a certain crop" as far north as Champaign and Macon Counties in central Illinois. It was against this excessive optimism and distortion that John A. Kennicott, one of the best-known agricultural authorities in the Middle West, cautioned. He urged people to remember the excesses of farm journals and nurserymen in promoting the *morus multicaulis* and silkworm craze of the 1830's.[9]

Many farmers in southern Illinois did turn to cotton in a small way, but bad luck seemed to dog their efforts. In 1862

---

[8] *Charleston Courier,* May 23, 1862, quoting the *New York Herald; T. R.* Strobridge: "The Letters of D. C. Donohue, Special Agent for the Procuring of Cotton Seed," *Tennessee Historical Quarterly,* XXI (December 1962), 379 ff.; *Chicago Tribune,* Jan. 8, 1862; Gates: *Illinois Central Railroad,* pp. 283 ff.

[9] *Rural New Yorker,* XIII (Jan. 25, 1862), 29, and XIV (May 23, 1863), 171; Illinois State Agricultural Society: *Transactions,* V (1861–4), 31, 67, 69, 87, 504 ff.; *Prairie Farmer,* IX (Jan. 25, 1862), 50; *Country Gentleman,* XIX (Apr. 10, 1862), 241.

part of the seed arrived too late for planting and some of it was not in good condition. In 1863 the severe frost of August–September hurt the cotton. In 1864 the crop was still meager. Not until 1865, when the war was over, did it reach a million pounds. Although Illinois continued to produce small quantities of cotton for years thereafter, the state was not well adapted to cotton culture. Osborn's faith in cotton as a crop that could be-

COTTON CROP OF ILLINOIS
(*in pounds*)

1862	6,770
1863	91,596
1864	384,480
1865	1,581,400

SOURCE: U.S. Department of Agriculture, *Monthly Report,* February 1866, p. 89.

come established in southern Illinois did not die easily. As late as 1872, the Illinois Central was advertising that its lands in southern Illinois were well adapted to cotton and tobacco.[1]

Osborn's efforts to secure Federal aid for cotton growing in the North won an odd recruit in Jim Lane, senator from Kansas. Lane seems to have convinced himself, notwithstanding all previous talk, that with the high prices prevailing Kansas could be changed "from a corn and wheat producing to a cotton growing state." In his rough, homespun way he called for an appropriation of $20,000 to "encourage the culture of cotton north of lattitude 36 30." Astonished senatorial colleagues managed to reduce the sum to $3,000 and to put in literate form Lane's amendment to provide for the purchase and distribution of cotton and tobacco seed. Lane's efforts to transform Kansas agriculture met with little success, the cotton crop of 1870 being 24,000 pounds.[2]

[1] The Illinois State Agricultural Society: *Transactions,* VI (1865–1866), 66, gives the yield of cotton for 1865 as 7,609 bales, varying from 350 to 475 pounds each. *Guide to the Illinois Central Railroad Lands. 340,000 Acres of the Best Farming and Fruit Lands for Sale* (Chicago, 1872), p. 14.
[2] *Cong. Globe,* 37 Cong., 3 Sess., part 1, Feb. 2, 1863, pp. 671, 677–678; Act of Feb. 25, 1863, 12 Stat., p. 691.

Had the same amount of effort been spent to promote the production of cotton in Kentucky, where in the southern and western counties it had long been raised for domestic use, better results might have been achieved. In 1849 the Bluegrass state grew 758 bales of cotton, but no cotton crop was shown for 1859. In 1863 it was said that cotton had matured well in Kentucky despite the unfavorable season, and that the crop was being picked and the gins were in operation. But few people familiar with the growing of cotton could have been optimistic about efforts to produce it in any considerable amount north of Tennessee and North Carolina.[3]

Cotton in Utah was more of a surprise. Finding little else from which they could make a living, farmers in the Little Dixie corner of southwest Utah Territory, recently established there by the Mormon Church, turned to cotton in a minor way in 1862. About 200 acres were put into the staple in very small tracts and irrigated at the expense of much labor. The resulting yield was surprisingly good—75,000 pounds, or an average of 350 pounds to the acre of fair upland cotton. California, not to be outdone, offered prizes in 1862 to encourage the production of cotton, tobacco, sugar from sorghum, raw silk, tea, coffee, indigo, and rice.[4]

Many people thought the best substitute the North could get for the South's cotton would be flax and hemp fibers. Prior to the war much flax was being raised for its seed. Some flax fiber of poor quality had been produced. People knew that flax fiber, properly prepared, could be used on spinning jennies as cotton was, and they hoped that with greater care in preparing the fiber and technical refinements in manufacturing, it might be possible to "cottonize" flax so that it could replace the Southern staple. Congress was persuaded to appropriate $20,000 for an investigation of the practicability of preparing cottonized thread from flax and hemp. It is not clear whether Congress knew that the New York legislature had appropriated $2,000 a year earlier to test machinery for use in manufacturing cottonized flax, and that the committee appointed to carry out the tests had reported back

---

[3] *Natchez Courier*, Sept. 10, 1863.
[4] C. H. Howard of Salt Lake City, Jan. 10, 1863, in *Rural New Yorker*, XIV (Feb. 14, 1863), 54; *Prairie Farmer*, X (July 5, 1862), and XI (Feb. 7, 1863), 83.

that no such machinery existed and had declined to use the appropriation.[5]

Although both flax and hemp had long been raised in the United States with government aid, neither was a thriving branch of agriculture at the outbreak of the war. Indeed, flax production had sharply declined in the previous decade. The commission to test the practicability of cultivating flax and hemp as a substitute for cotton consisted of an undistinguished Pennsylvania congressman, a well-known horticulturist who contributed a number of articles to the annual volume of the Department of Agriculture, and a relatively unknown man from Providence. Their report of February 27, 1865, came too late to have any effect. It consisted chiefly of information lifted bodily from encyclopedias, with some material from correspondence which the Commissioner of Agriculture had invited. It had no value to farmers, professors, or manufacturers, and none to the country. Another step taken by the Congress in an effort to encourage the growth and use of flax was to exempt machines adapted to the manufacture of fabrics from flax or hemp from tariff duties.[6]

Flax production did increase greatly during the sixties as a result of the $15 a ton duty on imports as well as of the demand. New York, the leading state in 1860, increased its output from 1,518,000 pounds to 3,927,000 in 1865 but was outdistanced by Ohio, which had a great increase in production. In 1870 Ohio's yield was 17,880,000 pounds out of a total for the country of 27,133,000 pounds, almost all of which was produced in the North. In 1880 the yield had fallen to less than two million pounds despite the continuation of high tariff protection. Some progress was made in cottonizing flax, at least to the extent that calico and cotton flannel containing 50 per cent flax was produced, as well as a variety of other products containing more or less flax. Perhaps the most important factor in preventing extensive cultivation of flax was the great amount of labor and careful attention needed

[5] *Rural New Yorker*, XII (Feb. 23, 1861), 61, and XIV (June 13, 1863), 190 Act of Feb. 25, 1863, 12 *Stat.*, p. 691; *Cong. Globe*, 37 Cong., 3 Sess., part 1, pp. 675 ff. Flax when rotted, cleaned, and chemically treated was said to be cottonized. *Rural New Yorker*, XII (Mar. 16, 1861), 85.
[6] *Report of the Flax and Hemp Commission Appointed under Act of Congress February 25, 1863*, 96 pp.; Act of June 30, 1864, 13 *Stat.*, p. 216.

to separate the woody core from the fiber or lint. Few farmers cared to give the time to perform this task satisfactorily.[7]

Of far greater importance in easing the cotton famine than all activities to encourage the cultivation of cotton, flax, and hemp in the loyal states were the operations of the Federal troops in capturing Beaufort, New Orleans, Nashville, Memphis, and Atlanta and in bringing under Federal control large portions of the Delta of the lower Mississippi. The quantity of cotton captured and traded through the lines was many times greater than all that was raised in the North.

There remains for another chapter a discussion of the substitution of wool for cotton and the remarkable success of the United States, Australia, and the River Plate in increasing their production of wool so as to prevent the runaway prices of wool which had been generally anticipated.

---

[7] E. A. Whitman: *Flax Culture* (Boston, 1888), p. 92; *Rural New Yorker,* XIV (June 6, 1863), 182; Commissioner of Agriculture: *Report,* 1862, p. 116; I. P. Roberts: *Autobiography of a Farm Boy* (Ithaca, N.Y., 1946), p. 30.

7

Livestock Farming

WITH THE FIRING on Fort Sumter and the beginning of the war, it was time for Northern farmers to replan their operations so that they could carry on with a smaller labor force. They also had to make sure that they were producing the staples which were most needed and for which they and their land were suited. The *Rural New Yorker* of May 4, 1861, in urging farmers to work longer and harder to make up for the shortage of manpower and to compensate for the destruction of food that always accompanies war, stressed the importance of increasing the production of beef, pork, and wheat by careful management of livestock and enlargement of the acreage sown to grain. Strangely, it said nothing about substitutes for cotton, particularly wool, which was one of the mainstays of New York agriculture, outranked in importance only by dairy products.[1]

The number of horses, cattle, and hogs, as well as the production of all grains, had steadily increased throughout the fifties, but the number of sheep had been nearly stationary. They had increased only 3 per cent, whereas population grew 35 per cent, dairy cattle increased 34 per cent, beef cattle 43 per cent, and swine 10 per cent. Both excessive production costs in the older states, where land values were high, and better profits in dairying contributed to the decline in the number of sheep. Other factors

---

[1] *Rural New Yorker*, XII (May 4, 1861), 141.

were the great damage done by dogs in killing and worrying the sheep and the competition of wool and woolen imports from countries where costs were low. Neither the forties nor the fifties had brought favorable prices for wool except for short periods. Many farmers in the older states found the care of sheep not commensurate with the returns and were either selling off their stock completely or sharply reducing the numbers. Between 1840 and 1860 New England and New York, which had been the center of the sheep industry, cut their stock by more than half.

As the tide of settlement moved west, a new sheep-raising area had developed in Ohio, Michigan, Indiana, and Illinois. By 1860 Ohio had more sheep than any other state, a lead it held until it was displaced by California in 1880. Abundance of cheap land doubtless was a factor in the westward movement of sheep raising, but in Ohio by 1850 land values were higher than they were in Vermont. Ohio's sheep industry was concentrated in the twelve east-central counties of the state, extending from Licking on the west to Columbiana on the Pennsylvania line. Across the panhandle of Virginia in Pennsylvania, Washington County led all counties in the number of its sheep: 351,252 in 1860. In this county the average number of sheep per farm was 91.[2]

Nowhere else was there such concentration of sheep, but they were to be found in every county in Indiana and Illinois and in all the well-developed counties in Michigan and Iowa. In fact, one writer maintains that "practically every pioneer farm . . . in Iowa had its own flock of sheep," though on many they were raised for the wool used within the household and not for commercial purposes. Illinois, which seemed to excel in everything relating to size in agriculture, had several large flocks of sheep. The best known were those of James McConnell in Sangamon County, which ranged from 17,000 to 21,000 sheep in the fifties. Nearby were eight other large sheep operations with flocks numbering from 1,000 to 8,000.[3]

[2] E. A. Carman, H. A. Heath, and John Minto: *Special Report on History and Present Condition of the Sheep Industry of the United States* (Washington, 1892), borrows heavily from H. S. Randall's works (which are cited below).

[3] E. N. Wentworth: *America's Sheep Trails* (Ames, Iowa, 1948); James Caird: *Prairie Farming in America* (New York, 1859), p. 57; *Springfield Journal* in *Prairie Farmer*, XVI (Oct. 28, 1865), 320.

Few flocks in the Middle West were outstanding for the quality or amount of wool they produced, being mostly grade stock with small fleeces. McConnell and John Wentworth of northern Illinois, it is true, imported purebred Merino rams and ewes from Europe and doubtless their importations improved the quality of sheep in their vicinity, for it had been sufficiently demonstrated that the breeding of purebred Merinos with grade stock had a marked effect in raising the quality and quantity of wool of the offspring. It was the somewhat better prices of 1859 and 1860 and of the war years that induced Middle Western sheepmen to invest heavily in Vermont Merino breeding stock.

Although Ohio led in the number of sheep in both 1850 and 1860, the census figures show that here too, interest in sheep and wool was declining. In 1854 Ohio flocks numbered 4,845,189; in 1858, 3,366,840. Similar declines were noted in Indiana, Illinois, and Kentucky. The only important gains were in California, New Mexico, Michigan, and Missouri, in all of which there was an abundance of cheap land held by the government.

The fact is that the United States had become heavily dependent on wool and woolen goods from abroad. Imports of raw wool were at least equivalent to half the amount produced domestically, and imports of manufactured wool constituted one ninth of the value of all imports. With Southern cotton unavailable and all other plans to replace it with Northern-produced goods failing, with shipping costs high as a result of the losses inflicted by Confederate privateers, and with the high rate of consumption by the army, it might be expected that runaway inflation in wool prices would result. But as Chester Wright has effectively shown, there was no such increase in terms of gold. Instead, the average gold price of all grades of wool increased during the war by only 5 per cent over the average price for 1852–61, though the rise in terms of currency was 67 per cent. It is remarkable that during the war the gold price of fine wool never reached the level it attained in 1859 and 1860.[4]

Sheep raisers had suffered from poor prices for their wool in 1858, but during the next two years prices were reasonably

---

[4] *U.S. Economist* in *Rural New Yorker*, XVI (Apr. 20, 1865); C. W. Wright: *Wool-Growing and the Tariff* (Boston, 1910), pp. 156 ff.

NUMBER OF SHEEP IN LEADING WOOL-PRODUCING STATES

	1860	JAN. 1, 1864	JAN. 1, 1865	JAN. 1, 1866	JAN. 1, 1867
Vermont	770,216	1,112,969	1,252,089	1,377,296	1,335,980
New York	2,718,646	4,237,324	4,576,310	5,117,148	5,373,980
Pennsylvania	1,831,776	2,610,458	2,871,503	3,230,440	3,456,568
Ohio	3,863,883	4,779,662	5,795,340	6,568,052	7,159,177
Michigan	1,329,059	2,465,360	3,020,066	3,473,075	4,028,767
Iowa	389,932	1,032,912	1,456,754	1,950,752	2,399,425
Illinois	1,023,515	1,627,983	2,455,913	2,446,081	2,764,072
Indiana	1,137,209	1,933,790	3,020,066	2,783,367	3,033,870
United States	22,471,275	24,346,391	28,647,269	32,695,797	39,385,380

SOURCE: The statistics for 1860 are a compilation of the data in *Eighth Census of the United States, 1860, Agriculture*, pp. 184, 192. Those for later years are estimates made by J. R. Dodge and published annually in the *Reports* of the Commissioner of Agriculture. The statistics given for the entire United States are not very meaningful for the states of the Confederacy or for California, Oregon, and Nevada. A number of territories are omitted from the United States total in columns 2, 3, and 4, and California, Nevada, and Oregon are omitted from column 5. There were 4,999,767 sheep in the states of the Confederacy in 1860 and 3,542,401 in 1867. The *Census of New York*, 1865, p. ciii, shows 5,521,610 sheep in New York in 1865.

favorable. Wool prices dropped to their lowest level for years in 1861. A large mill owner of Watervliet, New York, prepared a table of the average cost of his wool bought in New York, Ohio, Michigan, and Vermont for the years since 1852 which reveals this sharp decrease:

AVERAGE COST OF 600,000 TO 700,000 POUNDS OF WOOL USED IN WATERVLIET MILLS

1852	38 1/7¢ per lb.		1857	41 3/4¢ per lb.
1853	48 1/4	"	1858	34 1/3	"
1854	36 1/3	"	1859	44 1/2	"
1855	33 1/10	"	1860	45	"
1856	39 5/8	"	1861	33 1/3	"

SOURCE: Letter of James Roy, Jan. 16, 1862, to H. S. Randall, Randall MSS., Regional History, Cornell University.

Wool prices recovered in 1862, and for the remainder of the war the gold price of wool never dropped to the level of these two poor years. In currency, the price of wool was 76 to 85 cents in October 1863, 90 cents to $1.00 in July, and $1.00 to $1.18 in September 1864. An expansion of the sheep industry surpassing anything before witnessed was the natural result. The number of sheep in the loyal states but exclusive of the Far West increased from some 15,100,000 in 1860 to an estimated 32,600,000 in 1866. In every Northern state from New Hampshire and Vermont to Illinois the number of sheep on farms had declined in the forties and fifties; now in every state save Rhode Island, Delaware, Kentucky, and Missouri the number greatly increased. Even New England, where costs of raising wool were said to be more than double what they were in the West, increased its sheep by 81 percent. Although Ohio and New York still had the largest number of sheep, the biggest increases were in Iowa, Wisconsin, California, Illinois, and Michigan.

This sharp change from virtual stagnation to extraordinarily rapid growth could only have been made because farmers withheld their young and mature stock from market for longer periods than formerly. We may deduce this also from the fact that mutton, despite the great increase in the number of sheep, was consistently higher in price during the war, both in currency and in gold, in relation to previous prices than beef, pork, wheat, or corn.[5]

Intensified interest in sheep breeding accompanied the expansion of the sheep industry. Early in the nineteenth century Spanish Merino sheep had been brought in and were doubtless mixed with later introductions of Silesian, Spanish, and French Merinos. They were bred with increasing care and attention to certain points that connoisseurs were demanding: dark color, heavy yolk, and large, fine fleeces. Merinos were raised for their wool and were not in demand for their mutton. Coarse-wooled English breeds were raised more for mutton.

From the first, New England took the lead in breeding

[5] *Davenport Daily Gazette,* Apr. 29, 1863; Wright: *Wool-Growing,* pp. 127, 175, 192. The quotations are from the *American Agriculturist,* the *New York Tribune,* and Wright.

Merinos, gradually improving upon the early strains until by the mid-nineteenth century they were hardy and much heavier than their European counterparts, with fleeces that averaged five to six pounds. It was in Addison County, Vermont, that sheep breeding reached its highest development. Buyers came to Addison County and neighboring counties for the choice and well-advertised American Merinos of the Paular, Infantado or Atwood, and French or Rambouillet families. The fine wool of these Merino families brought premium prices in contrast to the coarse wool of the English breeds. The most successful breeders had a national—indeed an international—reputation for their stock. Among them were William R. Sanford, Charles Rich, Solomon W. Jewett, Edwin Hammond, and Alonzo and Merrill Bingham.

Henry S. Randall, biographer of Thomas Jefferson, was better known to nineteenth-century farmers for his writings on sheep. He had a 360-acre sheep farm in Cortland County, New York, on which he maintained 800 Merinos acquired from the best flocks. Sheep and sheep farming constituted his principal interest. He traveled widely, lecturing to agricultural societies and gathering material for his major treatises on sheep. His first important work was *Sheep Husbandry in the South,* later *Sheep Husbandry.* Published first in 1848, it went through many printings in Philadelphia, New York, and San Francisco and was in print as late as 1883. Though much of it is a compilation of writings by others, there was sufficient original material adapted to the South to make it attractive. It stirred up deep interest in that section, where prejudices against sheep had long existed, and led to the introduction of purebred Merinos, many of which were acquired through Randall.[6] Randall's second and more important work, *The Practical Shepherd,* published in 1863, borrowed heavily from *Sheep Husbandry,* but contained news items about leading sheepbreeders and fresh matter relating to Vermont Merino families, marketing of wool, and breeding practices. A third small book, *Fine Wool Sheep Industry,* published the same year as his *Practical Shepherd,* is in some respects the most interesting, because it is largely Randall's work and deals with the

---

[6] Randall's correspondence with a prominent sheep rancher of Texas, George W. Kendall, has been edited by H. J. Brown in *Letters from a Texas Sheep Ranch* (Urbana, Ill., 1959).

part of the sheep industry in which he was intimately concerned, Merino breeding. All three works are useful manuals, providing much sound common-sense advice on many problems relating to sheep and warning against tendencies already apparent among the breeders, notably the overemphasis upon wrinkles and yolk, that were later to turn sheepmen against the Merino strains. A recent Australian historian of the Merino has said that Randall's *Practical Shepherd* was "the most famous and certainly the most reliable of . . . early sources."[7]

In the preparation of *The Practical Shepherd* Randall corresponded with nearly every prominent sheep breeder, visited many of them, inspected their flocks, and pumped them for their recollections. He also corresponded with wool dealers, from whom he assembled information concerning fluctuations of prices and buying practices. As is indicated by everything he wrote on sheep, he favored the Merino of the Infantado and Paular families, of which his own flock was composed, but he gave attention to other Merino families and to the coarse-wooled breeds. There is no doubt that he was in the market to sell his choice sheep for breeding purposes.

The publication of Randall's *Practical Shepherd* was an overwhelming success, as had been anticipated by D. D. T. Moore, the publisher, who had taken great pains to include numerous illustrations, an analytical table of contents, and a detailed index, as well as to have both covers stamped in gold with a superb drawing of a sheep and to print the book in attractive type. In 1863 the book was in its twelfth printing, in June 1864 it had gone to its nineteenth, and it ultimately reached thirty. Meantime, Moore, doubtless impressed with the reception the book received, invited Randall to become editor of the department of sheep husbandry on the *Rural New Yorker,* the most widely circulated and influential farm journal. Randall had been editor of the *Wool Grower and Stock Register* during its short life before insufficient patronage and unwillingness "to sell its influence to speculators" had forced it to suspend.

In accepting the invitation Randall was joining a distinguished editorial staff, including, in addition to Moore, Charles

---

[7] H. B. Austin: *The Merino* (Sydney, Australia, 1947), p. 20.

D. Bragdon, formerly of the *Prairie Farmer* and a courageous supporter of currency reform and group action among farmers, and Patrick Barry, partner of George Ellwanger in the "most notable of all American nurseries." Randall disavowed any intention of fostering his favorite sheep breeds and families but said that he would not hesitate to express his preferences. Nor did he, for engravings of Merinos, especially Infantados, and records of their ancestry mark the pages of the *Rural New Yorker* while Randall was associated with it. Sheep farming had surely come into its own when the most widely circulated farm journal devoted so much attention to fine-wooled sheep and to the "sheep grandees" or "sheep kings" of Vermont such as Edwin Hammond and Merrill Bingham.[8]

Vermonters had brought sheep breeding to a high point by careful selection, by breeding "in and in," and by the continued importation of the best blood in France and Spain. Their sheep produced fine wool in increasing quantities in each generation. Ewes with ten or more pounds of premium wool and rams with fleeces of twenty, even thirty, pounds, unwashed weight, offered prospect of substantial profits if costs were not too high. Vermont fleeces were well above the average for the country and exceeded those of every other state by a substantial margin in both 1860 and 1870. Indeed, with less than half as many sheep as the total number in Texas, Arkansas, Mississippi, South Carolina, and Florida, Vermont produced more than twice as much wool. Furthermore, in Addison County, where the Infantado and Paular sheep breeding was centered, the disparity was even more marked.

For years sheepmen from all over the country had been journeying to Vermont to buy choice rams and ewes, but during the war this trek set in "with the regularity of a bountifully fed river," said Randall. While he was the guest of the Hammonds for two weeks, as many as fifteen buyers a day came to examine their sheep.[9] As demand rose the prices skyrocketed, with the

---

[8] Geo. Geddes, Nov. 1, 1863, to Randall, Randall MSS., Regional History, Cornell University; *Rural New Yorker*, XIV (Nov. 28, Dec. 12, 1863), 381, 398; U. P. Hedrick: *History of Horticulture in America to 1860* (New York, 1950), p. 243.
[9] *Rural New Yorker*, XV (Feb. 13, 1864), 54.

AVERAGE SIZE OF FLEECES FOR ALL SHEEP
(in pounds)

	1860	1870
United States	2.6	3.5
Illinois	2.6	3.6
New York	3.6	4.8
Ohio	2.9	4.1
Vermont	4.1	5.3
Addison County	4.8	5.9

SOURCE: *Ninth Census of the United States, 1870, III, Industry and Wealth.*

Bingham and Hammond sheep bringing the highest prices. The service charge for the top rams was ten and fifteen dollars, which made their owners reluctant to sell. Records of sale of rams at $3,500 and $5,000, and a refusal of $10,000 for the famous ram Gold Drop, seem well authenticated.[1] Visitors in Addison County marveled at the high prices sheep were bringing, the palaces the grandees were building, the additional farms they were buying, the barns that looked like manufactures, and the landscaping of their grounds.[2]

By 1864 so great was the craze for Vermont Merinos that sheep peddlers in Ohio and Michigan could sell at a premium anything they claimed to be from Vermont. It was said that Vermont flockmasters were culling their sheep and selling the unwanted ones at ten dollars a head to go to the West, where they might be claimed as products of Hammond's "brag ram." A *Rural New Yorker* correspondent declared that Gold Drop "has gotten more brothers and half sisters than the cutest Yankee ever had cousins, and some of them have found a relation at every stopping place from the Penobscot to the Rocky Mountains."[3]

Because of the premium the Addison County sheep brought, sheep hawkers sheared their sheep early in the spring so that by late summer their wool would be long and suggestive of heavy

---

[1] Details of sales at prices up to $5,000 for rams are given many times in the *Rural New Yorker,* the *Cultivator,* and the *Prairie Farmer.*
[2] *Ohio Farmer,* XV (June 30, 1866), 201; New York State Agricultural Society, *Journal,* XV (August 1865), 49.
[3] *Rural New Yorker,* XIV (Oct. 10, 1863), 325.

fleeces. To give their inferior sheep the dark color associated with the heavy yolk or oil of the choice Merinos, they rubbed in linseed oil and burnt umber. Since the best of the Vermont sheep had heavy wrinkles, which made shearing difficult but increased the weight of the fleece, the sheep jockeys found it possible to shear their animals to simulate wrinkles. "This is Vermont ice, stubble shearing." Many farmers in Ohio and Michigan, continually hearing of the superiority of Vermont sheep, were induced to purchase for premium prices grade sheep said to have been raised in Vermont but properly sheared and umbered to give the appearance of belonging to one of the choice flocks. The *Prairie Farmer* warned its Western readers that better than common sheep could be bought from local breeders and that so-called Vermont sheep offered at $50 or less were likely to be no bargain. Sheep from the flocks of Sanford, Hammond, Rich, and Bingham were of the very best quality and were worth the price charged for them, but it was far higher than $50.[4]

Throughout the West flocks of Vermont-bred sheep were being built up, especially in California, where by the Civil War two of the best-known Addison County sheepmen had established themselves. Solomon Jewett had long been one of the heaviest importers of French and Spanish Merinos. He had bred them to a state of perfection and had built up a market for his rams and ewes in Michigan and throughout the West. In 1859 he accompanied his first shipment of sheep to California. Later he trailed sheep across the plains to California. He established his ranch near Bakersfield in the upper San Joaquin Valley, where by 1862 he had 12,000 sheep, young and old, from which his wool clip was 18,000 pounds. His sheep, three fourths of them Merinos, yielded an average of six pounds of wool each, which brought them to the Addison County level. Jewett was able to adapt himself to conditions in California and became one of the most successful and prosperous of the California ranchers.[5]

Jewett was not the first to drive sheep across the plains to

---

[4] M. W. C. Wright, Jan. 20, 1862, to Randall, Randall MSS.; *Prairie Farmer*, XV (Feb. 25, 1865), 120.
[5] *Cultivator*, X (June 1862), 194;

H. S. Giffen and Arthur Woodward: *The Story of El Tejon* (Los Angeles, 1942), p. 46.

California and to establish himself there as a rival of the Addison County grandees with their high-quality stock. The Flint-Bixby Company consisting of three Maine men left Keokuk, Iowa, in May 1853 trailing 1,400 sheep destined for California, where they arrived the following year. In the back country of Monterey they acquired a large ranch which they stocked with a mixture of local and Merino sheep. They continued to bring in premium rams, buying partly the Hammond Infantados. In 1859 they were reported to have 26,000 sheep, of which 2,000 were pure Merinos. Their wool clip of 1858 was 70,000 pounds; in 1862 it was between 85,000 and 90,000 pounds, and in 1864 they clipped 200,000 pounds of wool from 40,000 sheep and lambs.[6]

Another Addison County sheepman who transferred his major interest to California was A. L. Bingham, who operated the Feather River ranch of Sam Brannan. By 1862 he had 400 full-blooded French Merinos. He imported and sold top-quality breeding stock and introduced into California the sheep-shearing festival that had marked the New England industry. Bingham declared that the cost of raising sheep in Vermont was four times as great as in California.[7]

The severe drought of 1863–4, which was a calamity for cattle in California, did not affect sheep to the same degree. For the state at large, the number of cattle declined in the sixties by more than 50 per cent, while the number of sheep nearly tripled. It was such men as Flint, Bixby, Jewett, Bingham, and Hollister who, by introducing high-quality stock and grading up the poorer native sheep, rapidly made California the major wool-producing state. In 1870 it was outranked only by Ohio, in 1880 it led all states in the number of sheep, and in 1890 its sheep were producing larger fleeces than the sheep of all other states, including Vermont. Other states and territories that were to be important sheep producers in the future and that were increasing

[6] *California Farmer*, IX (Apr. 22, 1859), 92; *Prairie Farmer*, XXVII (July 19, 1862), 35, quoting the *Bulletin*.
[7] *California Farmer*, VIII (Sept. 18, 1857), 78, and XXII (Oct. 7, 1864), 81; *Alta California*, Mar. 14, May 9, 1862; Wentworth: *America's Sheep Trails, passim;* A. L. Bingham, Mar. 29, 1860, to J. L. L. F. Warren, J. L. L. F. Warren MSS., Bancroft Library.

their flocks in the sixties were Oregon, Utah, Washington, Colorado, and Nevada. New Mexico had long raised large numbers of sheep.[8]

According to the Census Bureau, four fifths of all the sheep in the country in 1870 were either purebred or grade Merinos. They were liked because their wool generally brought better prices, though their fleeces might be lighter than some of the coarse-wooled breeds. The premium on their fine wool diminished during the war because of the army's great demand for blankets and other goods made of coarse wool.[9]

AVERAGE PRICE OF OHIO WASHED WOOL PER POUND

YEARS	FINE	MEDIUM	COARSE
1852–61	$.51	$.43	$.37
1862–65	.75	.73	.70

SOURCE: C. W. Wright, *Wool-Growing and the Tariff* (Boston, 1910), p. 158.

In view of the great improvement in the price of the coarser wool, it might be expected that the English breeds would have come into favor at this time, the more so because serious questions were being asked about the wisdom of "in and in" breeding of Merinos to produce the heavy yolk and wrinkly skins sought after by specialists. Merino fleeces were difficult to sheer and lost much weight when washed. Some Merino breeders were already using French Rambouillet stock to produce a larger animal with a heavier but slightly coarser fleece and with more palatable mutton. Others were learning that Merinos which were mixed with English sheep, especially Southdowns, retained some of the best qualities of both.

Among the types grown more for mutton than wool were the Leicesters, the Cotswolds, the Southdowns, the Hampshire Downs, the Shropshire Downs, and the Oxfordshire Downs.

[8] *Cultivator*, XIII (January 1865), 12; *American Agriculturist*, XXII (June 1864), 166.
[9] *Census of 1900*, V, p. cciii.

There was a tendency for farmers living near urban markets to concentrate on them because of the better quality of and demand for their mutton. None of these breeds, however, had an outstanding authority to champion their qualities, as Randall did for the Vermont families of Merinos, though Orange Judd, editor of the *American Agriculturist,* did give considerable space to the Southdowns.[1]

Of all specialized farm groups, sheep raisers were the most sensitive about the use of governmental powers for or against their welfare. Unlike the producers of other farm commodities, sheep raisers were in competition with the sheep interests of Great Britain, Australia, and Buenos Aires, where costs were lower. Like the sugar cane planters of Louisiana, they were convinced they should have protection for raw wool at least at the same rate the manufacturers of woolen goods enjoyed. The Walker Tariff of 1846 had given them this equality, though it had not given them the amount of protection they desired, but in the tariff of 1857 the equality of treatment granted raw wool and woolen manufactures was dropped, and lower-priced wool went on the free list. Sheep raisers gained a little from the tariff revision of 1861, but not enough to provide them with the protection they felt they needed. In 1864 when high protectionists were in power (though they were more representative of manufacturers than producers of raw materials), the rates prescribed did not satisfy the sheep raisers, who felt that their interests were being sacrificed to benefit manufacturers advocating cheap raw materials.[2]

In the fifties the amount of wool produced in the United States increased more from improvement in the sheep than from a rise in their numbers. Wool imports increased at a more rapid rate than American flocks. The war, with its enlarged demand for wool, caused partly by the shortage of cotton, led to an extraordinary expansion of the sheep industry and a great increase

---

[1] *Rural New Yorker,* XIV (Sept. 19, 1863), 301; *American Agriculturist,* XXI (September, October, 1862), 265, 303, and XXII (October 1863), 299.

[2] H. J. Brown: "The National Association of Wool Manufacturers, 1864–1897," Ph.D. dissertation, 1949, Cornell University Library, pp. 10 ff.

in the production of wool, both in the United States and abroad:

PRODUCTION OF WOOL
(in millions of pounds)

YEAR	EUROPE & GREAT BRITAIN	NORTH AMERICA	AUSTRALIA & NEW ZEALAND	RIVER PLATE	OTHER
1860	640	90	60	43	102
1864	650	165	110	137	119
1870	650	176	175	197	112

SOURCE: C. W. Wright, *Wool-Growing and the Tariff* (Boston, 1910), p. 164.

A considerable part of this huge increase in foreign wool moved into the American market and kept down the price which the sheep people felt was necessary for them to prosper.[3]

Both the wool producers and the wool manufacturers felt seriously the competition of foreign wool and woolen goods, and both came to recognize the advisability of organizing into national associations to achieve their objectives. The manufacturers moved first at a meeting in Springfield, Massachusetts, in November 1864, creating the National Association of Wool Manufacturers, one of the first of the national trade associations and the prototype of many that were to come later. News of its organization, with 200 members paying dues of $25 a year, and of its alleged action in giving the Speaker of the House of Representatives—Schuyler Colfax—a suit of broadcloth, confirmed many in the belief that its main purpose was to assure low prices for raw wool.[4]

Wool producers were not far behind in taking group action that culminated eventually in their national association. Already they had experimented with wool depots at Buffalo and Cleveland to which many consigned their wool. There it was graded and sold at auction. The depots provided cooperating farmers with sacks and twine for binding and furnished them with market in-

[3] Wright: *Wool-Growing*, p. 166, shows that imports of wool averaged 70,000,000 pounds for 1862–4 as compared with 30,000,000 pounds for 1858–60.

[4] *Prairie Farmer*, XV (Jan. 28, 1865), 50; Brown: "The National Association," pp. 68, 82 ff.

formation, for which the depots took a small percentage of the price. Promising as these movements were, they were not followed up. Instead, the wool growers resorted to the convention, sometimes in association with the state fair, to bring the interested people together to lay plans for action. They may have been influenced by the success of the sorghum conventions which flourished in 1862 and 1863 from Ohio to Wisconsin and brought enthusiastic growers together to discuss the problems of the new crop.[5]

County, regional, and state meetings of wool growers sprang up almost simultaneously in late 1863 and 1864 in New York, Vermont, Ohio, Illinois, and elsewhere. Principal speaker at a number of these conventions was Henry S. Randall, who seemed best able to express the issues and grievances of the producers. At the organization meeting of the Illinois Wool Growers Association in late 1863, the demands of the sheep farmers were clearly set forth:

1. Protection against dogs and wolves.
2. Compensation for sheep destroyed by dogs.
3. A tariff on raw wool to protect the grower as the manufacturer was protected and assure the grower 75 cents a pound.
4. An independent and reliable press free of influence by any particular group.
5. A combination of wool growers to meet combinations of those antagonistic to their interests.

The association denounced the *United States Economist* for being an organ of the wool speculators who were interested in depressing prices, and expressed regret that so many newspapers followed its lead on tariff matters.[6]

Randall strongly supported these demands, even to the extent of declaring that special-interest organizations such as wool growers' associations were much better equipped to fight farmers' battles than were the agricultural societies. "The mission of

---

[5] *Ohio Farmer*, V (Feb. 16, May 31, 1856), 26, 80, VI (Jan. 3, 1857), 5, and VIII (Aug. 13, 1859), 260; *Prairie Farmer*, XII (March 1852), 150 ff.
[6] *Rural New Yorker*, XIV (Nov. 7, 1863), 356. On Jan. 9, 1864, the Illinois State Agricultural Society demanded a duty of at least ten cents a pound on imported wool. Illinois State Agricultural Society, *Transactions*, V (1861–4), 92.

these societies is ended. . . . they control nothing; do not dictate to anybody; have no positive influence in politics and in shaping public policy." Randall believed that the day of these organizations had passed and that they needed to be replaced by the young, vigorous organizations of special agricultural interests prepared to meet and challenge the unique power gathered in the hands of the boards of trade, the corn exchange, chambers of commerce, mercantile associations and butchers' combinations.[7]

On September 1, 1864, the New York Sheep Breeders and Wool Growers Association was formed. Randall, who had taken the initiative in organizing it, was chosen president. In explaining the objective of the association, Randall declared that it was not a combination "against any other industrial interest," that it did not propose to interfere with the "ordinary and healthy" transactions in wool, and that it would not inaugurate an aggressive attack on wool manufacturers. He could not conceive of the wool manufacturers and wool growers not having common interests that would assure close and amicable relationships. If, however, the manufacturers pressed for congressional actions unfavorable to the growers, which he could not believe they would do, then the growers were prepared to advocate in Congress and elsewhere such steps as would counteract all unfriendly action. Cooperation was thus offered to the manufacturers, but the veiled threat was apparent.[8]

Sheep growers' uneasiness about the establishment of the National Association of Wool Manufacturers was aggravated by the tariff of 1864, which, although it raised the duty on wool, did not give the growers the rate they had hoped for. In their bitterness they could not fail to remember the scandal brought out by a congressional investigating committee in 1858, to the effect that certain Massachusetts wool manufacturers had in 1857 contributed $100,000 to hire lobbyists, such as Thurlow Weed, to secure a large reduction in tariff duties on wool. The stratagem had been successful. In this "cruel and oppressive" manner Congress had stripped from the grower all protection on

---

[7] *Rural New Yorker,* XIV (Nov. 7, 1863), 357–8.
[8] *Rural New Yorker,* XV (Aug. 20, Oct. 1, 15, 1864), 269, 317, 333; Brown: "The National Association," *passim.*

cheaper wool while retaining protection for the manufacturer.[9]

Defeated in 1857 because of lack of organization, and dissatisfied with the rates of 1864, the wool growers were now well organized through their state wool growers' associations and well captained by Randall. Stimulated in part by the sample petitions Randall printed in the *Rural New Yorker,* petitions poured in on Congress from farmers calling for minimum tariff rates of ten or twelve cents a pound on all foreign wool. Having won the confidence of the wool manufacturers and been elected an honorary member of their trade association, Randall was in a strong position to bring together the growers and the manufacturers in a joint meeting where the tariff question could be thrashed out. From this meeting came an agreement that "adequate" protection was necessary for both and that only by both working together with the House Ways and Means Committee could satisfactory rates be established.[1]

Representatives of the wool growers' associations of Vermont, New England, New York, Ohio, Illinois, and Wisconsin also met separately and organized the National Wool Growers' Association. Randall, as the one outstanding figure in the sheep industry in whom there was general confidence, was elected president. Thus, for the first time, a major branch of American agriculture that touched upon the lives and prosperity of large numbers of farmers was prepared to see that its interest in tariff and tax questions were not overlooked in Washington. For the first time, these farmers could register their complaints about the unfair practices of wool buyers in discounting the weight of fleeces for grease and dirt, in bearing the market, and in quibbling unfairly about grades.[2]

Sheep growers had now become a formidable organized special-interest group, with strong backing in the important wool-growing states and effective representation in the House.

---

[9] "Alleged Corruption in the Tariff of 1857," *House Reports,* 35 Cong., 1 Sess., no. 414, May 27, 1858, p. 4 and *passim; Rural New Yorker,* XVI (Oct. 12, 1865), 334. For a comparative table showing the various tariff rates on wool from 1789 to 1883, see W. D. Lewis: *Our Sheep and the Tariff* (University of Pennsylvania, *Political Economy and Public Law Series,* II, 1890), 94.

[1] *Rural New Yorker,* XVI (Nov. 25, Dec. 23, 1865), 374, 406, 431.

[2] *Rural New Yorker,* XVII (Jan. 6, 1866), 5.

The representatives were such men as Justin Smith Morrill of Vermont, chairman of the Ways and Means Committee, Columbus Delano, himself a sheepman, powerful in the Republican Party and later to be president of the National Association of Wool Growers, and Josiah B. Grinnell, likewise a sheep raiser, who did some valuable favors for his railroad friends and thereby accumulated support that might be useful to sheep growers. Petitions and memorials from state legislatures, wool growers' associations, and sheepmen poured into Congress. Leading wool growers rushed to Washington to plead for at least a ten-cent tariff on Merino wool. Randall worked hard in Washington to continue the alliance he had formed between the growers and the manufacturers. A group representing the manufacturers kept pushing for a higher tariff on woolen goods but cooperated at the same time with Randall and the Wool Growers. The time seemed propitious for both groups. Taussig's charge that the wool growers were "the most uncompromising and even fanatical among the protectionists" surely applies with equal force to the wool manufacturers.[3]

In 1867 the wool producers and manufacturers showed their newly assembled strength by putting enough pressure on Congress that it adopted the Wool and Woolens Act of March 2, which gave both parts of the industry essentially what they wanted without including in the measure tariff boons for other special-interest groups. Indeed, in view of the efforts of the iron manufacturers and other groups to obtain higher rates for all manufactures, something which clearly could not be granted at the time, the wool interests were remarkably successful in getting what they wanted. On fine Merino wool a duty of ten cents a pound, plus an ad valorem tax of 11 per cent, was levied.[4] The new high rates did little to prop up the rapidly declining sheep industry in New England, though they may have stimulated the sheep industry in the new commonwealths in the Rocky Mountain country. After 1867 numerous Vermont sheep growers

---

[3] F. W. Taussig: *Some Aspects of the Tariff Question* (Cambridge, Mass., 1915), p. 301. Brown: "The National Association of Wool Manufacturers" is indispensable for any analysis of the maneuvering of the wool growers and manufacturers.

[4] 14 *U.S. Stat.*, p. 559.

THE ILLUSTRATED LONDON NEWS

No. 1175.—Vol. XLI.]   SATURDAY, NOVEMBER 22, 1862.   [With a Supplement, Fivepence

THE COTTON DISTRESS.—TO THE RESCUE!

① The Cotton Famine in England
   Distributing tickets for bread, soup, meat, meal, and coal at Manchester
② Yankee Soldiers Going into Camp

③ THE MILK RATION
④ YANKEE SOLDIERS FORAGING IN LOUISIANA
⑤ COTTON HOARD IN SOUTHERN SWAMPS

NOTICE.

To the Farmers of Campbell, Franklin, Henry, Patrick, Grayson, Carroll, Floyd, the Western part of Pittsylvania and Halifax, and the Southern part of Bedford Counties :

The surplus Forage in the above district has been set apart for the purpose of feeding the Public Animals not in service.

All the Corn, Rye, Oats, Hay, Fodder and Straw, not required for the use of the people in the above Counties and parts of Counties, will be wanted by the Government for the purpose above stated.

Stables are being erected at suitable stations in the District, at which Farmers will be expected to deliver their surplus Forage, and for which they will be paid the prices fixed by the State Commissioners. The following are the Schedule Prices at present :

Corn unshelled, $3,95 per bushel; Corn shelled, $4,00 per bushel; Rye, $3,20 per bushel; Oats, $2,00 per bushel; Sheaf Oats, $3,70 per 100 lbs.; Hay, per 100 lbs. $3,00; Wheat Straw, $1,30 per 100 lbs; for baling Long Forage, 50 cts. per 100 lbs.; for hauling Long Forage, 8 cents per mile per 100 lbs.; for hauling Corn, 4 cents per bushel per mile.

It is with great difficulty that the necessary transportation for armies in the field can be furnished. The Government, therefore, cannot supply the teams to haul the Forage from the farms to the stations at which it is needed. It will be necessary for the farmers to do the transportation, for which, they will be paid liberal prices.

JAS. G. PAXTON,
Maj. and Q. M.

Fair Grounds, near Lynchburg, Nov. 13th, 1863.

JOHNSON & SCHAFFTER, PRINTERS, LYNCHBURG, VA.

SPECIAL EXEMPTIONS.

1. Each head of a family, not worth more than five hundred dollars.

2. Each head of a family, with minor children, not worth more than five hundred dollars for himself, and one hundred dollars for each minor living with him, and five hundred dollars in addition thereto for each minor son he has living, or may have lost, or had disabled in the military or naval service.

3. Each officer, soldier, or seaman, in the army or navy, or who has been discharged therefrom, for wounds, and is not worth more than one thousand dollars.

4. Each widow of any officer, soldier, or seaman, who has died in the military or naval service, the widow not worth more than one thousand dollars. *Provided*, the farmer or planter shall not pay a tax in kind upon corn, when he does not produce more than two hundred bushels, or upon Irish potatoes, when he does not produce more than fifty bushels, or upon peas and beans, when not more than twenty bushels are produced; and the forage derived from the corn plant shall also be exempt in all cases where the corn is not taxed in kind; neither shall any farmer or planter, who does not produce more than fifteen pounds ginned cotton for each member of his family, or ten pounds of wool, be subject to the tax in kind.

5. Such portion of said crops as may be necessary to raise and fatten the hogs of such farmer, planter, or grazier, for pork.

TAX IN KIND

Form No. 1. Estimate No. 14

Mr. H. L. Warren

14 day of Oct 1864

TAX IN KIND.

FORM NO. 1. ESTIMATE NO.

Estimate and Assessment of AGRICULTURAL PRODUCTS which are taxed in kind, agreed upon by the Assessor and Tax Payer, and the value of that portion thereof to which the Government is entitled, in accordance with the provisions of "An Act to lay taxes for the common defence, and carry on the Government of the Confederate States," and an "Act to amend said Act, approved 17th of February, 1864," said Estimate and Assessment to be returned to the District Quartermaster on or before the 1st day of September of each year.

AGRICULTURAL PRODUCTS	QUANTITY OF GROSS CROPS	QUALITY	TITHE	VALUE OF TITHE
Wheat	200	1	20	200 00
Oats	60		6	48 00
Sheaf Oats				
Rye				
Cured Hay	1000	1	100	5 50
Wool	50		5	40 00
			Total Value, $	293 50

⑨ Drove of Virginia Cattle
⑩ A Farm Road
⑪ Virginians Drawing Rations from the Federal Government

⑫ CRADLING AND LOADING WHEAT
⑬ PENNSYLVANIA GERMAN FARMER PACKED TO FLEE FROM CONFEDERATES

⑭ Hubbard's Mower
⑮ Seymour, Morgan and Allen Self-Raking Reaper
⑯ Emery's Patent Changeable Railroad Horse Power and Thrashing
    Machine

17 Iowa Land for Sale at $1.50 an Acre
18 Not All Unimproved Land in the West Was Free

⑲ PERSONNEL OF THE U.S. DEPARTMENT OF AGRICULTURE, 1867
    *Left to right: Meyers, Saunders, Whitaker, G. B. Newton, Isaac Newton, Sr.,
    Gardiner, Dodge, Antisell, Isaac Newton, Jr., Glover*
⑳ HENRY S. RANDALL
    Authority on Merino sheep (and Thomas Jefferson)

limited themselves to the breeding of Merinos, which probably brought them far greater returns than the fleeces had ever provided.[5]

Sheep growing was to continue to expand for two years after the war. But before then, some areas were showing a marked reduction in the number of sheep, while in others sheep were increasing. New York State illustrates both tendencies. In the Genesee Valley, where the greatest concentration of sheep existed, a prominent wool grower observed early in 1865 that wool growing was the leading business among the farmers. In that year the number of sheep in his county, Orleans, increased by more than 10 per cent. About the same time a sheepman of Dryden in Tompkins County wrote that in his neighborhood "cows are running out sheep." More favorable prices for butter and cheese in comparison with prices for wool were making dairy farming especially attractive. In Tompkins County the number of sheep declined in 1865 by approximately 2 per cent.[6]

Sheep farmers had only a short time before the gold price of wool fell from its war level and caused the sheep industry to contract rapidly and painfully throughout the East. In every Eastern state except Delaware the number of sheep fell more than 50 per cent by 1870. A saving feature was that, outside the breeder counties of Vermont and some of the very large sheep farms in Illinois, most farmers who had small flocks were at the same time raising cattle, selling butter, cheese, or milk, and making their living out of numerous other ventures. The decline of sheep growing was another blow at farming in the Northeast, particularly in New England, and contributed to that rural abandonment which is the subject of Harold Wilson's *Hill Country of Northern New England*.

One is left with this question: What effect did the sheep-growers' insistence upon high duties on wool in the war years, and their organization into state and national pressure groups under Randall, have upon farmers' attitudes toward protection

---

[5] In Addison County alone 80 breeders and dealers advertised Merino sheep in Hamilton Child: *Gazetteer and Business Directory of Addison County, Vt.* (Syracuse,

N.Y., 1882).
[6] E. B. Pottle, Jan. 10, 1865, to H. S. Randall and Jos. McGraw, 1865 (day and month unclear), to Randall, Randall MSS.

in later years? Prior to the war, in the older states most farmers had kept small flocks of sheep, and one gathers that many, perhaps most, continued to keep a few animals, just as they pursued so many other activities on a small scale.[7] Did the small investment in sheep convert them to the doctrine of protection to such an extent that long after they had given up raising sheep, they were susceptible to arguments for protection? When Justin Smith Morrill, staunch defender and writer of protectionist tariff schedules, first came to Congress, his state of Vermont had by far the highest number of sheep per farm. Morrill then seemed to represent the prevailing views of his constituents on tariffs, but as time passed he appeared to be more concerned about the position of the manufacturer than of the wool producer. This increasing concern for the manufacturer, however, may again have been a reflection of changing circumstances in Vermont, where the number of sheep and of sheep farmers was rapidly declining and the manufacturing interests growing.

Much has been made, perhaps too much, of the individualism of the farmer as a carryover from pioneer days. The record of the many state and county agricultural societies that early sprang up, of sorghum conventions, wool growers' meetings, horticultural society gatherings, even historical associations, all suggest a hungering for intellectual companionship, a desire to learn the best and to profit from the experiences of others, and a feeling of the need for associational meetings at which group objectives could be framed and plans for achieving them laid.

Beef cattle and hogs, the mainstay of America's meat diet, were in heavy demand throughout the war by the office of the Commissary General of Subsistence of the War Department, by wage earners whose incomes were higher than in normal times, and by foreign purchasers. While there was a sharp decline in shipments abroad of beef in barrels and of hogs and cattle, all of which represented a small part of the exports of meat products, the exports of ham and bacon increased sixfold, lard and tallow fourfold, and pork 50 per cent.[8] This previously unparalleled

---

[7] A writer in Lake County, Ill., remarked in 1865 that "nearly all the farmers keep a few" sheep. *Prairie Farmer*, XV (Apr. 21, 1865), 325.
[8] The statistics of exports of 1860 and 1863 are from the Secretary of the Treasury: *Report on Commerce and Navigation* for these years.

foreign demand for the meat and meat products of the Northern states, added to the wartime domestic needs, in part explains why the North's supply of hogs and cattle had been sharply reduced by the close of the war, whereas the number of sheep had greatly increased. Ohio, which has the best statistics for the war years, illustrates these changes:

LIVESTOCK IN OHIO			
YEAR	CATTLE	HOGS	SHEEP
1860	1,779,061	1,918,225	3,442,856
1861	1,837,938	2,595,981	3,943,436
1862	1,824,774	2,765,900	4,448,227
1863	1,734,788	2,239,358	5,042,439
1864	1,436,990	1,646,506	6,305,796
1865	1,244,327	1,455,695	6,305,796
1866	1,199,208	1,799,417	6,227,252

SOURCE: Ohio State Board of Agriculture, *Annual Reports,* 1861–6.

Estimates of the number of livestock on farms were prepared by the statistician of the U. S. Department of Agriculture beginning with January 1864, and though they are decidedly out of line with data collected by both New York and Ohio, they may be useful for the trends they reveal when compared with the census statistics of 1860.

LIVESTOCK IN LOYAL STATES, EXCLUSIVE OF CALIFORNIA, NEVADA, AND OREGON					
YEAR	ALL CATTLE	HOGS	SHEEP	HORSES	MULES
1860	13,668,102	17,060,035	15,104,272	4,199,141	301,609
1864 (Jan. 1)	14,840,721	16,148,712	24,346,391	4,049,142	280,847
1865 (Feb.)	12,840,721	13,070,887	28,647,269	3,740,933	247,553
1866 (Jan.)	12,674,968	13,616,876	32,695,797	3,899,019	250,151

Another factor contributing to the decline in the number of livestock was the heavy damage to the corn crop of Ohio, Indiana, Illinois, and Iowa by the frost of August 29, 1863, which reduced the amount of feed grain for fattening cattle and made it necessary to send cattle to market before they had reached their best stage of development. Never did cattle come through the winter so poorly as in 1863–4. Losses were heavy—as high as 20 to 30 head on some farms.[9]

Although California had not supplied Eastern markets with cattle prior to the Civil War, cattle were increasing so rapidly in that state that it promised to become a source of supply. However, the great drought of 1863–4 came close to wiping out the cattle industry of southern California. Many owners of ranchos were forced into bankruptcy and others were obliged to drive their cattle northward in the hope of finding forage for their animals. Abel Stearns, the largest of the stockmen and owner of over a hundred thousand acres, is said to have lost 12,000 cattle in this long drought. Santa Barbara County lost four fifths of its 76,000 cattle and Stanislaus County lost one third. The *Napa Register* of June 4, 1864, commenting on the large droves of cattle that were going through the city on their way to pasturage in the Eel River Valley, said that losses in the lower counties were running as high as 75 per cent.[1]

There was some good with the bad, however, according to James L. L. F. Warren, editor of the *California Farmer,* who welcomed the destruction of the Spanish cattle because they were wild and practically worthless save for their hides. Starvation made it easier to gather the hides, for it was not necessary to knock the cattle down. Another boon that some expected from the drought was the breakup of the huge Spanish and Mexican ranchos. The slightly developed ranchos with their poor Spanish cattle were assessed at only 10 cents an acre and $2 per head for the livestock, whereas if they could be divided into small farms and stocked with good American cattle, Warren thought they would be assessed at $5 and $20 respectively.[2]

By the opening of the Civil War, the corn belt, stretching

---

[9] *Prairie Farmer,* XII (Sept. 5, 12, 1863), 153, 161, 165; *Davenport Daily Gazette,* Sept. 1, 29, 1863; *Cincinnati Commercial,* Sept. 14, 1864, and Sept. 13, 1865; *New York Tribune,* May 3, 1864; *Nashville Dispatch,* May 11, 1864; *Country Gentleman,* XXIII (Jan. 7, 21, May 26, 1864), 20, 52, 340.
[1] *California Farmer,* XXI (Apr. 1,

1864), 68, listed Stearns's losses as 12,000, but A. F. Rolle: *California* (New York, 1963), p. 344, makes them 30,000.
[2] *California Farmer,* XXI (Apr. 1, 29, 1864), 68, 98; *Bi-Monthly Report of the Agricultural Department,* September–October 1864, pp. 20–2, and the same for November–December 1864, pp. 25 ff.

from Ohio through central Indiana and Illinois and into Iowa, and clearly marked in dot maps showing density of production of corn, had come into existence. Here the rich soils are admirably adapted to the growth of corn in a rotation system of two years in corn and three in small grains and clover. They were so fertile and productive that farmers planted corn on the land year after year without apparent reduction in yield. Greedy farmers, anxious to make as much as possible out of their land, cropped it regularly and sold the product without trying to maintain its fertility. Others who thought of their investment as a longer-range venture fed their grain to livestock, spread the manure over the land, and raised considerable grass for hay to carry their horses and cattle through the winter. Farmers naturally turned to hogs and cattle to utilize their corn, which brought low prices off the farm. The corn belt thus gradually became a corn and hog belt, but beef cattle were secondary only to hogs in utilizing the corn.

The feeder cattle business had begun to develop before the war. The best days of the feeders and drovers of the Scioto Valley of Ohio had passed, and in the fifties and sixties it was the Illinois and Indiana bonanza farmers who started as cattle buyers, used their profits to build up large ranches, and conducted their operations on a large scale. The ablest of them held onto their great ranches for a generation by turning from cattle to corn and from hired hands to tenants. Some were able to pass their holdings to children and grandchildren who became the modern landlords of the twentieth century and frequently absentee owners.[3]

John T. Alexander is the best known of these bonanza farmers and cattle kings because of the place he won for himself in that classic of the cattle industry, Joseph G. McCoy's *Historic Sketches of the Cattle Trade of the West and the Southwest.* During the war Alexander was one of the largest, probably outdoing all other drovers from the West in shipping cattle to the

---

[3] *Rural New Yorker,* XII (July 27, 1861); P. W. Gates: "Hoosier Cattle Kings," *Indiana Magazine of History,* XLIV (March 1948), 1 ff., and "Cattle Kings in the Prairies," *Mississippi Valley Historical Review,* XXXV (December, 1948), 379 ff.; P. C. Henlein: *Cattle Kingdom in the Ohio Valley, 1783–1860* (Lexington, Ky., 1959).

New York market. A careful judge of cattle and a shrewd buyer, Alexander was invariably credited with having the best cattle arriving in New York.[4]

From the rich corn and cattle feeder counties of Ohio, Indiana, and Illinois, cattle had been driven all the way to New York, Philadelphia, and Baltimore, but the coming of the railroad greatly changed the movement of livestock. Thereafter, cattle were driven to the railhead, later to towns like Springfield, Peoria, Bloomington, and Decatur in Illinois, Indianapolis and La Fayette in Indiana, and Chillicothe and Columbus, Ohio. At these centers they were loaded on the stockcars for the long hot ride to market. Solon Robinson, the tart-tongued market reporter of the *New York Tribune,* commented weekly on arrivals of stock from the West, giving the names of the drovers, the number and condition of the cattle, and the prices they brought. He was critical of the railroads for not providing water for stock going all the way from Illinois to New York. They arrived battered, bruised, and greatly dehydrated and had still to be driven to the cattle yards. Only at the Harlem freight yard was it possible to unload direct from the car to market. Robinson's price quotations, statistics of arrivals, and statements of the condition of the market were summarized in many farm journals and had much to do with the flow and price of cattle in the New York market.[5]

Robinson's statistics on the origins of the cattle reaching New York show how important cattle feeding was to Illinois, Indiana, and Ohio. Illinois was far in the lead in sending beef cattle to the New York market, though some of the cattle listed as coming from Illinois may have been raised in Iowa or Missouri and brought to the feedlots of Illinois for fattening.

During and long after the war, dual-purpose cattle of Shorthorn and Devon stock were by far the most common, whether in the dairy herds of New York or on the beef cattle ranches of Indiana and Illinois, and there was little inclination to experiment with other breeds. They were well adapted to the conditions of farm life, in which they received little care and

---

[4] McCoy: *Historic Sketches of the Cattle Trade of the West and the Southwest* (Kansas City, 1874), pp. 163–178.

[5] *New York Weekly Tribune,* June 21, 1862, Mar. 28, 1863.

ANNUAL RECEIPTS OF BEEF CATTLE
IN NEW YORK MARKET

YEAR	NUMBER	AVERAGE PRICE PER POUND	
1855	155,564	10	cents
1860	226,933	8	"
1861	222,835	7.75	"
1862	239,486	7.66	"
1863	264,091	9.25	"
1864	267,609	14.11	"
1865	273,274	16	"

SOURCE: *New York Tribune*, in *Country Gentleman*, XXVII (Jan. 18, 1866), 49.

not particularly nutritious food; they were healthy and not easily affected by disease; and they produced beef that seemed quite satisfactory to American taste. Because of the ease with which they could be driven to nearby markets or the frequency with which buyers appeared in rural areas, every farmer could raise one or two surplus animals. Not until after the war did the great flood of Western beef cattle into Eastern markets gradually impel farmers in the older states to abandon the dual-purpose animals and move out of the beef cattle business.

Major changes were to occur in the cattle industry at the conclusion of the war. Texas, with its huge reservoir of cattle,

NUMBER OF BEEF CATTLE SHIPPED TO NEW YORK CITY

STATE	1862	1863
Illinois	103,741	118,692
New York	36,919	28,985
Ohio	31,575	19,269
Indiana	16,599	14,232
Kentucky	8,641	6,782
Michigan	7,379	9,074
Other states		16,330

SOURCE: *Country Gentleman*, XXIII (Feb. 4, 1864), 81, and *Genesee Farmer*, XXIV (February 1863), 53, both citing the *New York Tribune*.

was prepared to undertake the "long drive" to stock the ranges of Kansas, Nebraska, and Dakota Territory. But already the Spanish fever, which was brought into Kansas and Missouri by a tick accompanying the Texas cattle, was destroying the local cattle of Shorthorn blood. It led to the adoption in Kansas of an act banning the importation of Longhorns from April 1 to November 1 of each year.[6] Meanwhile, the westward push of the Kansas Pacific, the Santa Fe, the Burlington, and the Union Pacific Railroads made it possible to bring in blooded stock, at first Shorthorns, then Herefords, to upgrade the Longhorns. The railroads also provided the means by which these improved cattle could be shipped to market. The war perhaps slowed the opening of the Great Plains, but the release of men from the army, the offer of free homesteads, and the ease with which people could get to the West by the new railroads swiftly made up for the delay.

Farmers concentrating partly on beef cattle, like the dairymen, were much disturbed by the accounts coming out of Europe of rinderpest or the cattle plague, which L. H. Bailey called the "most fatal disease affecting cattle." J. R. Dodge of the U. S. Department of Agriculture, in a long account of the ravages of the disease abroad and the efforts to stop it, expressed the view that Congress could not be expected to take the necessary steps to counteract it. He urged the states to consider legislation for quarantining affected herds, for providing for the slaughter of diseased animals and compensation to the owners, and for obtaining competent veterinary surgeons to inspect herds and enforce quarantine regulations.[7]

The supply of hogs, like the number of beef cattle, was bound to decline during a long war. On the other hand, because of the frequency and size of their litters, the number of hogs can easily be increased if the corn-hog ratio is favorable. The Ohio figures previously given show substantial increases in the number of hogs during the early days of the war, but by 1863

---

[6] *General Laws of Kansas*, 1861, p. 280; J. F. Smithcors: *The American Veterinary Profession* (Ames, Iowa, 1963), pp. 435 ff.
[7] L. H. Bailey: *Cyclopedia of American Agriculture* (4 vols., New York, 1907–9), III, 145; J. R. Dodge: "The Cattle Plague in Europe," in Commissioner of Agriculture, *Report*, 1865, pp. 550 ff.

their number had begun to decline and continued to do so through 1864 and 1865. The frost of 1863 and the early slaughter of pigs it made necessary, the ravages of cholera, and the heavy purchases by the army all reduced the number of hogs in the older portion of the corn belt.

The damage to livestock from hog cholera was greater than that caused by all other diseases. Losses were biggest among closely confined hogs, especially those kept by distilleries and breweries. Within a hundred miles of Cincinnati 60,000 hogs are said to have died in 1861. Many farmers were so frightened of the disease that they dressed off their hogs well before they were ready for butchering. In Illinois, contributors to the *Prairie Farmer* wrote despairingly of wholesale losses, frightful ravages, the "great scourge," and the few surviving hogs. In one farming community where a farmers' club kept statistics, 3,564 hogs died of cholera and 3,193 were butchered. Of the 2,791 survivors, a large number were less than a month old. Other reports were that losses ranged as high as 50 per cent, while some farmers reported total destruction of their animals.[8]

The best breeds and the most likely specimens seemed to be most susceptible, said a distressed observer. Farmers met to discuss symptoms and remedies, but they could do little more than vie with each other in relating their losses. Frequent mention was made in both Illinois and Iowa of the bold way Massachusetts had dealt with pleuropneumonia by destroying afflicted animals, isolating those that had been exposed, and adopting regulations concerning the movement of exposed cattle. Unfortunately there was no clear idea how similar action could be taken against hog cholera. For years farmers in the corn and hog belt had to learn to live with the disease.[9]

In Iowa, Wisconsin, Michigan, and Minnesota, where government land still existed and homesteading and agricultural expansion were proceeding, the number of hogs showed no decrease, although these states were not exempt from the cholera.

[8] Ohio State Board of Agriculture: *Annual Report*, 1861, pp. 343 ff.; *Quincy Whig and Republican*, Feb. 3, 1863; Illinois State Agricultural Society, *Transactions*, V (1861–4), 365; *Prairie Farmer*, VIII (Aug. 8, Sept. 12, Oct. 31, 1861), 68, 147, 294.
[9] *Prairie Farmer*, VIII (Nov. 14, 1861), 319; Iowa State Agricultural Society: *Eighth Report*, 1861–2, p. 129.

As a result of this northward expansion of the corn-hog area, as well as of the closing of the Mississippi and the stoppage of trade south from Cincinnati and Louisville, Chicago replaced Cincinnati as the great market to which hogs were brought for packing. An expanding market in the United States, plus the enlarged demands of the British for American pork products, the frost of 1863, and the necessity for farmers to reduce the numbers of their cattle, all aided in keeping the price of pork and pork products at a favorable level and made hog raising one of the more profitable features of corn belt agriculture.[1]

At the close of the war consumers of pork in the East and corn and hog farmers of the Middle West were panic-stricken by the discovery in Germany that trichinae (parasitic nematode worms that frequent the intestines of pigs) can be passed on to humans and cause death from trichinosis. A number of serious cases of trichinosis and speedy deaths from it occurred in 1864 and 1865 in Germany. In America, where pork was a major item in the diet of many people, this news caused so much alarm that New York quotations on pork fell by half, reported the *Country Gentleman*. Later dispatches from abroad showed that the danger had been exaggerated, and on investigation it was found that the proportion of American hogs infected with trichinae was small and certainly not a general menace to the health of pork eaters. The excitement quickly subsided, but years later it was the alleged presence of trichinae in American pork that was the basis of excluding it from the markets of a number of European countries until meat inspection had been set up.[2]

Purchases by the War Department of more than a half million horses and a quarter million mules for the cavalry, artillery, and quartermaster departments were a heavy drain upon agriculture. These purchases constituted 10 per cent of the number of horses and a far larger percentage of the mules on farms in

---

[1] The *Cincinnati Commercial* of Sept. 13, 1865, shows that pork prices were relatively higher than other farm commodities. Following are the average prices it offered: 1861–2, 3.28¢ per lb.; 1862–3, 4.45¢; 1863–4, 7¢; 1864–5, 14.62¢.
[2] *Country Gentleman*, XXVII (Apr. 5, 12, 26, May 31, 1866), 227, 242, 272, 349, 353; Department of Agriculture: *Monthly Report*, March 1866, pp. 127–42; R. A. Clemen: *The American Livestock and Meat Industry* (New York, 1923), pp. 320 ff.

the North in 1860. In Illinois 150,000 horses, many of them mares, were obtained, to the regret of the state agricultural society, which feared that they were needed at home and that the loss would take years to make up. Vermont Morgans were especially desired for the cavalry, for they were said to stand campaigning better than other breeds. Agents scoured the Green Mountain state in search of good mounts and within a short time purchased 10,000 horses, or 14 per cent of the total number recorded in the census of 1860. Prices generally were around $110 in the first two years of the war. Then they rose to $120 and $133, and in the last year cavalry horses brought from $144 to $185 and artillery horses from $161 to $185. The price paid for mules ranged from $95 to $133 in 1862 and 1863, and from $170 to $195 in 1865. At such low prices farmers tried to pass off their culls which were affected by heaves, ringbone, spavin, and blindness. Such culls did not last long with the army but might have continued useful for some time on the farm. Enough horses and mules were offered that the army was able to maintain adequate supplies for the most part, notwithstanding neglect and mistreatment of the animals that caused the unnecessary death of 30,000 in Tennessee in the winter of 1863–4. Only when the army was hard pressed by Lee just before Gettysburg was it necessary to authorize the seizure of animals intended for export.[3]

Not everyone found selling horses to the government an easy matter. One person thought it "such an ordeal to go through with" that it required considerable nerve to push a trade to its completion. All mares were rejected, he claimed, because when in heat their neighing would give their position away. Close inspection by four different persons, numerous rejections for age,

---

[3] Illinois State Agricultural Society: *Transactions*, V (1861–4), 21; *Prairie Farmer*, X (Nov. 22, 1862), 324. The Vermont State Agricultural Society denied that first-class Morgans could be bought for the usual price the government paid, contending that they ordinarily sold for $200 to $400. *Burlington Daily Times*, Jan. 8, 1862. R. L. Jones: "The Horse and Mule Industry in Ohio to 1865," *Mississippi Valley Historical Review*, XXXIII (June 1946), 81; *House Ex. Doc.*, 37 Cong., 3 Sess., 1862, IV, no. 1, 83; *House Ex. Doc.*, 38 Cong., 1 Sess., 1863, V, no. 1, 64; Secretary of War: *Annual Report*, 1865, p. 1; *O.R.*, ser. 3, V, 220; *Cultivator*, X (September 1862), 289; Smithcors: *American Veterinary Profession*, pp. 188–9.

unsoundness, or other weaknesses, and the payment, after some delay, in scrip which brokers shaved by 5 to 8 per cent—all made it easier to sell to intermediaries rather than directly to the government. Another source indicates that the army restricted the purchases of mares to one third of the total number of horses it was buying because they were more "ticklish" and less manageable than geldings.[4]

A few weeks before Lee's surrender, Secretary of War Edwin M. Stanton reported that the army was acquiring 500 horses daily, which was about the average number destroyed. Twice during the last eight months the cavalry of the Army of the Potomac had been remounted. "The production of the country seems to be able to bear the immense drain upon its horses and mules, and the stock, judging from the current prices, gives no signs of exhaustion or diminution." Doubtless the ease with which the army was able to meet its needs for horses justified to some extent Stanton's optimism concerning supplies. Others closer to the farmers, however, were much concerned about "the scarcity of horse flesh," the difficulty of finding replacements, and the danger that the sales to the government might seriously deplete the numbers and quality of the stock remaining on farms.[5]

Estimates prepared by the statistician of the Department of Agriculture on the number of horses in the Northern states at the conclusion of the war show that Vermont had lost 28 per cent of its horses, Kentucky 41 per cent, and Missouri 35 per cent. Defections to the South and the plundering of both sides account to a considerable extent for the losses in Kentucky and Missouri, while Vermont's figures show that the Yankees were quite ready to make a fast buck from their horses as well as from their sheep. On the other hand the states which were still receiving immigrants, creating new farms, and expanding the area in cultivation increased the number of their horses markedly. Outstanding among the growth states were Wisconsin with an increase of 33 per cent, Iowa with an increase of 40 per cent, and Minnesota with an increase of 55 per cent. Farm machines

---

[4] *O.R.*, ser. 3, IV, 201, 769, 1212; *Prairie Farmer*, XIV (Nov. 19, 1864), 323, quoting the *New Na-* tion.
[5] *American Stock Journal*, IV (April 1862), 112.

such as reapers, cultivators, drills, rakes, and mowers required increased numbers of draft animals, and oxen, which had previously been extensively used, were not adaptable to hauling the new machines.

At the conclusion of the war Northern farms were still well stocked with cattle, hogs, sheep, and horses, despite the heavy drain upon them. Many farmers had unwisely sold horses they could ill spare, but they had an opportunity to recoup their forces when at the conclusion of the war the Quartermaster's Office sold 104,000 horses and 102,000 mules. There had been no reason, unless it was labor problems, for farmers to dispose of their dairy cattle, and their number had shown a steady increase. Heavy drains on beef cattle and hogs had sharply cut into their total number, and perhaps this might have created problems for the North had the conflict lasted another year or two. Prices of beef and pork were low throughout 1861 and well into 1862, and indeed it was not until 1863 and 1864 that the big rise occurred. Producers who were not seriously affected by hog cholera, who fed their own grain, and who watched market quotations closely and got their livestock to market when prices were highest managed to do very well.[6]

---

[6] These estimates were not prepared with the accuracy that crop reports are assembled today and are presented here only to show trends. The percentages are computed from data in the Commissioner of Agriculture: *Report*, 1863, p. 606, and *Report*, 1865, p. 67. Ohio's assessors' data on horses in the state are probably more reliable than the estimates of the Department of Agriculture: 1860, 692,503; 1861, 738,427; 1863, 716,825; 1864, 716,825; and 1865, 681,284—as compared with 1860, 709,713; 1862, 727,245; and 1864, 625,644. They are taken from the *Reports* of the State Board of Agriculture, 1859–65. R. F. Weigley: *Quartermaster General of the Union Army* (New York, 1959), 331.

8

Dairy Farming

I N THE MID-NINETEENTH CENTURY dairy farming went through
major changes which were, if anything, slowed down by the
Civil War and yet in the long run were to be favorably influenced
by it. The most important of these changes was the effect the
construction of railroads had in enabling farmers to market their
milk in New York City, Boston, Philadelphia, Baltimore, and
other urban centers. Before the coming of the railroads the major
source of milk in the cities, aside from supplies brought in from
nearby farms, was the huge dairies run in connection with the
distilleries and breweries or operated by dairymen using their
swill. These dairies kept from 300 to 4,000 cows that were fed
largely on the hot fermented mash—swill or slop, as opponents
called it; "spent grain," as a recent historian of a brewing company dubbed it.[1] The slop, containing a very small amount of food
in a great quantity of liquid, was constantly kept in troughs in
front of the cows, who, to get enough to satisfy their hunger,
had to consume 30 to 60 gallons a day. Sometimes a little hay
and grain was given to aid the digestive process.

In New York, where there were 814 people listed as brewers
and distillers in 1865, the slop dairies were located mostly on

---

[1] T. C. Cochran: *The Pabst Brewing Company* (New York, 1948), p 107.

the West Side near the Hudson on 9th, 15th and 16th, 38th and 39th, and 45th and 46th Streets. Johnson's at the foot of 16th Street was the best known and most widely patronized. At least one 700-cow dairy was located in Brooklyn. Altogether these swill dairies kept some 13,000 cows, of which 2,000 were said to die annually. In some of these stables milk dealers rented stalls, paying five dollars a year, while in other cases nearby residents bought slops from brewers or distillers for seven to nine cents a barrel.[2]

The milk from cows fed this "smoking hot" distillery mash was bluish, watery, and insipid and, because of the careless way the cows were milked, contained excrement, urine, dust, and dirt, and doubtless germs of the diseases against which modern pasteurization is directed. Being fed an unnatural diet, living under conditions that were thoroughly unsanitary, and being milked by persons only interested in getting as much liquid from their udders as possible, the cows became subject to "functional derangements" such as bloody murrain, diarrhea, pleurisy, consumption, and foot rot; their flesh "became flaccid, with tendency to putrescence, scabs and cutaneous erruptions, teeth decay," said a legislative committee in 1854. Fed to pigs, the slop assured "scrofulous and measly pork"; fed to cows, it produced "bloated and diseased carcases."[3]

Man's inhumanity to man is well illustrated in the long survival of this "detestable" swill milk business, for as early as 1840 the secretary of the New York State Medical Society had called attention to the high rate of mortality among infants fed the contaminated milk of the swill dairies. The Medical Society and the Academy of Medicine followed up this early attack in 1847, 1858, 1860, and 1864, providing abundant evidence of the dangers in the use of the milk and describing the frightful con-

---

[2] Gurdon Evans: *The Dairyman's Manual* (Utica, N. Y., 1851), pp. 63 ff.; John Mullaly: *The Milk Trade of New York and Vicinity* (New York, 1853), pp. 43 ff.; Council of Hygiene and Public Health of the Citizens Association of New York: *Report on the Sanitary Condition of the City* (New York, 1865), p. 263.

[3] New York Senate, Select Committee on petition of Citizens and Physicians of New York for an act to prevent the sale of impure or adulterated Milk, Mar. 29, 1854, *Senate Documents*, 1854, II, no. 100, pp. 1–7.

ditions under which it was produced. Medical society opinion, though based on scientific and indisputable evidence, needed popular support if a campaign to outlaw the sale of swill milk was to succeed. This came in 1858 when *Frank Leslie's Illustrated Newspaper* brought the question into the open as nothing previously had done by illustrating with graphic woodcuts accounts of the diseased and unhealthy cows kept in filthy, crowded, and unventilated stables, the adulteration and contamination of the milk, and the high rate of serious illness and death among the children of poorer families who used it. Three years later *Leslie's* related with pride its experiences in exposing the "infamous Swill Milk traffic" which had "grown shameless by tolerance." To ferret out information it engaged an army of detectives, many of whom were threatened with death in the pursuit of the investigation. It employed chemists to test the "poisonous trash" and lawyers to defend suits for damage. Arrayed against *Leslie's* were the large firms engaged in the milk traffic and the city authorities, who were on the side of the vested interests, as were the judges. The newspapers later took up the campaign against the swill dairies, and action seemed called for.[4]

Halting steps were taken in New York to outlaw the sale of contaminated milk. A Select Committee of the Senate brought in a searing indictment of the traffic in 1854 and the Senate passed a measure to ban it, but the House only referred the measure to a committee. In 1855, 1860, and 1861 a similar measure was under consideration, and in 1861 it passed the Assembly. Finally, Ezra Cornell in 1862 pushed through a measure "to prevent the adulteration of milk, and prevent the traffic in impure and unwholesome milk." For the moment it seemed that the police would close down all the swill dairies, and Solon Robinson optimistically thought the law was being made to work. He soon learned better, however, for the swill milk dairies were actually increasing their operations and found a ready market for all the

---

[4] "Report of the Committee on City Milk, New York ... Communicated by the New York Academy of Medicine," Mar. 2, 1859, *New York Assembly Documents*, 1860, IV, no. 111; S. M. Percy: "On the Food of Cities," in Medical Society of the State of New York, *Transactions*, 1864, pp. 75 ff.; *Leslie's Illustrated Newspaper*, XI (Apr. 6, 1861), 305.

milk they produced. A second measure in 1864 specified that adding water to milk was adulteration as the term was used in the act of 1862 and declared swill milk to be unwholesome. All such early laws were loosely drafted and full of loopholes, and they rarely provided for enforcement. Also, there were chemists who could be hired to swear that the distillery slop was nutritious and that the milk from cows fed on it was pure and unadulterated, and there were judges who were willing to decide against enforcement. The result was that so far as the state or, indeed, the city of New York was concerned, the swill milk dairies could and did flourish.[5]

Meantime, the public was becoming aroused at other insanitary and foul-smelling places that many thought produced disease. Among them were the slaughter pens, bone- and offal-boiling, fat-melting, and hide-dressing establishments, piggeries, offal decks, and dunghills which were found in Hell's Kitchen and elsewhere in lower Manhattan. A concerted effort to attack them led to the creation of the Metropolitan Board of Health in 1866 with power that promised alleviation of the worst of the conditions.[6]

Other factors were to be as significant in reducing the swill milk business in the city as regulation. Among these were the rising value of real estate, which tended to drive the distillers with their associated dairies to the more remote parts of the cities, public opinion aroused by the high incidence of illness

---

[5] Eric Brunger: "Changes in the New York State Dairying Industry, 1850–1900," Ph.D. dissertation, 1954, Syracuse University; *New York Senate Journal*, Apr. 13, 1854, p. 774; *Assembly Journal*, Mar. 3, 1855, p. 916, and Apr. 3, 1860, p. 953; *Senate Journal*, Apr. 12, 1861, p. 544, and Apr. 17, 1862, p. 596. Before its enactment the measure was weakened by changing "to prevent the sale of milk from cows fed on slops" to "prevent the adulteration of milk and prevent the traffic in impure and unwholesome milk." *Supplement to Fifth Edition of the Revised Statutes of New York*, 1863, p. 371. As late as 1876

Dr. R. O. Doremus of City College testified that distillery waste was nutritious for cows. *The People vs. Daniel Schrumpf. Misdemeanor, Adulteration of Milk, in the Court of Gen. Sessions in City and County of New York*, December 1876.

[6] Citizens Association of New York: *The Public Health. The Basis of Sanitary Reform. The Metropolitan Board of Health* (New York, 1866), *passim*. For difficulties in the path of the public health movement see Roy Lubove: *The Progressives and the Slums. Tenement House Reform in New York City* (Pittsburgh, 1962), pp. 11 ff.

and death among the poorer people, the educational work of public-health-minded people, and, perhaps most important, the construction of railroads into rural areas, which made it possible to bring country milk into the city.

Dairies feeding distillery slop were to be found in all larger communities, and in most of them public indignation, aroused by statistics of infant mortality and by the active and courageous efforts of some leaders of the medical profession, attacked the problem by legislation. Massachusetts tried to prohibit the adulteration of milk in 1856, authorized the appointment of inspectors for milk in Boston in 1859, and in 1864 banned the feeding of distillery waste to dairy cows and the sale of milk from diseased cows. Complacent Boston inspectors reported that samples of milk contained from 7 to 50 per cent added water, that few complaints were being made of violation of the law, and that the statute was too complicated to enforce. They thought the amount of milk sold in the city from slop-fed cows was not large. New Hampshire forbade the sale of milk from cows fed on distillery refuse in 1860. In Washington efforts were made in 1863 to clean up unsanitary cow yards and in 1871 to ban adulteration of milk. Chicago tried regulation of milk in the sixties and labeling of skim milk in 1870. Inspection of dairies and the use of veterinarians to inspect cows were not to come for years. The sale of meat from diseased animals was only second in danger to the distribution of contaminated milk.[7]

On the whole, the movement for public health legislation and for outlawing swill dairies had not proceeded far by 1865. Indeed, for long years afterward distillery slop-fed cows continued in many cities to provide dangerously contaminated milk for children in poorer families. In 1894 Paul Leicester Ford shaped a romantic story out of Peter Stirling's campaign against the swill dairies in New York. As late as 1906–8 distillery dairies

---

[7] Reports of Inspector of Milk, *Boston Documents*, 1863, I, no. 49, p. 4, and 1864, I, no. 437, pp. 1–10; *Session Laws of New Hampshire*, 1860, Act of July 4, 1860, p. 2245; *Acts of the General Court of Massachusetts*, 1863, Act of Apr. 6, 1863, p. 453; *Prairie Farmer*, X (Aug. 30, 1862), 131; J. F. Smithcors: *The American Veterinary Profession* (Ames, Iowa, 1963), p. 403; B. L. Pierce: *History of Chicago* (3 vols., New York, 1937–57), II, 335.

filled with sick cows living under unsanitary conditions still flourished in Cincinnati.[8]

Gail Borden's milk condensing plants at Wassaic, New York, and Burrville, Connecticut, were established in 1859, at a time when the country was being alerted to the danger of the adulterated and contaminated milk commonly sold in cities. Borden's process eliminated three fourths of the water in milk and sterilized it. More important, he devised testing and sampling procedures to determine butterfat content and purity as well as to evaluate previous care in handling milk. These procedures made it possible for him to reject all but first-quality milk. In 1861 his condensed milk was being recommended by physicians and was delivered to 3,000 families in New York and Brooklyn. The Civil War brought an unparalleled demand for Borden's milk, including government orders for it as part of regular field rations and for use in the Navy and in hospitals. The demand led to the opening of new plants in York, Pennsylvania; Livermore Falls, Maine; Brewster, New York; Winsted, Connecticut; and Elgin, Illinois. The price paid at the condensery was comparable to that farmers received for their milk at nearby railroads. A new business had been born, safe milk was assured those who patronized it, and fortunes came to Gail Borden, the inventor and entrepreneur, and to Jeremiah Milbank, the financier.[9]

The most important factor in reducing the swill dairy business was the gradual extension of the railroads into the hinter-

---

[8] P. L. Ford: *The Honorable Peter Stirling* (New York, 1894); H. N. Parker: *City Milk Supply* (New York, 1917), p. 183. In London the same adulteration, the feeding of brewery swill to cows, and the sale of impure and unsafe milk was common in the 1870's. A. H. Hassall: *Food: Its Adulteration and the Methods of Detection* (London, 1876), pp. 404, 418 ff. It was said that at the high point of the operations of the distilleries in Peoria, Ill., in 1893, 28,038 animals were chained to the food troughs and fed the refuse. E. L. East: "The Distillers' and Cattle Feeders' Trust, 1887–1895," in Illinois State Historical Society, *Journal*, XLV (1952), 105.

[9] New York State Agricultural Society: *Journal*, XII (July 1861), 13; Joe B. Frantz: *Gail Borden. Dairyman to a Nation* (Norman, Okla., 1951), *passim*; X. A. Willard: "Among the Butter-Makers of Orange County, with Suggestions on Cheese Dairying," in New York State Agricultural Society, *Transactions*, 1865, p. 251.

land of cities like Boston and New York, so that milk from cows fed a more natural diet and kept under better conditions was brought into the cities. The railroads provided farmers who lived within 5 or 6 miles of stations, and perhaps not more than 40 to 60 miles from the cities, a distant market for their fluid milk that made it unnecessary for them to churn it into butter on the farm. Preoccupation with through traffic has prevented some historians from realizing how important the shipment of milk was to the railroads, though the farm journals were aware of it. Thus, the *New England Farmer* in 1861 commented on the attention the railroad executives and the farmers had given to the transportation of milk to Boston from the beginning of railroad construction in the 1830's, and the *New York Times* called the milk train in 1865 the most profitable train on the Erie Railroad.[1]

The historian of the Erie makes much of the effect of building the railroad into Orange County, which was then noted for its premium butter made in its model dairies. With the coming of the railroad through this rich dairying county, experimental shipments of milk to New York City were made. As Mott tells the story, the farmers' return of two cents a quart for fluid milk, when compared with fifteen cents a pound for butter (which required 12 quarts of milk), was so favorable and relieved them of so much labor that in less than two years "there was scarcely a farmer within reach of the railroad who did not ship his milk to New York and genuine Goshen butter . . . became a thing of the past." "Within reach" was regarded in 1861 as 1 to 5 miles from the railroad, and 70 to 100 miles was about the greatest distance milk could be safely hauled by rail. Thus began that most characteristic practice of railroads from Maine to California, running a milk train on most lines leading to the cities.[2]

---

[1] *New England Farmer*, XIII (September 1861), 435; E. C. Kirkland: *Men, Cities and Transportation. A Study in New England History, 1820–1900* (2 vols., Cambridge, Mass., 1948); *New York Times*, Aug. 15, 1865.

[2] Mott was quite wrong about the disappearance of Goshen butter made in Orange County, as is seen below. E. H. Mott: *Between the Ocean and the Lakes. The Story of the Erie* (New York, 1908), pp. 406 ff.; *Rural New Yorker*, XII (Aug. 3, 1861), 245. S. L. Loomis: "The Consumption of Milk," in Commissioner of Patents, *Report, Agriculture*, 1861, pp. 214–16; Edward Wiest: *The Butter Industry in the United States* (New York, 1916), p. 93.

In the fifties the Harlem and the New York and Hudson River Railroads were thrust northward from New York to Albany, bringing many hundreds of additional farms within close touch of modern transportation. Similarly the New York and New Haven and the Long Island Railroads were being pushed into additional territory which thereby made its milk tributary to New York City. At the same time additional feeder lines were being projected in the dairying region of the Walkill Valley of Orange County, where milk, cheese, and butter were expected to exceed all other freight traffic. On the Harlem Railroad the returns from hauling milk in 1861 constituted better than half the entire freight earnings and, a critic said, might be substantially increased if the railroad handled its business properly.[3]

Between 1,300 and 1,500 farmers in Westchester, Putnam, Dutchess, and Orange Counties were sending 124,000 quarts of milk daily into New York City in January 1861 and as much as 201,000 quarts in midsummer. Country fresh milk, commonly watered and sometimes treated with bicarbonate of soda to retard souring, was winning the battle in competition with swill milk, since slop-fed cows were furnishing a diminishing proportion of the milk consumed. When country milk first appeared in New York it sold for less than swill milk, but this was not for long; soon it brought a premium of one cent, sometimes two. Adulteration of the farm milk, however, kept its price down.

QUARTS OF MILK HAULED INTO NEW YORK CITY		
RAILROAD	DAILY, AUG. 1860	YEAR ENDING JUN. 30,1861
Harlem	88,000	27,507,080
Erie	80,000	24,414,608
Hudson River	18,000	—
Long Island	10,000	3,326,730
New York & New Haven	4,000	—
New Jersey	1,600	—

SOURCE: *New York Tribune* in *Dairy Farmer*, I (September 1860), 132; Commissioner of Patents, *Report*, 1861, *Agriculture*, p. 214.

[3] *American Railroad Journal*, XXXV (Mar. 8, Dec. 27, 1862), 178, 1027, and XXXVI (Mar. 14, Dec. 5, 1863), 257, 1152.

By 1865 the *New York Times* could say that the sale of swill milk was on the way out, since only five establishments feeding swill were left, and that, aside from the usual adulteration of milk by the addition of salt and one fifth water, the milk supply was fairly satisfactory. It attributed this to the railroads, which were now bringing in 88,000 quarts by the Erie, 100,000 quarts by the Harlem, and 15,000 by the Hudson River, as contrasted with the 75,000 quarts which were produced in the city. The *Times* was overly optimistic about the quality of the milk and the degree of adulteration, as the later news items showed. For example, one of its writers, after examining the milk fed to inmates of Blackwells Island, said that the product of the "cow with the iron tail" was watered by one half to two thirds and that this was altogether too common. There may have been some pure, unadulterated milk sold in the city at the premium price of 10¢ to 14¢ in 1865, but the preponderance of opinion seems to be that farmers, creameries, wholesalers, and peddlers either skimmed off the cream or added water, salt, corn meal, chalk, and other adulterants in a greater or less degree to their milk.[4]

In Boston the milk was notorious for being "heavily freighted with Cochituate water." Henry David Thoreau is quoted as saying, "Some circumstantial evidence is very strong, as when you find a trout in the milk." In 1863 when the price of cheese and butter had risen favorably with respect to that of milk, a Middlesex farmer complained that unless the milk were watered its price would have to go up an additional cent or there would be a scarcity of fluid milk. Not until then would farmers turn from butter and cheese making.[5]

In the summer of 1864 there was a stoppage of the distilleries and breweries in New York, and the dairies dependent on their swill were forced to feed hay and grain instead. Higher costs seem to have driven some of the proprietors out of business,

---

[4] *New York Times*, Aug. 22, 1864, Jan. 22, 1865. In Aug. 15, 1865, the *Times* observed that the Erie was hauling 140,000 quarts of milk daily to New York.

[5] *New England Farmer*, XV (April 1863), 121; P. W. Gates: *The Farmer's Age* (New York, 1960), p. 237.

but the reopening of the brewing and distilling establishments saved others. For the remainder of the war the hot liquid mash was scarce. Milk prices naturally rose with inflation, greater demand, higher costs of transportation, and the reduced output of the swill dairies. By 1864 city watered milk brought seven cents, country milk, which might also be watered, brought eight, and ten and twelve cents were paid for pure milk. Swill milk was often sold as country milk. Most of the increase in the price of milk seems to have gone to buyers, deliverymen, and railroads. Even before the outbreak of the war it was said that dairymen were doing well near cities, where the demand for fresh country milk was developing rapidly. There is no reason to doubt that they continued to fare well during the war. The astonishing feature about the increasing demand for fluid milk in the cities is that it attracted so little attention in the farm journals. They failed to foresee how dairy farming would become greatly changed by this development.[6]

In 1861 Dr. Silas L. Loomis prepared an article on the consumption of milk which appeared in the agricultural volume of the Patent Office of that year. Although the source of his data is not clear and some of his classifications are not easily understood, the analysis is interesting. He found the total production of milk from Maine to Virginia, including Wisconsin, to be 5,858,-000,000 quarts in round figures. Of this total 40 per cent was "used as food"; 54 per cent was used to make butter. One would like to compare these statistics with those for 1870 taken by the Census Bureau, but the latter are so exaggerated and bear so little relationship to other data as to be useless. What stands out is that, notwithstanding the growth of the urban demand for fluid milk, butter remained the principal method of utilizing milk throughout the Civil War and for years afterward. Nevertheless, there was a progressive decline in the production of butter in the milksheds of the cities, where the sale

---

[6] Solon Robinson reported in the *New York Weekly Tribune* of Nov. 26, 1864, that milk brought up to 12¢ a quart in New York, and on Mar. 11, 1865, he quoted dealers charging 12¢ and 14¢ for unadulterated milk. His comments in the *Weekly Tribune* of 1864–6 contain much on the difficulties of the swill milk dealers. See also *Country Gentleman*, XVII (Feb. 14, 1861), 106.

of fluid milk was increasing. This can be shown best for the New York milkshed and the smaller hinterlands of the minor cities of New York.[7]

In other states one finds the same development: city distillery dairies with their thin, bluish, dirty, and contaminated milk gradually being contracted as the railroads brought in supplies of farmers' fresh milk, adulterated by the addition of water but certainly much safer than milk from swill-fed cows. Milk trains from Worcester, Fitchburg, and Lowell brought 24,228,000 quarts into Boston in 1864. Chicago was extending its rail connections and building its milkshed in northern Ilinois in the same period. The Galena and Chicago Union Railroad, later a part of the Northwestern, brought 120,000 quarts to Chicago in 1853 and 1,606,000 quarts in 1860.[8]

Extension of the milksheds by the railroads and the growing market for cheese both at home and abroad made it possible for farmers in the East to turn to dairy farming at a time when they badly needed new opportunities for the investment of their labor and land. No longer could they compete with Western-grown wheat and corn-fed sheep and beef cattle, for their land— planted to grain for years in succession—had become infested with destructive insects, depleted of its essential minerals by exhaustive cultivation, and priced too high in relation to the fertile lands being opened up in the new West. Dairy farming was to prove the salvation of farmers in the older states of the Northeast, who now began to give their cows better housing and care and to remove the manure regularly and spread it on the land. They improved their stock through the use of good-quality, if not purebred, bulls and the elimination of scrub and low-producing animals. Hay of better quality was raised and carefully stored, cows were put on silage when the pastures dried up, and grain and hay or silage was fed in winter. Ice and milk houses with running spring water, clean and comfortable cows, and airy but not drafty stables were the objectives of the good dairy farmer. Thought was also given to the rotation and re-seeding of pastures, the elimination of the Canada thistle, and

---

[7] Commissioner of Patents: *Report, Agriculture*, 1861, p. 211.

[8] *American Railroad Journal*, XXXIV (July 27, 1861), 538.

EXPANSION OF MILK SOLD AND DECLINE OF BUTTER PRODUCTION IN NEW YORK MILKSHED

COUNTY	GALLONS MILK SOLD		BUTTER PRODUCTION IN POUNDS			
	1864	1869	1849	1859	1864	1869
Orange	8,835,052	13,741,983	3,769,034	3,033,805	2,363,661	1,403,400
Dutchess	8,964,574	5,013,384	1,544,201	2,134,209	1,358,722	1,232,252
Westchester	2,928,845	4,442,393	1,547,504	1,315,528	525,032	430,737
Putnam	2,841,453	3,591,343	785,330	465,235	272,924	277,759
Queens	929,131	1,590,194	561,230	505,986	424,063	362,250

GROWTH OF SMALLER NEW YORK MILKSHEDS

COUNTY	GALLONS MILK SOLD		BUTTER PRODUCTION IN POUNDS			
	1864	1869	1849	1859	1864	1869
Albany (Albany)	464,885	779,355	970,142	1,318,223	1,066,196	1,142,783
Erie (Buffalo)	489,859	7,116,859	1,544,201	2,128,107	1,558,573	2,149,358
Monroe (Rochester)	358,400	760,759	1,258,735	1,651,914	1,374,890	1,631,050
Onondaga (Syracuse)	262,946	3,039,355	2,147,518	2,363,284	2,149,141	2,375,577
Rensselaer (Troy)	556,638	1,035,906	1,336,281	1,279,844	1,144,726	1,271,128

SOURCE: *U.S. Censuses*, 1850, 1860, 1870, and *Census of New York*, 1865.

the replacement of the wasteful worm and stump fences. Increasing concentration upon the production and sale of fluid milk gradually led farmers to adopt a more modern system of agriculture.

In 1865 the *New York Times* devoted four columns to a detailed examination of the dairy business under the caption "Milky Ways." The condition of farming over the last ten years, declared the *Times*, had greatly improved. Farmers now raised most of the forage and grain their stock consumed, since nearly everyone had a mowing machine which permitted him to raise more hay than formerly, and a horse-drawn hayrake to aid him in seasoning it and getting it into the barn. With less labor than they used to have, farmers could now care for more cattle. They had larger herds—crosses of Devons, Durhams, and natives— which produced an average of 1,800 quarts a year. At four cents a quart for their milk, farmers were doing well, grossing $1,000 to $1,500 a year. In fact, the *Times* was assured there was less poverty in Orange County than anywhere else in the country. Even so, Orange County farms were not as productive as the *Times* writer thought they could be. Little had yet been done to drain their wet areas, their zigzag fences wasted much timber and land, and their output of milk was small, doubtless owing to the fact that the milk breeds, particularly the Ayrshires and Jerseys, were rarely to be found in the herds.

The rise in the price of milk in New York caused farmers to feel that the spread between the price they received and the price for which their milk sold was too great. Some farmers in the New York milkshed organized cooperatively to sell milk directly in the city, only to find the city dealers so powerful and so determined to halt such competition by fair means or foul that their operations were not altogether successful. Finally, when the city dealers offered to pay more to the producers, the promising little cooperative folded, at which point the dealers cut their price to the farmers to the previous level. The *Times* writer declared that farmers "must meet combination with combination" if they were to obtain fair treatment.[9]

Dairy farmers well located with respect to railroads and

---

[9] *New York Times*, Aug. 15, 1865.

growing cities and towns were able to relieve themselves and their wives of much of the drudgery of making butter and cheese by selling their milk. But that fortunate group constituted a small part of the total. The larger number had to devote a considerable amount of their time to the many tasks involved in butter and cheese making. They depended for their cash income on the sale or barter of these items and on the sale of old cows, as well as on the sale of hogs and calves that were partly raised on skim milk, buttermilk, or whey. Trade in butter, cheese, beef, and pork was well institutionalized by 1860, with quotations being carried regularly in the farm journals and newspapers having rural patrons.

New York led all other states in dairy farming and provided standards that for years were to be the basis for judging dairy products. As the New York farmers went West to begin farming anew in Michigan, Illinois, Wisconsin, and elsewhere, they carried with them their experience and knowledge, and they developed the great dairy industry of the newer commonwealths which was destined to surpass that of the Empire state. The preeminence of New York's dairy industry is shown by the following table.

PERCENTAGE OF NATIONAL TOTALS OF COWS AND DAIRY PRODUCTS

	NEW YORK		PENNSYLVANIA		OHIO	
	1860	1870	1860	1870	1860	1870
Milch cows	13	14	8	8	8	7
Butter	22	20	12	11	10	10
Cheese	44	42	11	2	22	15
Milk	—	57	—	—	—	—

SOURCE: *U.S. Censuses* of 1860 and 1870.

In 1860 the average amount of butter produced on each farm in New York was 533 pounds, in Vermont 502, New Jersey 386, Pennsylvania 375, Connecticut 303, Ohio 270, and Michigan 248. A decade later Vermont, supreme in its choice sheep, Morgan horses, and maple sugar, led with an average of 527 pounds of butter per farmer. Next came New York with 495, Pennsylvania with 349, Connecticut with 263, New Jersey with 260, Ohio with 256, and Iowa with 236. In New York the heaviest butter-producing areas were upstate, well away from the milk-shed tributary to New York City, but in Pennsylvania the butter-producing area was in the counties closest to Philadelphia. Elsewhere in the major dairy states, butter production was widely distributed, with no areas of concentration.

In 1860 cream separators were still far in the future. The dasher churn, in which the dasher was plunged up and down for forty to fifty minutes in a closed barrel, was in general use. In larger dairies the barrel-type churn, operated by hand or by sheep, dog, or horse power on treadmills, was used. In the very largest dairies steam or water power was harnessed to churns. Over 700 patents had been taken out on improved devices for churning butter, but one shrewd observer declared that most of them had proved useless.

The writings of Charles L. Flint, Harvard graduate, participant in the founding of Massachusetts Institute of Technology, a founder of Massachusetts Agricultural College, and a long-time Secretary of the Massachusetts Board of Agriculture, provided dairy farmers with excellent advice on all matters relating to breeds of cattle, stables, pastures, grasses, milking, and butter and cheese making. His *Milch Cows and Dairy Farming,* first published in 1858, went through numerous printings and must have been used by many farmers. X. A. Willard, whose articles frequently appeared in the reports of the U. S. Commissioner of Agriculture, the transactions of the New York State Agricultural Society, and the *Rural New Yorker,* was more concerned with cheese and butter making. His writings were brought together and published as *Practical Dairy Husbandry* in 1871.[1]

In few farm commodities was the spread in price between the top quality and the lowest as great as in butter. For example, Orange County butter in pails was quoted in the *New York Weekly Tribune* on January 11, 1862, at 22 to 25 cents per pound while grease butter was quoted at 7.5 to 9 cents a pound.

Orange County or Goshen butter early acquired a reputation for purity, taste, and the clean conditions under which it was made, and for a time Orange County or Goshen was a com-

---

[1] American Institute of the City of New York: *Annual Report,* 1865, p. 157; C. L. Flint: *Milch Cows and Dairy Farming* (New York, 1858); X. A. Willard: *Practical Dairy Husbandry* (New York, 1871).

WHOLESALE BUTTER QUOTATIONS, JAN. 10, 1862

Orange County, in pails	22–25 cents
State choice	18–20 "
Welsh tubs choice	18–20 "
Welsh tubs, fair to good	15–17 "
Western Pennsylvania choice	14–15 "
Western Pennsylvania fair	11–13 "
Western Reserve choice	14–15 "
Western Reserve fair to good	11–13 "
Western common	9–10 "
Grease butter	7.5–9 "

WHOLESALE BUTTER QUOTATIONS, NOV. 4, 1864

Orange County and Goshen	60 cents
Sussex	52–55 "
Illinois, Iowa, Minnesota	32–36 "
Western Reserve	45–47 "
Central Ohio	37–42 "
Pennsylvania	48–55 "

SOURCE: *New York Weekly Tribune,* Jan. 11, 1862, Nov. 5, 1864.

mercial term applied to top-quality butter, whether made in Orange County or elsewhere. Rivaling the position of Orange County butter in Philadelphia was "Philadelphia print," which was made in Chester, Lancaster, and Delaware Counties on some of the finest farming country in the United States. Famous for its "sweetness, solidity and golden color" (though it must be said that the color was artificially produced both winter and summer), this butter also brought premium prices.[2]

Butter continued to be produced largely on the farm, whereas cheese was being produced increasingly in factories. Throughout the war no great expansion in the production of butter occurred in the East, though there was a good deal of

---

[2] The *National Intelligencer,* Feb. 25, 1862, carried an ad listing 35 tubs and firkins of prime Goshen butter for sale. The *Atlanta Commonwealth,* June 25, 1861, described the butter brought into Atlanta as just so much lard and tallow mixed, and so indifferently prepared that it became sour or rancid in a short time. It acknowledged that Tennessee produced good butter and later declared that "much so called Goshen butter" was produced in the South. *Ibid.,* Nov. 11, 1861. "Philadelphia Butter," in Commissioner of Agriculture, *Report,* 1868, pp. 291 ff.

shifting of production from districts near cities to those more remote. The big increase in production was in the upper Mississippi Valley, plus Michigan. Ohio just held its own as the leading state in butter production in this region; it was in Illinois, Iowa, Minnesota, Wisconsin, and Michigan that dairy farming was developing rapidly. For example, Iowa, which produced less than three million pounds of butter in 1850 and was eleventh among the states in butter manufacture in 1860, jumped to fifth place in 1870. In 1864 and 1865 Iowa was shipping eastward over a million pounds.

It is understandable that the market did not value the butter from these new states as it did New York's production, for it had taken the New York producers years to learn how to make a high-quality product. A Bureau County, Illinois, farmer described the general quality of butter made in the West as quite mixed, ranging from " 'sloshy' that needs a spoon to lift it, upward through various grades to the firm, sweet, yellow butter that is seldom found in groceries and stores. . . ." Only when farm families decided to concentrate on management of milk cattle and the production of butter, and learned how great a difference there was in the cash return from the top-grade product and that of lower quality, did they refine their processes. It was the small farmer who made a little butter in the height of the grass season and took little pains with it who turned out butter of poor quality that could be classed as "grease" or "grease butter."[3]

Although New York State or Orange County butter brought premium prices, not all New York dairy farmers were tidy and sanitary in their milking and butter making. A speaker at the New York State Fair took them to task for the "filthiness" of their dairies, their failure to clean the cows before milking, the muck that was allowed to fall into the milk, the dirty pails they used, the storage of milk near hogpens and other foul-smelling places, and their general want of cleanliness. Cows were still milked in the pasture or barnyard, rain or shine, and in regions where mild weather prevailed, cows were never housed. Farther north they were kept in barns only in the worst of the winter

---

[3] Iowa State Agricultural Society: *Reports*, 1864, pp. 17–22, and 1865, pp. 21–32; *Prairie Farmer*, XVI (Dec. 9, 1865), 414.

months. Clearly, all insanitary and careless methods in handling the milk were not confined to the slop dairies. However, the experts' advice concerning the effect of impure and insanitary milk on the quality of cheese and butter was beginning to have results. Some farmers were taking greater care of their livestock. They were feeding them better, especially in the winter, to assure milk when the price was at its best level; they were building spring-fed milk houses to keep their milk and butter cool; and they were taking greater pride in the manufacture of their dairy products.[4]

In his recent study of the Wisconsin dairy industry, Eric Lampard has shown how bitterly farmers of the Badger state fought efforts to protect consumers by outlawing contaminated and adulterated milk and unsanitary conditions on the farm. Much the same may be said of New York dairy interests. In 1864, when dealers protested against misbranding of butter firkins and tried to get effective legislation that required the correct weight to be stamped on them, the representatives of upstate New York were opposed.[5]

One of the largest dairy farm operations about which we have some detailed information was that of Zadock Pratt of Prattsville, Greene County, New York. Pratt cleared his upland area of 365 acres of hemlock, which he used in his tannery, and then turned to dairy farming. From 80 cows he made 17,976 pounds of butter during what he called the eight months' pasture season of 1863, and sold it for an average of 27 cents a pound, or $4,853.52. The skim milk was consumed by 49 hogs, 130 turkeys, and 120 chickens, and from their sale he grossed $691.33. Other miscellaneous income brought his total gross income to $5,620.85. From this he deducted $700 interest on $10,000 he had invested in the farm and $1216.45 for other expenses, including labor. As he figured it, the profit was $3,704.40. Other products, which presumably were used on the farm, were 1,107 bushels of ear corn, 1,500 bushels of carrots and beets, 130 loads of pumpkins, and 80 tons of hay. His help consisted of three

---

[4] Mullaly: *The Milk Trade of New York*, pp. 80 ff.; New York State Agricultural Society: *Journal*, XVI (November 1866), 109 ff.

[5] *New York Tribune*, Aug. 22, 1864. Such a measure was enacted in 1865. New York State Agricultural Society: *Transactions*, 1864, p. xvi.

men, three women, and three boys. Churning was done in barrel churns operated by an overshot waterwheel. The records he had kept since 1857 enabled him to show that the amount of butter sold per cow ranged from $30.95 in 1857 to $42.97 in 1860, $49.81 in 1861, $58.98 in 1862, and $60.66 in 1863.[6]

Farmers in the expanding milkshed of New York found that their dependence on the New York market for their sales weakened their bargaining position and enabled the milk dealers to determine price. Consequently, they tended to revert to butter manufacturing and some of them turned to group action. Orange County dairy farmers organized the Walkill Creamery Association, in which cooperating members pooled their resources and built plants for making butter and cheese. Thereafter expenses for operation and sales were shared in proportion to the amount of milk delivered to the plant. The association was a unique institution because, unlike the cheese associations of central New York which are discussed below, it concentrated about equally upon the production of butter and cheese, in addition to selling milk and cream. Its plan was to skim part, but by no means all, of the cream from the milk and make it into butter, while using the partially skimmed milk for cheese. In the best of the season nearly one pound of butter and two pounds of cheese could be made from 14 quarts of milk. From April 1 to December 1, 1865, the association received 627,174 quarts of milk and utilized it as shown in the table on p. 207. Expenses for labor, fuel, cheese boxes, salt, rennets, cartage, and purchase of hogs came to $3,235.33. The net which could be paid to the farmers was 4.1¢ per quart.

X. A. Willard, the compiler of these statistics, was impressed with the considerably higher return to the farmers from this butter and skim cheese operation than from sales of milk for cheese alone. Doubtless the association benefited from the reputation of Orange County butter and the experience and care shown by its participants in the management of their dairy operations, for

---

[6] Zadock Pratt: "The Dairy Farming Region of Greene and Orange Counties, New York, with Some Account of the Farm of the Writer," in Commissioner of Patents, *Report, Agriculture*, 1861, pp. 411 ff.; Commissioner of Agriculture: *Report*, 1865, p. 456; *New York Weekly Tribune*, Feb. 13, 1864; New York State Agricultural Society: *Journal*, XIII (June 1863), 46.

SALES OF MILK AND MILK PRODUCTS OF WALKILL
CREAMERY ASSOCIATION, APR. 1 TO DEC. 1, 1865

27,308 quarts of whole milk sold at 7¢	$ 1,926,22
1,561 quarts skim milk sold at 1 and 5/8¢	24.02
31,630 pounds of buttermilk sold at 42¼¢	13,344.21
81,778 pounds skim cheese sold at 14¼¢	11,659.08
5,908 pounds whole milk cheese sold at 18¢	1,065.44
2,261 quarts cream sold at 19.6¢	443.33
Hogs fed on whey	446.24
Buttermilk and sundries	207.49
Total	$29,116.03

SOURCE: New York State Agricultural Society, *Journal*, XVI
(May 1866), pp. 25 ff.

it received premium prices for its butter, and its skim cheese, which was shipped to China, got almost as much as the central New York factories received for their whole-milk cheese. Willard's conclusion, that the better lands in the Mohawk Valley were too high-priced to justify using their principal product, milk, for the making of cheese, was borne out, for the census of 1870 shows that in this area farmers were turning away from cheese making to the sale of milk and the production of more butter.[7]

Well-located dairymen had three choices in the marketing of their milk: They might sell whole milk, they might make and sell butter, or they might make and sell cheese. Some combined the last two. In the 1860's farmers shifted from one to another as the prices of milk, butter, and cheese varied, for it was a common complaint that there was a considerable spread in them. However, there were relatively few dairymen so situated as to be able to rely only on sales of fluid milk.

Commercial cheese making, unlike butter making, came to be centered in very limited areas in New York and Ohio, where in 1860 about 70 per cent of the cheese was produced. In New York, the Mohawk Valley, the counties bordering on the eastern end of Lake Ontario and the beginnings of the St. Lawrence River, and three counties at the eastern tip of Lake Erie constituted the principal cheese areas. From Herkimer County alone

---

[7] New York State Agricultural Society: *Journal*, XVI (May 1866), 25 ff.

in 1864 there were shipped 16,767,994 pounds of cheese valued at $3,353,538. In Ohio, there was an even greater concentration on cheese production, with six counties in the Western Reserve of northeastern Ohio producing 86 per cent of the state's total. Elsewhere, cheese production was scattered.[8]

Cheese making was both a mechanical and a chemical process, whereas butter making was purely mechanical. The former involved curdling the milk by heating it, adding an acid derived from the rennet, the inner lining of a calf's stomach, eliminating the whey or liquid after curdling by cutting up the curds and by pressure, and salting and coloring the product. Cheese could be made from cream, whole milk, skim milk, or buttermilk, but the best quality came from whole milk or milk with only a small amount of cream removed. Though farmers in all parts of the country made cheese, much was used locally, and only the larger or commercial dairy farms produced it in sufficient quantities to justify marketing. In Herkimer County, where the business was conducted during six or seven months in the year, a lively market developed. At Little Falls in the height of the season, farmers came with their wagons loaded with cheese, prepared to dicker with buyers who knew this was the best place to meet the producers. The bids accepted here had much to do with determining prices elsewhere. In June of 1865 their bids ranged from 10¢ for the poorer quality of skimmed and hay-made cheese to a high of 14½¢ for the top quality, made from the milk of cows fed on the best pastures. At these prices dealers could not afford to buy for the English market, but the Southern demand for Northern cheese helped to clear the market.[9]

Cheese making within the home continued to flourish, though it had certain disadvantages compared with production in factories. Farmers, instead of making cheese daily, let their milk accumulate; frequently it became sour or tainted because they did not have ideal facilities for keeping milk. Few farmers had designed their butteries or kitchens for cheese making, which called for space, shelving, protection from flies, odors, dirt, and sun in the summer, and washing, scouring, and scalding facili-

---

[8] New York State Cheese Manufacturers' Association: *Second Annual Report,* 1864, p. 40.

[9] *Utica Morning Herald,* May 3, 1864; *Prairie Farmer,* XV (June 24, 1865), 505.

ties. Also, few farmers were skilled cheese makers and the average quality of their product was not high.

In the early fifties farmers in Oneida County, New York, began to organize to manufacture cheese in factories. Their associations took various forms, but increasingly they became joint stock enterprises in which the stock was distributed among patrons as widely as possible. Elected trustees selected the manager and worked closely with him. Profits after all expenses, including dividends on the stock, were divided among the patrons according to the amount of milk they furnished. From the outset the factory system offered important advantages, including the most efficient equipment, savings by buying salt, bandages, boxes, and coloring matter at wholesale prices, a skilled staff, and the production of cheese of a more uniform and higher quality, which assured better prices. Such obvious benefits swept aside the natural conservatism of farmers, and between 1851 and 1860, 38 associations were organized in New York. During the war their number increased even more rapidly, reaching 454 in New York state alone. In 1864 the milk from 137,000 cows was brought regularly to these association factories, which were making about one third of the entire production of the state.[1]

At first, cooperating farmers, appreciating the burden they would slough off in transferring all responsibility for their cheese to the factories, thought little of carrying the milk daily to the factory. Soon, however, this daily trip came to be regarded as a nuisance. Then the factories sent out teams along major routes to pick up the milk. Farmers who had been feeding their hogs the whey remaining when the curds were pressed now found that they had little to feed hogs other than grain. Some factories maintained their own hogs to use the whey. In other cases the collecting teamsters brought back whey for use on the farms. Since hogs which were fed on whey from sweet milk gained well,

---

[1] H. E. Erdman: "The 'Associated Dairies' of New York as Precursors of American Agricultural Cooperatives," *Agricultural History*, XXXVI (April 1962), 82 ff.; X. A. Willard: "American Dairying; Its Rise, Progress and National Importance," in Commissioner of Agriculture, *Report*, 1865, pp. 433–4; "Extracts from the Report of the New York State Cheese Manufacturers' Association," in New York State Agricultural Society, *Transactions*, 1863, p. 197; *Census of the State of New York*, 1865, p. 402. There are major discrepancies between the state census figures and those of Willard.

the factory managers found that farmers taking the whey were more likely to bring in sweet milk. These and other minor problems of the cheese factories were more than compensated for by the one and two cents a pound premium their cheese sold for over that produced by single dairies.[2]

In the absence of clearly established standards for milk or methods of determining the amount of fat that had been skimmed from it before it was brought to the factories—or, indeed, in the absence of techniques for determining the sweetness of the milk, the managers were hard put to maintain the quality of their product. It was soon found that farmers were adding water, skimming off the cream, and palming off sour and tainted milk on the cheese factory and that there were great differences in the care with which the milk had been handled. At least half of the patrons of cheese factories were said to tamper with the milk before it reached the plant. Doubtless the temptation to water or skim the milk destined for the factories was great, for the farmers' returns were so small. In 1866, when factory cheese sold for 17¢ a pound on the average, it took almost five quarts of milk for a pound of cheese. After costs, the farmer had little more than two cents a quart. Despite the poor quality of much of the milk that was brought to the factories, their cheese brought from one to two cents a pound more than cheese made at home.[3]

England had bought small quantities of American butter and cheese before 1861 but during the war years its purchases greatly increased, taking off the market a substantial fraction of the cheese and large amounts of butter. Almost 90 per cent of the cheese and between 65 and 77 per cent of the butter going abroad went to England. Manifestly, the foreign demand for cheese and its effect on price was more responsible for the expansion of cheese making than the war. Americans have long been aware that English farmers tried to prevent the importation of beef cattle and later of "dead meat" in the seventies and eighties, but may not know the effect the intrusion of large quantities of American dairy products had on British agriculture.

---

[2] *Rural New Yorker*, XV (Feb. 6, 1864), 45.
[3] American Dairymen's Associa-

tion: *Second Annual Report*, 1866, pp. 68, 110; *Rural New Yorker*, XV (Feb. 6, 1864), 47.

EXPORTS OF BUTTER AND CHEESE

YEAR	BUTTER (POUNDS)	VALUE	CHEESE (POUNDS)	VALUE	TOTAL VALUE OF ALL EXPORTS
1855–1858 (Average)	2,871,000	$ 583,000	7,033,000	$ 695,000	
1860	7,640,914	1,144,321	15,515,799	1,565,630	$373,189,284
1861	15,531,381	2,335,985	32,361,428	3,321,631	228,699,486
1862	26,691,247	4,164,344	34,052,678	2,715,892	213,069,519
1863	35,172,415	6,733,743	42,045,054	4,216,804	305,884,988
1864	20,895,435	6,140,031	77,751,329	5,638,007	320,035,199
1865	21,388,185	7,234,173	53,089,468	11,684,927	306,306,758

SOURCE: Secretary of the Treasury, *Reports on Commerce and Navigation* for 1860–5.

English and Scotch producers of cheese were worried about the inroads American cheese was making in their markets, and they were warned that they must raise the quality of their product even more if they expected to hold their home market.[4]

In this country leading authorities in cheese marketing watched with concern the growing production of cheese which was not paralleled by an equal growth in consumption in the Northern states. It was easy for them to blame the low rate of consumption, as compared with the demand for cheese in England, on poor quality. Also, it was clear that the lower price American cheese brought in England was at least partly owing to its generally inferior quality.

Troubled by the low rate of consumption at home and the prejudice against their product abroad, and knowing that they were being victimized by the persistent action of farmers in bringing to the factories milk of poor quality which tainted the

[4] A Mr. Bowles of London expressed this warning at a meeting of the Ayrshire Agricultural Association. Willard picked up the speech and reported it to the Farmers' Club of Little Falls, and it was published in New York State Agricultural Society: *Transactions*, 1862, p. 417. A Tory lord regretted the income this sale of American cheese provided for the continuation of the Civil War and could not understand why English farmers were not able to supply all the cheese their market consumed. In his *English Farming Past and Present* (London, 1927 edition), Lord Ernle mentions American cheese glutting the English market only in the late seventies (p. 376).

LONDON PRICES OF ENGLISH AND AMERICAN
CHEESE, 1863

Cheshire per hundredweight	56 to 75 shillings
Double Gloucester	58 to 64 "
Cheddar	60 to 76 "
American	40 to 54 "

SOURCE: *Mark Lane Express* in *Genesee Farmer*, XXIV (May
1863), 142.

cheese, the elite of manufacturers met in Rome, New York, in
1864 to arrange for mutual protection. With thirty-three associated dairies and one private dairy represented, the meeting
organized itself as the New York State Cheese Manufacturers'
Association. They were following the practice of the sorghum
producers, horticulturists, wool growers, and livestock groups,
which organized local, state, and national associations to raise
standards, establish fair practices, and obtain helpful legislation.
The cheese manufacturers, who were close to the dairymen,
devoted time to discussing the adulteration and skimming of
milk and finally drafted a petition to the New York legislature
urging it to prohibit the adulteration of milk intended for the
factories.

Swifter action than usual followed. The same year the legislature enacted a measure declaring that anyone knowingly
selling to cheese factories any milk which was diluted with water
or in any way adulterated, or from which any cream had been
taken, should be fined not less than $25 or more than $100 for
each offense. One may doubt that such legislation was any more
enforceable than the measures to outlaw the sale of adulterated
and swill milk to consumers. Willard's frequently reiterated
insistence that enlightened self-interest should lead the farmers
to give greater attention to sanitation and to follow the best of
modern practices in assuring fresh and untainted milk was probably more effective in the end.[5]

It was not only the farmers who cheated in skimming milk

[5] *Rural New Yorker*, XV (Jan. 16,
30, Feb. 6, 1864), 22, 37, 45; New
York State Cheese Manufacturers'
Association: *Second Annual Report*, 1864, p. 171; Willard: *Practical Dairy Husbandry*, pp. 312 ff.

intended for the cheese factories. Some, at least, of the factory managers skimmed off a part of the fat and made it into poor butter which was said to be little better than grease. This practice made their cheese inferior. Much of the cheese brought into the Little Falls market by factory managers and farmers was found to be inferior, with almost every load containing one or two defective cheeses that were too soft, too hard and dry, made of sour milk, lacking color, mottled white and yellow, or of a dark brick color. Willard's most common comment was that it was "badly skimmed."[6]

In 1866 the New York State Cheese Manufacturers' Association was merged into the broader American Dairymen's Association, whose membership extended as far west as Wisconsin, Iowa, and Minnesota. It claimed to represent 526 factories, of which 412 were in New York, 52 in Ohio, 25 in Canada, 10 in Massachusetts, and 8 in Vermont. The association decided to establish a weekly journal in the interests of dairymen and to maintain a dairy salesroom and depot in New York City. As the English market was becoming increasingly important to cheese makers, the association listened with great interest to criticisms of American cheese and the reasons it brought low prices abroad. These were voiced by a dairyman of Herkimer County who had personally examined a number of English dairies. Among the faults he found were porousness, lack of quality or richness, and bad flavor that frequently induced nausea. He said that some of the cheese was hard, dry, and brittle, and other cheese was watery and poor in appearance. The association determined to send a representative to England to investigate the style of cheese in favor there and the best methods of making that quality.[7]

The natural selection for this task was Xerxes A. Willard, the leading authority on cheese and butter making and dairy problems, whose writings and lectures in the *Utica Weekly*

[6] *Working Farmer*, XVIII (Apr. 1, 1866), 86; *Utica Weekly Herald*, May 3, June 7, 14, 21, 1864.

[7] "Cheese and Butter Manufacture," in New York State Agricultural Society, *Transactions*, 1866, pp. 16 ff.; New York State Cheese Manufac-

turers' Association: *Second Annual Report*, 1864, p. 49; American Dairymen's Association: *Second Annual Report*, 1866, p. 57; *Rural New Yorker*, XVI (Jan. 20, 27, 1866), 22, 30.

Herald, in farm journals, and in the publications of state and national departments of agriculture had brought him to the attention of agriculturists throughout the country. During Willard's six months' trip to England in 1866, he conducted intensive examinations of dairy farming and cheese making on farms and in factories "over a large part of England, from the extreme south to the extreme north—was in Scotland, Ireland, France and Switzerland." He found widespread prejudice against American cheese, but where English consumers were not aware of what they were eating, they liked the best quality of American factory-made cheese better than the average English product. Willard commented favorably on the care with which cows were milked in England and on the cool and airy stone-floored milk rooms, which were models of neatness and cleanliness. The bad flavor of much American cheese, he declared, was owing to haste in salting, the faulty separation of whey from the curds, the use of bad milk, bad rennet from half-starved calves, and improper curing. Willard touched upon sensitive issues, including the lack of adequate controls by the factories over the quality of milk brought to them. The attention given to his elaborate study promised well for improvement in the future.[8]

Association factories soon spread into Ohio, where at first they had a somewhat uncertain career. During the war they prospered there, however, and were to be found in all the major cheese-producing counties. When Willard compiled his list of factories in 1871, he recorded 103 in Ohio, 46 in Illinois, 34 in Wisconsin, 32 in Vermont, 25 in Massachusetts, 22 in Michigan, and 946 in New York, with other states having smaller numbers. The institution had also spread to Canada, where Willard lists 35.[9]

One might compare the social effect of the cheese and butter factories with the results of the introduction of the mowing machine and the reaper, for all three greatly changed the pattern of life and work in the home and on the farm. The drudgery of cheese and butter making was one of the hardest tasks of farm women. When both products were made, as they were on many

---

[8] American Dairymen's Association: *Report,* 1866, p. 45; *Ohio Farmer,* XV (Feb. 3, 1866), 34.

[9] Willard: *Practical Dairy Husbandry,* pp. 531 ff.

small farms where the occupants tried to produce all the food used on the place, the wife might have two or three bad days a week when, in addition to all her other work, she operated the dash churn and performed most of the operations involved in cheese making. A prominent cheese maker hailed with joy the factory system which replaced "the old system of family cheese making [that] has done more to injure the health of our wives and daughters than any other cause." It did relieve the women of much hard toil, but it was usually followed by an increase in the number of cows the farm family maintained and therefore by an increase in other chores.[1]

It was in California that the largest dairy ranches of tens of thousands of acres existed and that the dairy industry reached its highest degree of specialization. Herds of 300 to 1,000 cows are mentioned in an article on dairies and dairying in California in the *Overland Monthly* in 1870. One owner of 1,000 Devon, Durham, and Jersey cows reported that they yielded 200 pounds each of butter annually. On this ranch the milk was conducted to the dairy house through pipes and the churns were driven by a steam engine.[2]

Shorthorn cattle were the most popular of all breeds, as is shown by the attention and prizes bestowed on them at the numerous county and state fairs and by the space devoted to them in the farm journals and in the publications of the state agricultural societies. They were an all-purpose animal favorably regarded by buyers for the slaughter houses and capable of producing high yields of fairly rich milk. Shorthorn oxen were large, lumbering animals too awkward for use on the steep hillside farms of New England, and there the Devon, a smaller animal, was popular. Ayrshires, with their greater and richer milk yield, were becoming more popular, and by 1863 it was possible for one observer to say that knowledgeable people regarded them as the best dairy cows. It was in Massachusetts, in the developing Boston milkshed, that the Ayrshires were best established. Jerseys and a few Guernseys had been brought in

---

[1] W. H. Comstock: "The Comparative Advantages of the Old and the New System of Cheese Manufacture," in New York State Cheese Manufacturers' Association, *Report*, 1864, p. 67.
[2] *Overland Monthly*, IV (April, 1870), 357.

from the Channel Islands, but they were thought to be ugly and lacking in form. Though they gave the richest milk they were not held in favor, save by a few dairymen who specialized in them. Herefords could scarcely be regarded as dairy animals, though one or two of their most persistent advocates did argue that they were good milkers.[3]

Dutch or Holstein cattle were practically unknown. The few Holsteins which had been imported had brought pleuropneumonia and created great alarm among dairy farmers. This did little to make the breed popular. In a widely used book on *The Diseases of Cattle,* published in 1859, George H. Dadd, a veterinary surgeon and prolific writer on animal diseases, did give the comparatively unknown Holsteins a favorable write-up emphasizing their form, size, and high milk production. On the other hand, Francis M. Rotch, one of the best-known cattlemen in New York, in a 42-page treatment of "Select Breeds of Cattle and their Adaptation to the United States" published in the report of the Department of Agriculture in 1861, devoted 14 pages to Shorthorns, 6 to Devons, 3 each to Herefords, Ayrshires, and Jerseys, and one short paragraph to Dutch or Holsteins. He said that the Holsteins are reputed to be good milkers in Holland but those which have been imported to the United States are "generally coarse, ill-proportioned animals, with hard hides, and rarely take on flesh well, and its quality is inferior at best." This brief reference and the derogatory remarks may seem strange to readers of the twentieth century, when the Holstein is supreme in most dairy regions, but they expressed the attitude of cattlemen of 1861.[4]

In view of the prevailing preference for other breeds and the contempt generally felt for the Dutch cattle, it took courage for Winthrop Chenery of Belmont, Massachusetts, a well-to-do cattle importer, to bring in from Holland a few Dutch or Holstein cattle in 1852, 1857, 1859, and 1861 with the thought that there

---

[3] *American Stock Journal,* III (Feb. 1861), 4, and V (May, October, 1863), 42, 131; Massachusetts State Board of Agriculture: *13th Annual Report,* 1865, pp. 27 ff.
[4] George H. Dadd: *Dadd on the Nature and Treatment of the Dis-* eases *of Cattle* (Boston, 1859), pp. 311 ff.; Commissioner of Agriculture: *Report,* 1861, pp. 427 ff., 466. Also see Winthrop W. Chenery: "Holstein Cattle," in Commissioner of Agriculture, *Report,* 1864, p. 161.

might be a demand for them. Furthermore, the third group was infected with pleuropneumonia and all but one had to be killed. Two years later Chenery, despite indifference and indeed hostility, imported from Holland four cows and one bull and began a new herd of black and white cattle. Careful records of one of the cows showed that for short periods, thirty days on one occasion and seven on another, she gave 28 quarts and 35 quarts daily. In a brief article in the report of the Commissioner of Agriculture for 1864, Chenery managed for the first time to present to a national audience of agricultural authorities the claims of the Holstein cattle for a position on the American dairy farm. He concluded that "they are infinitely superior to any other breed for cheese-making, or for the production of milk for family use and for the supply of city markets. . . ." It was to take long years for the Holstein cattle to make much progress in the face of an almost solid support for Shorthorns, Devons, and Ayrshires, though it is interesting to note that the editor of the Shorthorn herdbook, Lewis F. Allen, in a general treatise on farming entitled *New American Farmbook* published in 1869, could say of the Holsteins: "Their trial, as a dairy cow, has thus far been most successful, as they show all the prominent points of great milkers."[5]

That Americans needed to give more attention to improving their dairy cattle's output of milk was the view of Silas L. Loomis. He concluded that the average production of milk per cow was a mere 1,800 quarts, and maintained that cows yielding less—and many yielded as little as 1,000 quarts—were not worth milking. He thought the average should be brought up to at least 2,200 quarts, which would require breeding only from high-producing animals of good stock. He argued that the high yield of Ayrshires, for example, justified buying good stock and breeding them with the native or older combinations of part Devon and part Shorthorn. An Ohio dairyman deplored the practice of selling the calves and depending on replacements from the West and South, which generally proved to be poorer milkers. Ezra Cornell, who had built up a herd of purebred Shorthorns,

---

[5] *Working Farmer*, XV (May 1, 1863), 104; L. F. Allen: *New American Farmbook* (New York, 1869), p. 371.

in his presidential address before the New York State Agricultural Society likewise pointed out the economic advantage of improving livestock. He cited statistics to show that in Tompkins County the average annual production of butter per cow had increased from 102 pounds in 1845 to 128 in 1860; in some dairies the average yield per cow was 200 pounds.[6]

Dairy farmers needed not only to improve their livestock but to safeguard it against diseases. They were already beset by two alarming diseases, pleuropneumonia and contagious abortion, and when they were threatened with a third that was raging abroad, rinderpest, they were panic-stricken and called upon government at all levels to help by authorizing research into the causes, quarantining exposed animals and destroying diseased ones, and banning further importations.

Contagious abortion became serious as the dairy industry began to flourish in central New York. By 1860 the disease was said to be doing such great damage among the herds of Herkimer County, New York, as to cause many farmers to abandon dairying and to turn to other uses for their land. The explanations suggested for the trouble were numerous: depletion of the soil, worrying of cattle by dogs, foul air in the stables, too much salt in the diet, change of residence, sudden changes in diet, and uncertain poisons in food, to name a few. Not only did the disease mean the loss of the calf and sometimes the cow, but the cows who survived were no longer good milkers. High losses were reported and farmers began to be panicky about the spread of the disease. Local groups collected data on its incidence and distribution in the hope that information about the common background of the disease would throw light on its cause. By 1865 and 1866 abortion had become a great scourge, sweeping through herds every year. Farmers pleaded for help, asking the New York legislature to provide for the appointment and support of a botanist, a microscopist, and a pathologist to make a "thorough and systematic search into the cause of the disease and its remedies." It was in searching for remedies for such ills that farmers

---

[6] Loomis: "The Consumption of Milk," p. 210; *Country Gentleman,* XXV (Feb. 2, 1865), 79; American Dairymen's Association: *Report,* 1866, p. 118; New York State Agricultural Society: *Transactions,* 1862, XXI, 27.

came to look ever more favorably on invoking government aid in solving their problems.[7]

Although pleuropneumonia had appeared in America earlier, the first big scare concerning it came in Massachusetts in 1859. The disease quickly spread through numerous herds and threatened heavy losses to farmers. The Massachusetts legislature and the governor moved swiftly and with imagination to stamp it out by destroying diseased animals and compensating the owners. For a time it seemed conquered, but it reappeared in 1863 and 1864 in Massachusetts and spread to New York, New Jersey, Michigan, and elsewhere. Again the Bay state legislature acted, appropriating $20,000 for the destruction of diseased animals and compensation to the owners. The Maine legislature also authorized town officials to quarantine exposed cattle and to destroy those ill with pleuropneumonia. Other states sent representatives to observe how Massachusetts dealt with the disease, but were less inclined to vote funds for destroying exposed and diseased cattle. The disease appeared in the brewery and distillery stables, where it became endemic or a "permanent disease," according to Solon Robinson. High death rates in the swill stables led to efforts to innoculate the cattle, but critics found the effects of the remedy worse than the disease. A saving feature seemed to be that as the epidemic continued, pleuropneumonia became less fatal than when it first appeared. Quarantining and isolating exposed cattle were favored as the more conservative approach over destruction.[8]

In 1865 the cattle plague or rinderpest swept over Europe and into England, where it caused heavy losses until vigorous action was taken to combat it. Accounts of the losses soon appeared in American papers and agricultural interests, recalling the damage resulting from the importation of the Dutch cattle

---

[7] *Dairy Farmer*, I (May 1860, March 1861), 3, 337; *Oneida Weekly Herald*, May 8, 22, 1864; *American Agriculturist*, XXIII (April 1864), 106; *Working Farmer*, XVIII (April 1866), 87; New York State Agricultural Society; *Journal*, XVI (April 1866), 35.

[8] Massachusetts slaughtered 842 cattle at a cost of $20,432 in its effort to stamp out the disease. *House Reports*, 36 Cong., 1 Sess., June 18, 1860, no. 651; Massachusetts Board of Agriculture: *Annual Reports*, 1862–5; *New York Weekly Tribune*, June 18, 1864.

which had brought in the germs of pleuropneumonia, became greatly upset and began a campaign to ban further importation of cattle.[9] Petitions poured into Congress from practically every agricultural society in the country urging an immediate prohibition on the importation of cattle until the plague had subsided abroad. Congress moved swiftly, permitting obstructionists to make no delays, and on December 11 and 13, 1865, banned the importation of cattle as long as the plague raged abroad. When questions were raised about livestock already on the high seas and the loss buyers would sustain if they had to be returned to England, supporters of the move declared their losses would be small compared with those to be expected if diseased cattle were admitted. On March 6, 1866, Congress went further, banning the importation of hides as well as neat cattle. The President was authorized to suspend the prohibition when the danger was passed.[1]

At the same time New York State, where dairying was the main agricultural interest, took steps to check the importation and spread of the disease. A report of the state agricultural society made at the request of the legislature described the rapid advance of the disease abroad, the losses sustained, and the alert methods used to control it in England, Belgium, France, and Prussia: quarantine and immediate slaughter of suspected animals. A measure embodying their recommendations was introduced into the state Senate by Ezra Cornell. The measure, which strongly supplemented the Federal law and provided for the destruction of cattle infected with rinderpest and the disinfection of all places exposed to the disease, was quickly enacted. Rarely have American legislative bodies moved so swiftly as they did in dealing with pleuropneumonia and rinderpest.[2] When,

---

[9] *Country Gentleman,* XXVI, has numerous references to the plague in England. L. H. Bailey: *Cyclopedia of American Agriculture* (4 vols., New York, 1907–9), III, 145; A. E. Erickson: "The Cattle Plague in England, 1865–1867," *Agricultural History,* XXXV (April 1961), 94.
[1] *Cong. Globe,* 39 Cong., 1 Sess., Dec. 11, 13, 1865, pp. 20, 38; Acts of Dec. 18, 1865 and Mar. 3, 1866, 14 *U.S. Stat.,* pp. 1–4; *Sen. Misc. Doc.,* 39 Cong., 1 Sess., 1865, I, no. 98. John Wentworth and John Sherman wanted hasty action to require importers to return to Europe all cattle then on the way by ship to the U.S.
[2] *New York Senate Documents,* 1866, II, no. 79; *New York Senate Journal,* Apr. 3, 11, 1866, pp. 632,

however, the leader of the public health movement began demanding action to assure purer supplies of milk and more hygienic conditions in dairies, the farmers and their representatives were not ready to support measures that would subject them to regulation.[3]

828; *New York Assembly Journal,* Apr. 18, 1866, p. 1654; *Country Gentleman,* XXVII (Apr. 12, 1866), 241.

[3] Brunger: "Changes in the New York State Dairying Industry," *passim;* Eric Lampard: *The Rise of the Dairy Industry in Wisconsin* (Madison Wis., 1963).

9

Farm Labor and Machinery

D URING THE 1850's agricultural expansion proceeded so rapidly in the United States that it dwarfed anything previously
seen in this country and probably in the world. In fact the growth
of agriculture outdistanced the growth of population, for whereas
the acreage in improved land increased by 44 per cent, population increased only 35 per cent.[1] The increased production of
staple crops in the fifties is as notable as the increase in improved acreage. Almost 600,000 new farms containing 114,000,-
000 acres were created and 50,000,000 acres were "improved,"
that is, cleared if forested, fenced, partly broken, and made a
part of operating farms with farm residences. This expansion
was made possible by a cycle of good years and favorable farm
prices, which were the result of Old World demand, an unparalleled flow of immigration from Europe, a reasonably liberal
public land system that provided for easy acquisition of government land at low prices, and the first great period of railroad
construction, which spread a network of steam lines through
Ohio, Indiana, Illinois, and Missouri and through Alabama and
Mississippi.

The Prairie state of Illinois led in the creation of new farms,
adding 67,000 and increasing its improved acres from 5,000,000

---

[1] Unless otherwise indicated, the
statistics in this chapter are from
the *Eighth Census of the United
States, 1860, Agriculture.*

to 13,000,000. Next came Indiana with 38,000 new farms and 3,200,000 additional improved acres, and Wisconsin with 49,000 new farms and 2,700,000 additional improved acres. Other states where much new land was improved were, in order of size of increases, Missouri, Iowa, Ohio, and California. These seven states of the Mississippi Valley together with California contained over half of the additional area brought into farms in the fifties. At the same time farmers in the original thirteen states were clearing and fencing additional land and creating new farms. Most outstanding in this respect were the premier agricultural commonwealths of New York and Pennsylvania, where, respectively, 26,369 and 28,780 new farms were created and 1,949,000 and 1,839,000 additional acres were improved.

The increased production of staple crops in the fifties is as notable as the increase in improved acreage. Cotton and tobacco crops increased more than 100 per cent while the wheat crop increased by 72 per cent. Like most farm crops, wheat was attacked by parasites and diseases, such as the midge, the chinch bug, the fly, rust, and smut, and the total yield of the country ranged widely from year to year. Drought, too much rain at the wrong time, or unseasonable frosts seemed to strike some portions of the major wheat-producing areas each year, but usually these misfortunes would be canceled out in the national crop by ideal weather in other areas. On the other hand, once in a decade or two a series of fortuitous circumstances or an equally unfortunate combination of bad weather might produce either a bumper crop or a disastrously small one. In 1859 crop conditions were favorable and the yield was good. Exports were small, and though the South bought grain and flour heavily, there was a large carryover.

Weather conditions throughout most of the North, save in Kansas, were near ideal for wheat growing in 1860. The wheat crop was reported to be "miraculous" and "wonderful" in Wisconsin and Minnesota, fully equal to 30 bushels to the acre, and the "best ever" in a part of Indiana. "A big river of produce to be poured through your tunnel for the next four months," said a commentator of the tremendous flow of wheat that would shortly be moving through Chicago. An Iowa reporter said that the farmers of Cerro Gordo County were sending off large quantities of grain to market and on their return were boasting of having "something besides rusty nails jingling in their pockets." These reports, in comparison with the usual lugubrious accounts of drought, excessive rain, unwanted cool or hot weather, early frosts, and damage by rust, smut, and chinch bugs, reveal how happy all were at the bumper crop. In the three states of Ohio, Wisconsin, and Minnesota, for which there are estimates of wheat production in 1860, the increase over the crop of 1859 amounted to 27,000,000 bushels, or 66 per cent. Though the South continued to draw upon Northern wheat as long as the Mississippi remained open, it could not absorb this large surplus, nor could the rest of the country.[2]

Poor crops in Great Britain and France saved the day for the American wheat farmer. The bumper crop of 1860, the smaller but more than sufficient crop of 1861, and the carryover from 1859 permitted large exports to these countries at a time when they were forced to go into the world market for much of their wheat and flour. Some historians have maintained that their dependence on American wheat and flour accounts for the refusal of both England and France to recognize the Confederacy. The point to be made here is that the crop of 1860, which was being drawn upon by the British in 1861, was not the result of any large expansion of the area seeded to wheat, but was owing to the combination of near-ideal weather and slight damage from disease and parasites. It was fortunate for the wheat farmers of the West that England needed American wheat, for Southern purchases, which had amounted to 10,000,000 bushels annually, ceased with the closing of the Mississippi. The states of the upper Mississippi Valley were hard hit by the loss of this market, by the failure of many banks whose circulation was based on Southern state bonds that now appeared worthless, and, for a time, by an almost complete stoppage of trade and commerce.[3]

---

[2] *Minnesota Farmer and Gardener,* I (December 1860), 54, 70; *Country Gentleman,* XVI (Aug. 9, 16, 30, Oct. 25, Nov. 15, 1860), 100, 116, 148, 273, 324; Iowa State Agricultural Society: *Seventh Annual Report,* 1860, pp. 348, 355.

[3] L. B. Schmidt: "The Influence of Wheat and Cotton on Anglo-American Relations during the Civil War," *Iowa Journal of History and Politics,* XVI (July 1918), 400 ff. Cf. F. L. Owsley: *King Cotton Diplomacy* (Chicago, 1959), *passim.*

In the midst of their distress, Western farmers could take hope from the review of the British corn trade for 1860 in the *Mark Lane Express,* which estimated that Great Britain would need 24,000,000 bushels of American wheat in the current season. In fact the exports to Great Britain for the fiscal year ending June 30, 1861, amounted to 24,510,961 bushels. In addition Great Britain took 2,429,117 barrels of flour, which were equal to 10,900,000 bushels of wheat. Doubtless most if not all of the 4,000,000 bushels of wheat that were shipped to Canada were also ultimately destined for Great Britain. Shipments to other countries as well brought the total amount of American wheat that went abroad in this year marked by the opening of the Civil War to the equivalent of 50,000,000 bushels, as compared with exports of 16,000,000 bushels in 1860. Furthermore, the average price of the wheat exported in 1861 was $1.23 as compared with 98¢ in 1860. The importance of this overseas demand for American wheat and flour in preventing a catastrophic drop in prices is demonstrated by the fact that even with the sale of 50,000,000 bushels there remained a "large surplus" from the crop of 1860 which carried over well beyond the harvesting and threshing of both winter and spring wheat crops of 1861.[4]

It was well that there was such a carryover, for the winter and spring wheat harvests of 1861 did not come up to those of the previous year. In Wisconsin the average yield per acre fell by nearly one half, resulting in a decline in the state's total production of nearly 14,000,000 bushels. Ohio produced 3,600,000 bushels less in 1861 than in 1860. Minnesota's yield was about a million bushels less. Only Illinois of the Western producing states did well. With some 100,000 acres less planted in the grain than in the previous year, its yield showed a decline of only 1,200,000 bushels. But nowhere was it possible to boast of a bumper crop comparable to that of 1860. Equally fortunate for American farmers and, indeed, for the American economy, was the continued ill success of English farmers and the "very mediocre" wheat crop of France. The foreign demand for wheat

---

[4] *Mark Lane Express* in *Country Gentleman,* XVI (Oct. 18, 1860), 256, and XVIII (Sept. 12, Oct. 10, 1861), 176, 244; Secretary of the Treasury: *Commerce and Navigation of the United States,* 1861, p. 48.

and flour led to the export of 37,280,572 bushels of wheat and 4,882,033 barrels of flour, or the equivalent of 58,000,000 bushels altogether, in the fiscal year ending June 30, 1862.[5]

Another fine crop of wheat in 1862, when England and France were still drawing heavily upon the United States for breadstuffs, greatly benefited the North, regardless of any influence it may or may not have had on American-British and -French relations. The estimated yield was 191,000,000 bushels, or 22,-000,000 more than both North and South produced in 1859. It was this huge increase which again made possible large exports of wheat and flour, amounting to an equivalent of 56,000,000 bushels in 1862–3 notwithstanding the heavy demands of the army and the destruction of food supplies caused by military operations. Foreign purchasing of American wheat and flour continued at a high rate through the fiscal year 1863–4, amounting to 23,681,712 bushels of wheat and 3,557,347 barrels of flour. Thereafter they subsided for a time to the prewar level. In the four years 1861–4, an equivalent of 203,000,000 bushels of wheat having a value of $265,000,000 had been exported.[6]

Europe's need for American ham, bacon, pork, and lard during the war was second only to its need for American wheat and flour. If we convert the meat products shipped abroad into corn needed to produce them, we find that between 37,000,000 and 66,000,000 bushels of corn were thus being used in 1862–4 to satisfy the European demand. Corn and meat products accounted for one tenth to one fourth of the total value of exports in the war years. Never before had Europe made such heavy drafts upon American foodstuffs and perhaps never had such drafts been so helpful to American interests. It was strange that the South had expected to influence English and French policy by its control of cotton, whereas it was the North that profited

---

[5] Illinois State Agricultural Society: *Transactions*, V, (1861–4), p. 28; J. G. Thompson: *Rise and Decline of the Wheat Growing Industry in Wisconsin*, p. 196; London *Agricultural Gazette*, Aug. 17, 1861, and Paris *Journal of Practical Agriculture*, Aug. 20, 1861, as quoted in *Country Gen-*

tleman, XVIII (September 1861), 176.
[6] The data on production of wheat are from the U.S. Commissioner of Agriculture: *Reports*, 1862–4, the Ohio State Board of Agriculture: *Reports*, 1862–4, and the Illinois State Agricultural Society: *Transactions*, 1861–4.

EXPORTS OF MAJOR FARM PRODUCTS, 1860–5

YEAR	HAM AND BACON (POUNDS)	PORK (POUNDS)	LARD (POUNDS)	CORN (BUSHELS)	CORN MEAL (BARRELS)	WHEAT (BUSHELS)	WHEAT FLOUR (BARRELS)
1860	25,844,610	204,551	40,289,519	3,314,155	233,709	4,155,153	2,611,503
1861	50,264,267	156,487	47,908,911	10,678,244	203,313	31,238,057	4,323,756
1862	141,212,786	309,102	118,573,307	18,904,898	253,570	37,289,572	4,882,033
1863	218,243,609	328,852	155,536,596	16,119,476	257,948	36,160,414	4,390,055
1864	110,886,446	317,597	97,190,765	4,096,694	262,357	23,681,712	3,557,347
1865	45,990,712	218,551	44,342,295	2,812,726	199,419	9,937,876	2,641,298

TOTAL VALUE OF EXPORTS OF PORK, BEEF, CORN, AND WHEAT PRODUCTS

1860	$28,458,558
1861	83,405,566
1862	108,565,722
1863	127,660,780
1864	94,159,130
1865	81,548,290

SOURCE: *Monthly Summary of Commerce and Finance*, VIII–XII (1899–1900), 2022, and the annual report of the Secretary of the Treasury, *Commerce and Navigation of the United States*, 1861–5.

so greatly by European demand for its wheat, corn, and meat products.

Corn, on which the welfare of Northern livestock depended, yielded well in the critical early days of the war. The excellent growing conditions in 1860 which had brought forth a bountiful harvest of wheat produced also an enormous crop of corn. Ohio, the only state for which we have reliable statistics, showed a 32 per cent increase over the good crop of 1859. There was a considerable increase in the exports of corn and corn meal in 1861 and 1862, but the amount was much less than the increased production and less, too, than the amount the South had customarily taken. Consequently, there was a big carryover into 1862 and, indeed, for the remainder of the war there was a large surplus of corn from one year to the next, except in 1863. The crops of 1861 and 1862 were both good, judging by the yields in Ohio and Illinois and the estimates of the U.S. Department of Agriculture. Only in 1863, when a late August frost hit the corn belt, was there a drastic reduction in the yield of corn, with government estimates showing a decline from the previous year of 26 to 35 per cent. The crop of 1864 was normal and that of 1865 was excellent.

New farms were being created during the war and the proportion of improved land in farms increased, although the growth was naturally smaller than what had occurred in the fifties. Even in New York 19,263 new farms were established in the sixties, but it was in the Middle West and California that the most marked growth occurred. Seven states of the upper Mississippi Valley added 258,466 farms, probably by far the larger portion after 1865. Some of these new farms and the additional improved acreage dated from the war years, however.

Estimates of acreages in grain and of the total acreage in crops prepared by the U.S. Commissioner of Agriculture for the six states of Ohio, Indiana, Illinois, Wisconsin, Michigan, and Iowa show an increase of 2,659,000 acres in all grains between 1862 and 1864. The land in oats, chiefly fed to horses, fell by 470,000 acres in Illinois, Indiana, Ohio, and Michigan between 1862 and 1864, according to these estimates. In the six states, the acreage in wheat and corn increased by 2,715,179 acres or 12 per cent, whereas the acreage in oats declined by 239,786 acres or 8 per cent. Expansion of the area in cultivation to grain, and substitution of wheat and corn for oats, help to explain the ability of the North to sustain itself and its army and to provide the large exports, not only of wheat and wheat flour but also of pork products, corn, and dairy products. The most important factor, however, was probably that, except for the corn crop of 1863, the crops of 1860–5 were good.

The five states of the "Old Northwest" with a population of 6,825,000 are said to have provided 1,000,000 soldiers, or 14 per cent of their population and 21 per cent of the total number of men serving in the Union army. The number who served for more than two weeks must be substantially discounted because of re-enlistments. If we eliminate some of the inflation and reduce the balance to three-year enlistments, we still have some 680,000 men in the army from these five states for most of the war, or one out of ten of the entire population. Approximately one half of the farm families must have provided men for the army. It is possible that army life attracted a larger portion of these states' 231,000 farm laborers, who, with smaller resources, fewer dependents, and less to tie them down, were more mobile than the 822,000 farmers; but the loss of a farm laborer was almost as serious a matter as the loss of a farmer.[7]

Second-generation farmers, having brought their land to a fairly high state of cultivation so that they were producing small surpluses of hogs, cattle, wheat, hay, fruit, vegetables, poultry, or eggs, might be fortunate enough to have sons on whom they could rely during the rush seasons when the hay and wheat had

---

[7] F. C. Bald: *Michigan in Four Centuries* (New York, 1954), p. 275; W. F. Raney: *Wisconsin* (New York, 1940), p. 164; A. C. Cole: *Era of the Civil War* (vol. III, *Centennial History of Illinois*, Springfield, 1919), p. 276; J. H. Levering: *Historic Indiana* (New York, 1909), p. 297; E. H. Roseboom: *The Civil War Era* (vol. IV, *History of the State of Ohio*, Columbus, 1944), p. 440; T. L. Livermore: *Numbers & Losses in the Civil War in America, 1861–65* (Bloomington, Ind., 1957), p.

1. Statistics of farmers and farm laborers are found in *Eighth Census of the United States, 1860, Population*, p. 662. Roseboom: *The Civil War Era*, p. 83, says that from one fourth to one third of the farm laborers of Ohio were in military service by 1863. There is much information on wages paid farm laborers in each state and the cost of cutting and stacking wheat and hay in 1866 in *Monthly Report of the Agricultural Department*, January 1867, pp. 4 ff.

to be harvested, the maple syrup made, or the supply of fuel wood prepared. But the sons grew up and went off to farm for themselves, leaving a gap that had to be filled unless the farming was to be contracted. Farmers who either lost or lacked sons employed hired hands during rush seasons; others found it necessary and profitable to employ labor the year round. Farm labor was then of two kinds, the one temporary and migratory, moving from farm to farm or from farm to town for employment, the other permanent, being employed throughout the year on the larger, better-financed and more successful farms.

Less is known about farm laborers than any other element in agriculture because, except for those who served as laborers only temporarily, they left few letters, no diaries, and no auto-biographies. That the New England farm laborer in the Civil War was very different from the hands who had worked on farms a generation earlier is attested by Donald Grant Mitchell, who wrote about farming in Connecticut from personal experience.

> There lived some twenty or thirty years ago in New England, a race of men, American born, and who, having gone through a two winters' course of district school ciphering and reading, with cropped tow heads, became the most indefatigable and ingenious of farm workers. Their hoeing was a sleight of hand; they could make an ox yoke, or an ax helve on rainy days; by adroit manipulation, they could relieve a choking cow, or as deftly, hive a swarm of bees. Their furrows indeed were not of the straightest, but their control of a long team of oxen was a miracle of guidance. . . . They certainly did not waste time at lavations; but as farm workers they had rare aptitude; no tool came amiss to them; they cradled; they churned, if need were; they chopped and piled their three cords of wood between sun and sun. . . . Rarest of all which they possessed, was an acuteness of understanding, which enabled them to comprehend an order before it was half uttered, and to meet occasional and unforseen difficulties, with a steady assurance, as if they had been an accepted part of the problem.

On the other hand, Mitchell wrote, the Irishman

> . . . balks at the first turn; he must have a multitude of chains; he needs a boy to aid him with the team, and another to carry a bar; he spends an hour in his doubtful

estimate of dimensions; but "begorra, its a lumpish tree," and he thwacks into the rind a foot or two from the ground, so as to leave a "nate" Irish stump. Half through the bole, he begins to doubt if it be indeed a chestnut or a poplar; and casting his eye aloft to measure it anew, an ancient woodpecker drops something smarting in his eye; and his howl starts the ruminating team into a confused entanglement among the young wood. Having eased his pain, and extricated his cattle, he pushes on with his axe, and presently, with a light crash of pliant boughs, his timber is lodged in the top of an adjoining tree. He tugs, and strains, and swears, and splits the helve of his axe in adapting it for a lever, and presently, near to noon, comes back for three or four hands to give him a boost with the tree. You return—to find the team strayed through a gate left open, into a thriving cornfield, and one of your pet tulip trees lodged in a lithe young hickory.

These and other such replace the New-Englander born, who long ago was paid off, wrapped his savings in a dingy piece of sheepskin, scratched his head reflectingly, and disappeared from the stage. He has become the father of a race that is hewing its way in Oregon, or he is a dignitary in Wisconsin, or thwacking terribly among the foremost fighters of the war.

Doubtless the picture of the earlier generation of farm laborers is somewhat overdrawn and that of the Irish hand is a reflection of the prejudice of the time. In older areas farm labor was more stable than in the West, the turnover was less, and the hands became habituated to their tasks. Mitchell maintained a tenant house for the family of his principal laborer on his large 200-acre farm, later increased to 360 acres, and he employed other hands. His instructions to his tenant in 1860 reveal a greater respect for him than is shown in the quotation.[8]

Labor scarcity was no new thing for the West. There were always men of means, bonanza farmers, and absentees, who wanted to develop their land, not as the actual pioneer did, by devoting a lifetime to the task, but within a year or two through the employment of others. Labor was also needed to build canals, railroads, and the new towns and cities springing up on the

[8] Donald Grant Mitchell: *My Farm of Edgewood: A Country Book* (New York, 1863), pp. 74 ff.; W. H. Dunn: *The Life of Donald G. Mitchell* (New York, 1922), pp. 282, 324.

frontier. These jobs were taken by immigrants coming in from the older states and from Europe who had spent all their funds in getting to the West and needed to earn a stake before starting for themselves. Thus everywhere in newly developing areas there were employers and employees, but the employee class was unstable since its members waited only for the day when they could strike out on their own. In 1860 when the census officials found 31,472 farm laborers in Wisconsin, or one each for 45 per cent of the farms, farmers were having the greatest difficulty recruiting sufficient hands to harvest, thresh, and market the bumper wheat crop of that year. Wages of $2 to $3 a day were being paid and still the number of workers was insufficient.[9]

Enlistment and the draft took many farmers and their sons away from agriculture, but not to the degree that conscription swept Southern farmers into the army. Overage men, those who could not pass the physical examinations of the army, others who had served and were discharged, aliens, and new immigrants, together with farmers' wives, constituted the labor force which was to carry on.

Neither the reaper nor the mower were new labor-saving devices suddenly called forth in response to the scarcity and high cost of labor during the war. It was estimated that by 1858 there were 73,000 reapers and mowers (many of the machines were designed for cutting both grain and grass) in the West, and that 70 per cent of the wheat in that section was cut by machine. Farmers in the East, particularly in New England, where wheat fields were small and hayfields rough and stony, were more cautious about introducing new machines, and the cradle was used on small fields somewhat longer than in the West. In New York there were at least twenty-two companies producing machines, which sold mostly in Pennsylvania, New York, and Ohio, and by the outbreak of war there may have been 15,000 or 20,000 on farms east of the Alleghenies.[1] The war years gave a tremen-

---

[9] *Country Gentleman*, XVI, (Aug. 16, 23, Dec. 6, 1860), 113, 129, 372.
[1] Leo Rogin: *The Introduction of Farm Machinery in Its Relations to the Productivity of Labor in the Agriculture of the United States during the Nineteenth Century* (Berkeley, Calif., 1931), pp. 72 ff.; W. T. Hutchinson: *Cyrus Hall McCormick, I, Seed Time, 1809–1856* (New York, 1930), *passim*.

dous impetus to the farm machinery business, as is shown by the sales figures for reapers and mowers: 1862—33,000; 1863—40,000; 1864 and 1865—each 80,000. By 1864 there were 250,-000 reapers and mowers in use in the North, or enough to provide three fourths of all farms over 100 acres with a machine.[2]

Reapers, whether McCormick, Hussey, Manny, Atkins, or one of the many other makes, with their reel, power takeoff and gears, hinged cutter bar that could be raised when necessary, and self-raking or hand-raking devices, were not complex machines, but it was frequently necessary to replace broken parts. Dealers interested primarily in the commissions they made on the sale of new reapers seem not to have stocked sufficient spare parts and were flooded with complaints when machines broke down and parts were locally unavailable. Farmers, delayed in harvesting, threatened never to buy another Kirby or Manny machine because some of their parts were too frail and impossible to replace when needed. They also complained that no one machine had all the useful features and urged that some combination of manufacturers be established that would bring the best points together in one reaper. Their complaints about the price of the McCormick reapers and the high profits made in their manufacture and sale doubtless had some share in the decision of the commissioner of the Patent Office not to extend certain McCormick patents in 1861.[3]

Reapers freed the farmers of the backbreaking labor of cradling the grain and made it possible to harvest the crop at the appropriate time, whereas with cradling it had been necessary to start cutting early or risk losing part of the grain from shattering on the ground. The reaper, combined with other equip-

---

[2] *Utica Morning Herald* in New York State Agricultural Society: *Journal*, XVI (1866), 67. Of the 125,000 machines in use in 1861, perhaps 80,000 had been constructed in the five previous years. The jump from 16,000 machines sold annually in these five years to 58,000 sold annually between 1862 and 1865 can scarcely be regarded as small. Cf. T. C. Cochran: "Did the Civil War Retard Industrialization," *Mississippi Val-*

ley Historical Review, XLVIII (September 1961), 202. Sales figures on mowers and reapers for a number of the principal manufacturers are found in *Eighth Census of the United States, 1860, Agriculture*, p. xxii.

[3] Out of $3,923,800 received from the sale of machines and parts, McCormick's profit was $1,351,596. *New York Tribune*, Nov. 19, 1861; *Prairie Farmer*, XIV (Aug. 6, 20, 1864), 83, 113.

ment, also enabled farmers to sow larger acreages. Two men with a hand-rake reaper or one man with a self-rake reaper could cut 10 acres of wheat, whereas it took five cradlers to cut the same area in a day. Each reaper was followed by two to four binders and each cradler by one. Cutting with a reaper and binding therefore required from three to six men and a horse, while cutting with cradles and binding required ten men. Another estimate is that a ten-man crew harvesting with a reaper could cut, bind, stack, and house the wheat of 10 or 12 acres a day, or as much as 200 acres in a season, which, without the reaper, would require fifteen men.[4]

General adoption of the reaper furthered the transition from part-subsistence to commercial agriculture, made farmers more dependent on a market economy, and encouraged them to enlarge their operations. Reapers cost $130. With credit extended by the better-financed producers or the new national banks, farmers could buy at this price knowing that one good wheat crop and fair prices might make it possible to discharge their debt. But most of all, the reaper enabled the farmer, if he was beyond draft age, not only to get along without the aid of his son who was in the army, but to enlarge the acreage he sowed and the volume of wheat he produced. It was a factor of major importance in making possible the high rate of production of wheat at a critical time when it was much needed. The *Minnesota Farmer*, in commenting on the excellent wheat crop of 1861 and the scarcity of help and high wages, said that "the addition of one thousand reapers to the already large cutting force, has materially helped to make harvest comparatively easy and of short duration."[5]

---

[4] Rogin: *Introduction of Farm Machinery*, pp. 126 ff.; Commissioner of Patents: *Report*, 1863, p. 13.
[5] *Minnesota Farmer* in *Country Gentleman*, XVIII (Sept. 26, 1861), 212; M. E. Jarchow: *The Earth Brought forth. A History of Minnesota Agriculture to 1865* (St. Paul, 1949), pp. 131 ff. Mitchell wrote in *My Farm of Edge-* *wood*, p. 78: "The tendency is now, . . . to centralize attention upon that line of cropping which is best suited to the land; this limits the range of labor, while the improved mechanical appliances fill a thousand wants, which were once only to be met by a dexterous handicraft at home."

In New England and northern New York, where from three fourths to four fifths of the cultivated land was in hay, it was mowing machines that were most helpful in replacing the labor of men gone off to war.[6] Whether they were reapers with the reel, platform, and self-raking device removed, or machines built solely for mowing grass, they were in such great demand throughout the war that frequently the plants producing them could not keep up with the orders. The lighter one-wheel mowers drawn by a single horse sold from $70 to $80 while the heavier two-wheel machines drawn by two horses and cutting a wider swath sold for $85 to $120. Best known of the makes were Ketchum, Manny, Buckeye, and Wood. Henry F. French, later president of the Massachusetts Agricultural College, declared after extensive travels in New England that almost every respectable farm had a mower in 1862. A little later he wrote that their use had increased tenfold as a result of labor scarcity. "Many farmers who keep but a single horse, find him worth a half dozen men, at what used to be the hand-work of mowing. . . . While the war has prevented extensive and permanent improvements upon the farm, it has . . . greatly hastened the introduction of useful machines, and of useful processes in farm labor."[7] An upstate New York farmer rejoiced that the mower had displaced the man-killing scythe, for with it and the horse-drawn rake the farmer was able to "command more leisure" for "pic-nics and parties, for berrying and visiting." The more common experience was that machines and improvements in agricultural techniques resulted in the farmers' increasing their acreage in cash grain or enlarging their herds of cattle, sheep, or hogs.[8]

Reapers and mowers could speed up the cutting of grain and hay, but to take full advantage of the enlarged operation they made possible, improvements were needed in plows, harrows,

---

[6] The ratio of the acreage in hay to the total acreage in crops may be seen in the estimates of land in crops in the *Reports* of the Commissioner of Agriculture for 1862–5.
[7] *New England Farmer*, XIII (July, August, 1861), 301, 352, 359; *Cultivator*, X (October 1862), 318; *Country Gentleman*, XXIII (Jan. 21, 1864), 41.
[8] *Rural New Yorker*, XII (Aug. 31, 1861), 278. This is an extremely rare statement of the existence of leisure time for such frivolities.

threshers, grain separators, drills, horse rakes, hay presses, sweep power mills and treadmills, and field rollers and crushers. The mechanical ingenuity of Americans is shown in their efforts to improve their agricultural machinery at a time when it was most needed. Agricultural societies offered generous prizes for improved machines and state fairs vied with each other in displays of new implements. The Illinois Central Railroad, which had large areas of prairie land useful at the time only for its grass, offered prizes of $250 each for a practical ditching machine and a corn cutter and stacker. These inducements, plus the demand for any device that would save labor, the prospect of rewards from royalties on improvements, and the examples of the successful Cyrus McCormick, J. I. Case, and John Deere implement companies, encouraged the tinkerers and inventers to experiment with "a great variety of improvements . . . in various farming implements and tools." The volume of patent applications increased from 5,038 in 1862 to 10,664 in 1865. A great number of these were directed "to the reduction and ease of manual labor, as well as a more perfect result and a richer reward," as the commissioner of patents quaintly put it. Among the patents sought in 1861 were 51 improvements for cultivators, 70 for harvesting implements, 26 for corn planters, 45 for seeding machines, and 19 for threshing machines.[9]

Next to the mower, the horse rake was the most important machine for increasing the efficiency of haying operations. Some early horse rakes were very crude and clumsy, but by 1861 there were light, well-made sulky rakes with removable curved spring teeth of steel that would rake the hay in windrows. In New England the horse-drawn hay tedder or kicker shook up the hay on the field and made speedier drying possible. Commonly the hay was drawn to the barn, where, with block and tackle to ride on carrier tracks under the ridgepole and a harpoonlike hayfork pulled by a horse, the load could be stored away in the mow in a

---

[9] *Prairie Farmer*, XI (Apr. 4, 1863), 216; Commissioner of Patents: *Report*, 1865, pp. 3, 14. The number of applications for patents on agricultural devices, exclusive of beehives and horse forks and rakes, increased from 350 in 1861 to 502 in 1863. See also *American Agriculturist*, XXI (November 1862), 326.

few minutes. Beater presses for compressing hay into bales for shipment were also improved.[1]

Hundreds of patents had been taken out on improvements for the plow—41 in 1861—and many more were to come. During the war progress was made in the use of cast-steel moldboards with German steel shares, and experiments were carried out with gang and sulky plows, subsoil plows, and straight draft plows. Huge, cumbersome breaking plows hauled by many oxen were still used for breaking the prairie sod, and big ditching plows were used for draining, but otherwise the plows were fairly light and efficient. A common two-horse plow without a wheel or extra point sold for $11.50. To eliminate excessive competition, seventeen farm machinery manufacturers established a schedule of prices for plows and parts in 1865 to which they agreed to adhere.[2] Great progress, too, was made in improving cultivators. The new two-horse cultivator covered twice as much acreage as the older double-shovel cultivator and, according to one authority on farming with machines, revolutionized the raising of corn.[3]

Wheat threshing took much labor, whether it was performed by the flail, which New England farmers still found cheaper to use for their small harvests, or by a crew of men with a threshing machine and horse-powered sweep mill or treadmill. The threshing machine of the war period, with separator and winnower, shelled the grain from the heads, separated it from the straw, and winnowed it from the chaff. The best-known and most commonly used, a Pitt thresher, which had a two-horse-powered treadmill or sweep power using four to ten horses, was too expensive for the average farmer to own, and migratory threshing outfits contracted to do the work on a toll basis, moving from farm to farm. Steam power had obvious advantages over horsepower and as the threshers became heavier and required greater power,

---

[1] *New England Farmer*, XIII (July, November, 1861), 336. For pictures of horse rakes see Ohio State Board of Agriculture: *Eighteenth Annual Report*, 1863, and *Twentieth Annual Report*, 1865; Clarence Danhof: "Gathering the Grass," *Agricultural History*, XXX (October 1956), 169; *Genesee Farmer*, XXV (October 1864), 301.
[2] *Rural New Yorker*, XVI (Apr. 8, 1864), 110.
[3] M. L. Dunlap: "Agricultural Machinery," in Commissioner of Agriculture, *Report*, 1863, p. 424.

steam threshers were introduced, though they were not common until well into the eighties.[4]

Prior to the war grain drills had not been made efficient, nor were they in general use; but, as with all promising labor-saving devices that were not too expensive, they were then widely adapted and improved. The advantages of drilling grain over broadcast sowing were that one fourth less seed was required, drilling could be done on windy days, and the seed rooted better, had better protection from drought and chinch bugs, and, being sown evenly at the same depth, ripened all at the same time. On the other hand, drilling required that the soil be better prepared. There remained some skepticism about the use of drills, but Isaac Newton, Commissioner of Agriculture, announced that the testimony of his many reporters was almost unanimous in favor of drilling. A two-horse corn planter costing from $35 to $46 which dropped the seed in two rows at a time did much, said the committee on agricultural implements of the Illinois State Agricultural Society, "to cheapen the growing of corn by substituting animal for hand labor." The drill was in extensive use by 1863.[5]

Other developments in agricultural machinery included improvements in and experiments with a portable steam engine, a potato planter and digger, a clover and grass seed harvester, sugar cane mill, corn huskers and shellers, butter worker, cheese press, dynamometer to test the draft of farm machines, self-regulating windmill, stump extractor, and smut machine. *The Working Farmer* of June 1, 1861, even contains a sketch of a milking machine operated by a hand pump.

By the close of the war most farms of any size possessed one or more of the new machines, which had become essential if production was to be maintained. The new improved implements had made some of the farmer's hardest tasks easier, had made him less dependent on hired labor, and had enabled him to

---

[4] *Rural New Yorker*, XIII (Feb. 22, 1862), 62; R. M. Wik: *Steam Power on the American Farm* (Philadelphia, 1953), pp. 16 ff.; *Minnesota Farmer and Gardener*, November 1960, back page.
[5] *Prairie Farmer*, VII (Apr. 11, 1861), 233; U.S. Department of Agriculture: *Bi-Monthly Report*, October 1864, p. 11; Ohio State Board of Agriculture: *Sixteenth Annual Report*, 1861, p. lix; Illinois State Agricultural Society: *Transactions*, 1861–4, p. 258.

manage larger acreages in grain and hay, but they had also increased the capital cost of farm making. It was no longer feasible for a person without capital to create a farm on the prairie, and it was becoming more difficult for a man to rise from laborer through tenant to owner.

In the two mid-century decades the manufacture of farm machinery became a major industry with a growing market both at home and abroad. At Chicago, Racine, Moline, Rockford, Milwaukee, Geneva, and elsewhere agricultural machines were being produced on a large scale and could therefore be offered at moderate prices, save where patent rights permitted a monopoly. Indeed, it appeared that American plows, reapers, mowers, and other implements were driving competitors out of the important European, British colonial, and Indian markets because of their technical proficiency and low cost. Statistics on the value of exports of agricultural implements first appear in the annual volume of *Commerce and Navigation* in 1864, when they reached $611,152. In 1865 they were higher than they were to rise again for many years to come: $1,385,000.

Mowers and reapers took the lead in the rapidly expanding production of agricultural tools and machines, though plows, harrows, and cultivators, as well as threshers and horse powers, were not far behind. In 1860, 73 plants with a total capitalization of $2,039,000 turned out machines worth $3,516,000. Four years later it was stated that 187 reaper and mower plants employing 60,000 men produced machines worth $15,000,000. It is startling to find that in 1870, when 100,000 reapers and mowers were manufactured, 103,643 grain cradles and 881,244 scythes were also produced. Other farm implements produced in 1870 include: corn shellers, 12,941; cultivators, 88,740; grain drills, 32,033; horse rakes, 80,819; plows, 864,947; and threshers, 22,931. The 300 per cent increase in the amount of capital invested in the manufacture of farm machinery, and the 359 per cent increase in the value of the products, are astonishing for a decade marked by one of the world's most destructive wars.[6]

---

[6] W. T. Hutchinson: *Cyrus Hall McCormick*, II, *Harvest, 1856–1884* (New York, 1935), p. 97 n.; *Mark Lane Express* in New York State Agricultural Society: *Jour-* nal XII (December–January 1861–2); *Eight Census of the United States, 1860, Manufacturers*, p. 733.

MANUFACTURE OF FARM IMPLEMENTS

	1850	1860	1870
Capital invested	$3,564,000	$11,477,000	$34,834,000
Value of products	6,842,000	17,487,000	52,066,000
Number of employees	7,220	14,814	25,249

SOURCE: *Ninth Census of the United States*, 1870, III, *Industry and Wealth*, 588–9.

Farmers had long been urged by farm leaders to maintain soil quality by spreading over their land the animal manures accumulating around their barns, and the better and more scientifically inclined farmers doubtless did so. Continued soil deterioration and declining production in the tobacco fields of Virginia led to experiments with the application of gypsum, marl, lime, wood ashes, compost, and night soil, and, in the forties, to the introduction of guano from Pacific islands off the coast of South America. All these produced favorable results—especially guano, but it was expensive. By the fifties fertilizers composed of various combinations of ground bone, phosphate, lime, guano, ammonia, night soil, and sand were being produced in numerous establishments and widely advertised in the farm journals under elaborate names such as Ammoniated Super Phosphate of Lime or Manipulated Phospho-Peruvian Guano. Seed houses, which had long maintained close relations with agricultural papers, now added fertilizers to their business and their increased advertising had a considerable effect on the flourishing character of the agricultural press. The manufacture of fertilizer was in process of becoming an important business, producing in 1859 $891,344 worth of fertilizers, of which some were good and some did not live up to their advertised analyses.

War prices and the desire of farmers to produce as much wheat, corn, hops, beans, peas, and other commodities as possible made the use of fertilizer expand rapidly. By 1864 New York farmers were buying as much as the entire country had used five years earlier. Farm journals were lavish in their allotment of space to promote the use of fertilizers, the New York State

Agricultural Society sponsored an elaborate series of experiments to determine the effect of the application of various chemical and mineral compositions to growing crops, and the U. S. Superintendent of the Census devoted much attention in 1864 to existing knowledge concerning the use of fertilizer on wheat and corn. To meet the demands, the fertilizer industry kept expanding, so that in 1869 it had a capital of $4,395,000 and an annual product valued at $5,815,000. Farmers were learning that not only were their yields improved through the use of fertilizer but also that the richness of their land was maintained.[7]

Immigration was another major factor making possible the expansion of agriculture in the North during the war. In 1861 and 1862 the flow slackened temporarily because of the outbreak of the war and the fear of compulsory military service, but the number of immigrants who arrived, though smaller than for any year since 1844, was still sizable: 91,918 in 1861 and 91,985 in 1862. The rate picked up in 1863 and 1864, and by 1865 it was back to the level of the mid-fifties. A total of 800,000 people immigrated to America in the years 1861–5. Included were 233,000 Germans and 16,000 or more Swedes and Norwegians, all of whom were more inclined than the Irish to go west, where so many of their fellow countrymen had preceded them, to enter farming. Some of the Norwegians and Swedes may well have been stimulated to immigrate to the West by Oscar Malmborg, the colonization agent whom the Illinois Central Railroad sent to Norway and Sweden. This first land-grant railroad was trying to settle Scandinavians on its line south of Chicago, but the greater portion of those arriving in Chicago in 1861 and 1862 went on to northern Illinois or Minnesota. Better results came

---

[7] L. C. Gray: *History of Agriculture in the Southern United States to 1860* (2 vols., Washington, 1933), II, *passim; Eight Census of the United States, 1860, Agriculture*, pp. xxxv ff.; *Ninth Census of the United States*, III, *Wealth and Industry*, pp. 395, 410; *Census of the State of New York*, 1865, p. 404; W. D. Rasmussen: "The Impact of Technological Change on American Agriculture, 1862–1962," *Journal of Economic History*, XXII (December 1962), 580 ff.; W. T. Jordan: "The Peruvian Guano Gospel in the Old South," *Agricultural History*, XXIV (October 1950), 216–17.

to the Illinois Central from the activities of another agent—
Francis Hoffman, who worked among German immigrants.[8]

Since many of the immigrants lacked the capital to purchase
land and equipment when they first came to the New World,
they either went into construction or factory work or served
"their apprenticeship on the farms of others," as the *Prairie
Farmer* expressed it. They were vitally important on the farms
in replacing those who had gone to war. But the status of hired
laborer or tenant was only a step to something better. As soon
as conditions warranted, they moved on to fulfill their dream of
independent proprietorship. After 1862 it was to the homestead
land of Minnesota, Michigan, and Kansas that they went.[9]

Another reservoir of labor which was drawn upon during
the war was the women of farm families. Except among immigrant families it had not been the custom for farm women to
work in the barn or field. Indeed, one might well wonder how they
could find time for anything more than the burdens imposed by
home, nursery, dairy, and poultry yard. Yet there is abundant evidence in the farm journals that women replaced their menfolk
by running mowers, reapers, rakes, drills, and even plows, as
well as driving loads of grain to market. A Wisconsin wife on a
grain farm told of women planting corn and hoeing it, harrowing
with oxen, operating all the farm machines, and binding grain.
Many women, especially Germans, worked in the fields as harvest
hands. On a New York farm a mother and seven daughters
plowed, dragged, sowed, and rolled 100 acres in wheat. In addition they milked twenty-two cows, made butter and cheese, and
helped shingle and lath an addition to their dwelling house and a
cheese house. When accounts of the work of these women appeared in farm journals, strong protests were made against women
working in the field and the barn. One critic said that continued
outdoor labor on the farm degrades women, coarsens their minds,

---

[8] P. W. Gates: *The Illinois Central Railroad and Its Colonization Work* (Cambridge, Mass.,
1934), pp. 188 ff. Some 11,000
Swedes and Norwegians came
through the major immigrant
ports in 1861–5, but more came
by way of Quebec and Montreal
and are not included in this fig-

ure. For the data on immigrants
coming through the principal
ports see U.S. Immigration Commission: *Report*, III, *Statistical
Review of Immigration, 1820–
1910*, Sen. Doc., 61 Cong., 3 Sess.,
1911, no. 756, pp. 27–9.
[9] *Prairie Farmer*, XII (Nov. 7,
1863), 292.

lowers their social position, and deforms their bodies. Others, including a woman, sharply and effectively rebutted every argument the original male critic had offered, contending that for the emergency there was nothing to be feared from the practice.[1] For the duration of the war bloomers continued to replace crinolines, said the *Rural New Yorker*.

Henry F. French, a practicing farmer, writer on agricultural matters, and educator, explained why the North was able to produce such great quantities of grain and meat during the war in spite of the heavy draft on its manpower. He thought that one half the labor of farmers was normally given to making permanent improvements on their land, such as extending the cleared portion, dragging off the stones for fencing, draining wet areas, erecting additions to their homes and new outbuildings, setting out fruit trees and grapevines, and working with their neighbors in improving roads and constructing churches. Moreover, when there was less pressure at the farm, the farmer or his older children sometimes took contracting jobs on bridges, canals, or railroads to add to their cash income. Under the emergencies of war and conscription all such work off the farm was suspended, improvements were stopped, and necessary but not vital work was slowed down or halted. Manure which in normal times would have been carried to the field was permitted to pile up, unused leaky roofs were not repaired, rotation schemes were abandoned, and wheat was sown on land in successive years. French deplored all this neglect of improvements, maintenance, and good farm practices, but he took comfort in the fact that Southerners were being shown how the North, without slaves to work the land, could fight and farm too.[2]

The letdown in good farm practices included not only the neglect of animal manures, but also the burning of straw, shallow plowing and poor cultivation, planting of wheat or corn on the

---

[1] *Galena Advertiser* in *Nashville Dispatch*, Aug. 8, 1863; *Rural New Yorker*, XIII (Nov. 15, 1862), 366, XIV (Mar. 7, May 23, June 6, July 11, 1863), 77, 165, 181, 222, and XV (Oct. 22, 1864), 342; *Country Gentleman*, XX (July 24, 1862), 61; *New England Farmer*, XV (May, July, August, September, 1863), 161, 229, 239, 287; *Prairie Farmer*, X (Oct. 4, 1862), 215.

[2] "The War and the Farmer," *New England Farmer*, XIV, (February 1863), 65–6; *Prairie Farmer*, VIII (Oct. 3, 1861), 224.

same land in successive years, and careless selection of seed. The result was the accumulation of weeds, insects, and diseases, deterioration of the soil, and declining yields. J. R. Dodge of the U.S. Department of Agriculture excoriated the grain farmers for their many faults, calling their method of tillage a "blind, senseless and suicidal system." These criticisms were not new. They had been made earlier of farm practices in the South, in the hill areas and Genesee Valley of New York, in Ohio, and even in Wisconsin. Furthermore, the continued cropping of land to wheat and the methods used to prepare the soil encouraged the multiplication of chinch bugs. These pests, together with declining yields and inferior wheat, which brought lower prices, caused farmers in Wisconsin, Michigan, Illinois, and Iowa gradually to shift from dependence upon wheat to hops and dairying. By the close of the war the wheat belt was moving farther west into the Red River Valley of Minnesota and Dakota, and later still into Kansas and Nebraska.[3]

Grain prices reached a low point in the summer of 1861 when the large carryover from the bumper crop of 1860, combined with the new winter wheat that was coming into market and the stoppage of trade with the South, drove prices down to a near-disaster level. Thereafter, European buying slowly lifted the surplus wheat and corn off the market. By late 1862 grain prices had risen to favorable levels. In March 1863 yellow corn was selling in New York at approximately double the price it had brought in July 1861; in the same period the price of wheat had risen 50 per cent in greenbacks, not gold. For the balance of the war, except in the late summer of 1863, prevailing prices enabled Northern farmers to replace badly worn or obsolete mowers, acquire better plows and harrows, pay off some of their debts acquired in the period of low prices, and even hire some labor on occasion.

Troubled by the rising cost of materials and wages, manufacturers of reapers and mowers, and probably of other farm implements, tried to raise their own prices—first by separate action and, when that failed, by price-fixing agreements among

---

[3] *Rural New Yorker*, XVI (Apr. 8, 1865), 110; J. R. Dodge in U.S. Department of Agriculture: *Monthly Report*, October 1867, p. 322; Thompson: *Wheat Growing in Wisconsin*, p. 58.

all producers. They found the competition for buyers so keen, however, that the agreements were almost impossible to maintain. Prices of mowers and reapers worked upward slowly and most producers enjoyed high profits, but they were not content. In 1865 they tried again to push up the price of mowing machines that had earlier sold for $120 and $130 to $180. They were threatened by a buyers' strike and sales were slow. A convention of manufacturers of agricultural implements met in Cleveland to try and maintain the price level at the very time economic conditions were turning downward. A critic contended that farmers should not have to pay wartime prices now that agricultural commodities and other items were slumping. He urged farmers to use their old mowers or borrow machines from others until the manufacturers were forced to lower their prices.[4]

Not all the farmers' costs were out of line with the prices they received. Interest on their debts, being payable in greenbacks, became easier to bear as agricultural prices rose. Debtors took advantage of the situation to pay off their obligations and everywhere property was being freed from mortgages. In one Wisconsin county 600 mortgages averaging $400 each were paid off and released. Civil suits for the collection of debts fell off by one half in Ohio. Banks and insurance companies had funds which they had loaned on mortgage paid off at such a rapid rate that they were hard put to find new investments. Since the cost of local improvements and the bonuses given to enlisted men were taken care of chiefly through bond issues, and since other expenses of local governments did not greatly change, farmers' taxes increased only moderately, save that they were required to pay some Federal taxes on production.[5]

The extension of railroad lines during the war made it easier for farmers to ship their wheat to market. Before the coming of the railroad, wheat was sometimes hauled as much as 150 miles by remote farmers desperately in need of cash to meet payments on their land and to acquire needed supplies. The high

[4] *Rural New Yorker*, XVI (June 10, 1865), 181; Hutchinson: *Cyrus Hall McCormick, Harvest*, pp. 92 ff.
[5] E. D. Fite: *Social and Industrial* *Conditions in the North during the Civil War* (New York, 1910), p. 120; A. C. Cole: *The Irrepressible Conflict* (New York, 1934), p. 358.

cost of hauling grain such distances, estimated to be a half cent a bushel for each mile, could only be justified by the fact that the farmer could haul in slack times and had no alternative way of raising funds. During the war railroads hauled grain for one seventh to one fourth the cost of hauling by ox teams. By 1864 and 1865, however, freight rates had risen. Farmers who now had to pay 25 cents a bushel for a 200-mile haul instead of the earlier charge of 12 to 15 cents were distressed, but others who had been hauling their grain long distances at much higher costs could well feel that the extension of the railroads was a great boon to them.[6]

Between 1861 and 1865, 1,803 miles of railroad were built in the Western states. Of this total, 385 miles were in Ohio, 367 in Illinois, 236 in Iowa, 213 in Minnesota, and 162 in Michigan, all major wheat-producing states. The coming (or the anticipation of the coming) of the railroad hastened the changeover from near-subsistence to commercial agriculture, a conversion which showed itself in rising wheat and corn production and in the rapid increase in hogs and cattle in the Middle West. The railroads brought in settlers looking either for the free government land or the railroad land which was offered on long credit terms. They were the principal influence in pushing the frontier westward into western Minnesota and Iowa, into areas of Michigan and Wisconsin which had heretofore been neglected, into Kansas, and into Nebraska.[7]

As has always happened in periods of inflation and favorable farm prices, farmers were induced in the latter part of the war, when prices were at their highest levels, to enlarge and intensify their operations through the use of borrowed funds. They had to have farm machinery if they were to give up their hired hands or older boys to the army, but many farmers went further by purchasing an additional forty, building a bigger barn, adding an ell to the house, or buying a choice Merino ram or an additional team of horses. Some who were drafted borrowed five hun-

[6] H. M. Larson: *The Wheat Market and the Minnesota Farmer, 1858–1900* (New York, 1926), p. 46; P. W. Gates: *The Farmer's Age* (New York, 1960), p. 161.

[7] R. E. Riegel: *The Story of the Western Railroads* (New York, 1926).

dred dollars or more to hire a substitute to serve for them. Thus despite the liquidation of debts during the first year or two of the war, by the end of it many farmers were back in debt for the improvements they had made or the additional acreage they had acquired. Corn belt farmers, who fed their grain to cattle and hogs and tried to maintain the fertility of their land, were much slower to add to the numbers of their livestock and were able to diversify more than the wheat farmers. Consequently they were not as vulnerable to changes in the price level as the others proved to be.

III

THE UNITED STATES

IO

Beginnings of Agricultural Education

ONE of the important measures enacted by the Federal government during the Civil War, a measure which was soon extended to the South upon its restoration to the Union, was the Morrill Act of 1862. This law, under which land was granted to the states for the establishment of colleges of agricultural and mechanical arts, has had an enduring influence on American society. The principle of the measure was not new. Government aid for education is deeply rooted in the American way of life. It had its origin in the early colonial period and was firmly established when the national government was formed. Aid for public schools was written into the Land Ordinance of 1785, which reserved one section in each township in the territory north of the Ohio for common schools. Thereafter every new state which was carved out of the public lands received the same allowance for education until 1850 when, with the admission of California, the grant was raised to two sections in each township, and with the admission of Oklahoma, Arizona, and New Mexico it was increased to four sections. During the same period, two townships, or 46,080 acres of land worth about $50,000, were granted to each new state as it entered the Union for a seminary of learning or university. Beginning with Ohio in 1803, thirty states, including Alaska, received these grants and twenty-nine succeeded in founding universities which survived, although in their early days their support was meager, their attendance sparse, and their variations from the classical tradition slight.

When strict or narrow interpretation of the Federal Constitution was common, the United States, with its abundance of government land, could somehow justify giving land but not money for higher education. Perhaps it was the colonial precedents of generous land grants given by the Crown of England to aid in establishing William and Mary College, and by New Hampshire and Massachusetts to found Dartmouth and Bowdoin Colleges, that first broke the constitutional barriers. In any case the United States initiated the university grants when the public lands were regarded as a national treasure to be husbanded carefully, were pledged for the payment of the country's debt, and were intended for sale only to the highest bidder at public auctions. It was expected that the states receiving the grants would follow the government's example and sell them at prices which would assure a substantial income when the returns were invested. The states and the universities they created were expected to share in the rising prices which the growing pressure on the supply of land would assure.[1]

Many private institutions likewise were opened with high hopes of profit from the land-speculating ventures into which their early promoters plunged. Oberlin, Knox, Grinnell, Coe, Augustana, and Blackburn colleges, not to mention those that did not survive, were as much involved in their early days in the real estate business as in education, and the success of the latter largely depended upon that business. Town promoters and real estate dealers found it desirable to attract population by locating a seminary or college in their communities, and if, in the process of town and college making, some of the fathers of both succeeded in advancing their own fortunes, who was there to complain?[2]

---

[1] E. D. Eddy, Jr.: *Colleges for Our Land and Time: The Land-Grant Idea in American Education* (New York, 1956); Allan Nevins: *The State Universities and Democracy* (Urbana, Ill., 1962).

[2] The promoters of Oberlin bought 6,000 acres, those of Knox 10,336 acres, and those of Grinnell 5,000 acres, from the profits of which it was hoped to produce flourishing institutions. J. H. Fairchild: *Oberlin. Its Origin, Progress and Results* (Oberlin, Ohio, 1871), p. 6; J. S. Miller: *Grinnell College* (Iowa City, 1953), p. 54; E. E. Calkins: *They Broke the Prairie* (New York, 1937), p. 46.

Between 1803, when Ohio was given land for what became Miami and Ohio Universities, and 1862, when the Morrill Act was adopted, members of Congress, particularly those who preferred to interpret the Constitution strictly, gradually gave way before the fresh nationalistic breezes coming out of the West. Many of them were induced to vote the same way as those whose minds were less bound to the past, so that Congress by degrees made grants to help build canals and railroads, construct state capitol buildings, and drain the states' swamplands. It was notable that when strict constructionists were faced with issues that promised to benefit their own states or districts, many of them could forget their constitutional scruples and vote in favor.

Dorothea Dix, whose concern for the welfare of the insane brought about far-reaching improvements in their care, seems early to have sensed the dilemma of the strict constructionists faced with measures their constituents really wanted. In her search for ways and means of aiding the states in establishing institutions for the care of the insane, she proposed that land grants be made to each state in a compound ratio of area and population. Since the older states would, for the first time, receive direct aid in the form of grants of land and the newer states would be given a bonus for their greater size, she hoped the measure would not be defeated by the strict constructionist arguments of the former and the anti-speculator views of the West. It is significant that Vermont, one of the poorest and least well endowed of the older states, was to provide the leadership in Congress both for the law to aid states in caring for their indigent insane and for the act creating agricultural colleges: Solomon Foot was the leader for the first and Justin Smith Morrill for the second.

Miss Dix induced Congress to pass her measure with its provision for land grants to all the states. Unfortunately, dour old Franklin Pierce found it necessary "to resist the deep sympathies of my own heart" and veto the measure, chiefly because it had an "eleemosynary object and, if sanctioned, might even lead the government eventually to provide care for all people suffering from calamities, which the constitution did not sanction." A Northern "doughface," Pierce anticipated the argument that was to be used by another Northern doughface, James

Buchanan, in his veto of the first Morrill bill. The Dix bill was important to the movement for agricultural colleges because the method by which it proposed to aid the states was to be copied by Representative Morrill in his bill.[3]

Another plan—calculated scheme is a better term—to enable the Eastern states to share in the distribution of the public lands was offered simultaneously with the Dix proposal by Representative Henry Bennett of a rural New York district. Bennett was a conservative who was outraged by the success of the Western states in securing grants of land for railroads and other public improvements—grants which might reduce the revenue expected from the public lands. He also deplored the efforts then under way to lower the price of public lands and to give them to actual settlers. He drafted a bill that would combine further modest subsidies of land to Western states for railroad construction with donations to the older states of 150,000 acres of land for each representative and senator they had in Congress. Through this sop to the West the older states would have come into the possession of 30,000,000 acres. Employing a devious parliamentary maneuver, Bennett managed to have his bill reported from the unfriendly Public Lands Committee and to secure favorable action by the House, but the bill was bottled up in the Senate— fortunately, if we may judge by the way Eastern states later managed the grants they received under the Morrill Act. With its donation to New York of more than 5,000,000 acres and to other states in proportion, the Bennett bill would have gone far to destroy the increasingly settler-oriented land system. Discussion of the merits of the Bennett and Dix bills contributed to the desire of the East to share in the public lands and thereby facilitated the subsequent passage of the Morrill Act.[4]

By the mid-nineteenth century there was increasing dissatisfaction among agricultural authorities with farming as practiced in the United States and the disinclination of farmers to consider

---

[3] I have discussed Miss Dix's plan for aiding in establishing institutions for the mentally ill in *The Wisconsin Pine Lands of Cornell University* (Ithaca, N.Y., 1943), pp. 11 ff. J. D. Richardson (ed.): *Messages and Papers of the Presidents* (9 vols., New York, 1904), V, 249; *Cong. Globe,* 33 Cong., 1 Sess., Mar. 8, 1864, p. 572.

[4] *Cong. Globe,* 32 Cong., 1 Sess., June 8, 1852, pp. 1536–9, and 33 Cong., 1 Sess., Apr. 4, 1854, pp. 849–51, 1000–1.

new ideas and improved methods. Belief in the inexhaustibility of the soil and of the supply of new land and preoccupation with immediate returns made farmers prodigal of the resources of the land and careless in their practices. Few could be induced to experiment with manure and fertilizer year after year. They resorted to thin plowing and row cropping of cotton, tobacco, and corn, and when the topsoil was gone and the productivity of the land sharply reduced, they moved on to other areas, heedless of the damage they had done. Southern planters either planned well in advance to remove their slaves and equipment to new areas, or acquired great tracts of land, only a part of which they could use at any one time, so as to have sufficient land for a lifetime.

In New England, which was less well endowed with first-rate soil, farmers found that they could not compete with richer lands farther west in the Genesee Valley of New York or the oak openings of Michigan and the prairies of Illinois. The result was that many farms, particularly the hillside farms which the pressure of population had forced New Englanders to cultivate, were abandoned. The state hardest hit by agricultural decline in the decade before the Civil War was Vermont where, as the result of emigration, one half the counties and 147 towns out of 246 lost population. New England, with its depressed agriculture and its traditional attitude toward public support for education, found it easy to advocate the use of public lands for education that might bring about improvement in its farms, particularly as such a plan would not be at the expense of local people. It seemed appropriate therefore that a Vermonter should lead the movement in Congress.[5]

The growing interest in improving agricultural practices was partly the result of increasing intellectual relations between European and American scientists, writers, travelers, journalists, and teachers. It was in Germany and Austria that agricultural science was most advanced and most extensively taught in universities, in thirty polytechnical schools, and in forty-six schools of agriculture. A graduate of one of these agricultural schools, Charles

---

[5] H. F. Wilson: *The Hill Country of Northern New England, Its Social and Economic History,* *1790–1930* (New York, 1936), *passim.*

Lewis Fleischmann, came to America in 1832. His extensive writings, his sharp criticisms of farming practices, and his call for technical education all contributed to the growing awareness that American agriculture was far behind that of most European countries. He maintained that the progress in agriculture made by European scientists could only become widely known and utilized in the United States by the establishment of agricultural schools.[6]

Henry Colman, who had studied agriculture for five years in Europe, was another who tried to alert Americans to the benefits of agricultural education. Colman had been commissioner of the Agricultural Survey of Massachusetts in 1837, editor of the *New England Farmer*, and a copious writer on farm problems before he was commissioned to make an agricultural survey of England, Ireland, France, and Italy. His *European Agriculture and Rural Economy*, published in two volumes in 1846, gave much attention to agricultural schools and experimental farms in England, Ireland, and France and included a plan for similar institutions which he hoped to see established in the United States.[7]

Germany's great chemist, Justus von Liebig, had a profound influence upon American agricultural authorities. Through the remarkable experiments he conducted in his world-famous laboratory at the University of Giessen from 1824 to 1852 and at Munich between 1852 and 1873, Liebig greatly expanded knowledge of the chemical constituents of soil and crops. Together with his other discoveries, his conclusion that plants drew upon the minerals in the soil, not the humus, for their growth, and that good soil management required replenishment of these minerals, brought him world fame. His writings, particularly his *Organic Chemistry in Its Applications to Agriculture and Physiology*, translated and published in England in 1840 and in the United States in 1841, created much controversy but great respect. Liebig

---

[6] Russell H. Chittenden: *History of the Sheffield Scientific School of Yale University, 1846–1922* (2 vols., New Haven, 1928), I, 20. I have dealt with Fleischmann's career in "Charles Lewis Fleisch-mann: German-American Agricultural Authority," *Agricultural History*, XXXV (January 1961), 13 ff.
[7] Henry Colman: *European Agriculture and Rural Economy* (Boston, 1846), *passim*.

emphasized that the minerals extracted from the soil by crops must be replaced, but he disregarded the value of ammonia from manure. The result was that some of his followers believed "laboratory tillage" would replace the use of manures and they thus justified the neglect and waste of farmyard manure that too many farmers permitted. Yet Liebig's mineral manure theory and his chemical analysis of soils and crops contributed much to agricultural science.[8]

Eager students from Europe and America flocked to Giessen, later to Munich, to learn the laboratory techniques Liebig had perfected. Naturally he came into demand as a lecturer and efforts were made to bring him to the United States, but he was not eager to take the long and somewhat dangerous voyage across the Atlantic. A follower, James F. W. Johnston of the University of Durham, himself an extensive writer on agricultural matters, was brought over in his place. Johnston toured portions of the country, studying its farming operations and lecturing on science in agriculture. At Yale a corps of students of Liebig and Johnston built a significant program of studies in chemistry and its relations to agriculture and industry. One of their first activities was an analysis of widely advertised brands of fertilizers which revealed extensive frauds in the claims made for them.[9]

Continued and increasing ravages of plant and animal parasites and diseases brought home to farmers how vulnerable their operations were to attacks by nature. Wheat, corn, cotton, rice, or tobacco was being planted on the same land year after year, with the result that pests accumulated. Cotton planters had to contend with the ravages of army worms, cotton lice, bollworms, cutworms, and the black rot; wheat growers were badgered by the Hessian fly, midge, jointworm, smut, rust, the chinch bug, and the weevil; tobacco growers had the hornworm; fruit growers

---

[8] *Country Gentleman*, III (June 8, 1854), 357; F. R. Moulton: *Liebig and After Liebig. A Century of Progress in Agricultural Chemistry* (Washington, 1942).
[9] J. F. W. Johnston: *Notes on North America: Agricultural, Economical and Social* (2 vols., Edinburgh, 1851); *Country Gentleman*, V (May 24, 1855), 333; *Cultivator*, IX (September 1861), 285; P. W. Gates: *The Farmer's Age. Agriculture, 1815–1860* (New York, 1960), pp. 362 ff.

had cankerworms and the curculio. Damages from insects and disease forced changes in farm practices and induced many farmers in New York, Illinois, and Wisconsin to give up growing wheat.

A series of crop and animal diseases, including the disastrous potato blight of the forties and hog cholera, pleuropneumonia, and contagious abortion in the fifties and early sixties, brought home to many the need for knowledge to deal with these evils. Entomology, animal husbandry, and veterinary science as well as agricultural chemistry and geology were appearing as possible aids to farmers. To bring to the attention of farmers the best of modern knowledge required the establishment of technical schools where scientists skilled in entomology, plant and animal breeding, chemistry, and geology could both conduct research and lecture on their results.[1]

Although many farmers resisted new ideas in farming and clung to the ways of their fathers, a widespread interest and respect for the ideas of modern science was developing, as is shown by the demand for the works of experts on various aspects of farming, some of whose books went through many editions and printings. The *American Agriculturist* for 1861 published a list of eighty-seven books "for farmers and others," including works of the most eminent scientists of Europe and America. Among these works were Liebig's *Lectures on Chemistry*, Boussingault's *Rural Economy*, Allen's *Diseases of Domestic Animals*, Dadd's *Modern Horse Doctor*, Johnson on *Manures*, Norton's *Scientific Agriculture*, Randall's *Sheep Husbandry*, and *Youatt on the Hog*. Some farmers in almost every community were experimenting with new ideas, searching for new methods of eradicating or curbing animal and plant diseases and harmful insects, and trying out new implements. Their successes produced not only respect for their accomplishments but also for their methods

---

[1] Illinois State Agricultural Society: *Transactions*, V (1861–4), p. 34; *Rural New Yorker*, XII (Aug. 3, Sept. 7, 21, 1861), 278, 286, 301; United States Agricultural Society: *Journal*, 1857, p. 56; Commissioner of Patents: *Report, Agriculture*, 1861, p. 147; *Oneida Weekly Herald*, May 22, 1864; *Working Farmer*, XVIII (April 1866), 87; New York State Agricultural Society: *Journal*, XIII (July 1862), 15.

—their learning. Practical education for farmers was winning support.

To this growing interest in agricultural education was added a demand by a combination of manufacturers and workers for the creation of institutions at which technical training in the mechanic arts could be provided. This movement has been described well by Earle D. Ross in his *Democracy's College*. The time seemed ripe for an attempt to secure Federal support in the form of land grants to help the states establish institutions for teaching the sciences involved in both agriculture and engineering. Proponents were particularly encouraged by the more liberal attitude of Congress in disposing of the public lands to railroads and to the states for various special purposes.

Many leaders contributed to the movement for Federal aid to agricultural education, and many historians have tried to assess individual responsibility for the adoption of the Morrill Act which finally emerged from this drive. Jonathan Baldwin Turner, a nurseryman of Illinois, did much to get the movement under way by drafting elaborate plans for state industrial universities, all of which were widely discussed in the farm journals. He proposed Federal aid to each state in the form of grants of land worth half a million dollars. In 1857 the United States Agricultural Society took the lead in the movement for land grants to establish agricultural colleges and publicized it to such an extent that few intelligent readers of the major papers of the day could have been unaware of it. With such influential members as Marshall Pinckney Wilder, the best-known fruit hybridizer and pear specialist; Joseph R. Williams, president of Michigan Agricultural College; Freeman G. Cary, president of Farmers' College of Cincinnati; Charles L. Flint, one of the most prolific writers on agriculture and secretary of the Massachusetts State Board of Agriculture; and Lewis G. Morris, eminent cattle breeder of New York, to mention only a few, the society was a powerful group of men of first rank in all fields of agriculture. Through its meetings in Washington, attended by two dozen or more congressmen, the society was able to focus attention upon the move for Federal aid and to win strong support in Congress. The lobbying of men like Wilder, Williams, Cary, Amos Brown, president of People's College of New York, and Evan Pugh, president of

259

Farmers' High School of Pennsylvania, caused Justin Smith Morrill of Vermont to see the political possibilities in the drive.[2]

Support for vocational education in agriculture and the mechanical arts was sufficiently strong in the fifties to make possible the founding of a number of schools, some of which were later to grow into the modern land-grant institutions. At Lansing, Michigan, Ames, Iowa, Center County, Pennsylvania, and Ovid, New York, significant beginnings had been made with the help of state appropriations. Unfortunately, none of these states had strongly committed themselves to continuing support for the schools, the presidents and faculties were not altogether certain how to introduce vocational education at the college level, and the results of the instruction in the pioneer period were not promising. Perhaps all they had done was to strengthen the demand for agricultural and vocational education. In the absence of adequate state support, advocates of this education now turned to the Federal government.[3]

It should not be thought that all Northern agricultural interests favored the establishment of agricultural colleges. In New England, where colleges were so well supported, the principal agricultural journal took a negative position concerning them. Simon Brown, the editor, regarded the Morrill bill as a wonderful scheme for politicians and expressed doubt that Massachusetts would move to accept the land grant in the next forty years. Senator John P. Hale of New Hampshire was firmly opposed to agricultural colleges; he could see no reason at all for them. Professor Samuel W. Johnson questioned whether the people who needed education in agriculture would attend. Solon Robinson, best known of agricultural writers, who had at first been an advocate of agricultural schools, later became soured on them, holding that they were as much needed as colleges for shoemakers, and maintaining in 1866 that few of the new institutions were any-

---

[2] United States Agricultural Society: *Journal*, 1857, pp. 10–11.
[3] A. C. True has summarized the work of the various public and private institutions in the teaching of agricultural science before 1862 in *A History of Agricultural Education in the United States, 1785–1925* (Washington, 1929),

pp. 24 ff. See also Madison Kuhn: *Michigan State, The First Hundred Years* (East Lansing, Mich., 1955); W. F. Dunaway: *History of Pennsylvania State College* (State College, Pa., 1946); E. D. Ross: *History of the Iowa State College of Agriculture and Mechanic Arts* (Ames, Iowa, 1942).

thing but sublime failures. The editor of the *Northern Farmer* was particularly caustic about agricultural colleges and the over-emphasis on the "soil analysis humbug" which had "originated with men of empty pockets." Finally, the *American Agriculturist* commented in 1867 on the popular prejudice against agricultural education which, farmers feared, would wean their sons from the farm. All these were the expressions of enlightened friends of agriculture.[4]

Justin Smith Morrill introduced his first agricultural college bill in the House of Representatives in 1857. He abandoned Turner's plan to grant each state land worth half a million dollars and substituted the grants of the Dix bill, which were based on state representation in Congress. Essentially, the Morrill bill provided for grants of 20,000 acres of public land to each state for each representative and senator it had in Congress, the land to be used as an endowment for the support of a college of agriculture and mechanic arts. Non-public-land states were to receive scrip (land-office money), which they were to sell. To avoid jurisdictional issues, they were prohibited from exchanging the scrip for land in Western states. The grants would range from 60,000 acres to states with small populations, such as Delaware and Florida, to 700,000 for New York and 540,000 for Pennsylvania. Since the Morrill bill did not have a clause establishing the amount of land on the compound basis of area and population, Rhode Island would be entitled to the same amount of scrip as Texas, and New Hampshire would be entitled to more than California.[5]

Morrill supported his measure in a lengthy speech, shrewdly contrived to meet constitutional objections and to show that farmers were the least privileged group so far as government

---

[4] *New England Farmer*, XI (April 1859), 172–3; *Journal of Agriculture* in New Hampshire Agricultural Society: *Transactions*, 1860, p. 86; Massachusetts Board of Agriculture: *Eleventh Annual Report*, 1864, p. 42; *Working Farmer*, XVIII (Mar. 1, 1865), 63; *Northern Farmer*, V (May 1858), 133; *American Agriculturist*, XXVI (August 1867), 279.

[5] A copy of the Morrill bill which is somewhat different from the Act of 1862 is in *Cong. Globe*, 35 Cong., 1 Sess., Apr. 20, 1858, p. 1697. The revived Morrill bill went through the House without discussion on June 17, 1862; hence I have relied on Morrill's speech of 1858. *Cong. Globe*, 37 Cong., 2 Sess., p. 2770.

handouts or aids were concerned. His opening paragraph was most effective.

> I know very well that when there is a lack of arguments to be brought against the merits of a measure, the Constitution is fled to as an inexhaustible arsenal of supply. From thence all sorts of missiles may be hurled. . . . I have also noticed that lions accustomed to roar around the Constitution are quite disposed to slumber whenever it is desirable for certain gentlemen . . . to leap over the impediment. . . . all the favor asked is, that the Constitution may not be strained and perverted to defeat a measure no less of public good than of public justice—just politically, just to all the States, and just, above all, to the manhood of our country.

He alluded to the support given to manufacturing and commerce and observed that when agriculture came with its hands out, it was coldly rejected although the prosperity of the country depended more on the farmers than upon any other class. Unfortunately, farming was not doing well in some parts of the country, and elsewhere, though farmers were improving their position, they were doing it at the expense of land that was being depleted of its fertility or topsoil.

Morrill showed his familiarity with the best agricultural literature of the times and the most recent developments in agricultural chemistry. European governments, he observed, were "alive to the wants of agriculture," as shown by their model farms, experiment stations, botanical gardens, agricultural and industrial colleges, and the many secondary schools which had as their purpose the improvement of the industrial and agricultural resources. Country by country, Morrill examined the many educational benefits they gave to agriculture and industry. He concluded that the "voice of our country . . . is believed to be overwhelmingly in favor of the establishment" of colleges for agriculture and mechanic arts.

Morrill's bill, with its assurance that the old states would draw direct benefit from the public lands without expense to themselves, brought eager support from representatives and senators who might otherwise have shown little concern for agriculture. New England representatives were solidly for the bill, New York and New Jersey were mostly in favor, Pennsylvania's support was tepid, and the South was strongly hostile. During the discussion Western congressmen argued that the older and wealthier states could afford to provide their own colleges, that it was in the newly developing territories and states that support for public institutions was needed, and that the public lands should be granted only to the states in which they were located. To this the Vermont Agricultural Society replied that the public lands belonged to all the people, not just to the new states.

Other than the conservative states' rights opposition of the South, which saw no advantage in educating at public expense the people who actually farmed, the chief and most vocal adversaries of the Morrill bill were Westerners who maintained that it was the settlement of the new territories and the transportation facilities for which the people paid that gave value to the lands and therefore absentee owners—whether states, institutions they created, or speculators—should not be permitted to profit from them. Land reformers in the West feared that the land speculator would buy up the scrip given to the Eastern states, exchange it for great tracts of land, and hold these for the rising values the settlement process would assure. Representatives from Western public-land states could argue too that while the East gained much, the West, with its small population and with the bonus for area provision of the Dix bill excluded, would receive small grants and would be saddled with speculator holdings for years to come. The bill passed the House on April 22, 1858, by a vote of 105 to 100 and the Senate on February 7, 1859, by 25 to 22. These margins were too close to promise passage over the veto of Buchanan, and the measure died for the time.[6]

By withdrawing from the Union in 1861, the Southern states removed the conservative element that had long prevented the adoption of important legislation affecting agriculture and the development of the West. In rapid succession Congress enacted the Homestead Act with its free-land policy, the Pacific Railroad Act with its liberal aid for the building of a railroad to the Pacific, the act creating the Department of Agriculture, the National

---

[6] *Cong. Globe*, 35 Cong., 1 Sess., Apr. 20, 1858, pp. 1692 ff., Apr. 22, 1858, p. 1742, and 35 Cong., 2 Sess., Feb. 7, 1859, p. 857. I have examined the votes by states on both the bill of 1857–8 and that of 1862 in my *Wisconsin Pine Lands*, p. 20.

Bank Act, and the Morrill Act, all of which had been held up by the shrewd politics of a minority section. Thus the Morrill Act became law in 1862, but with grants more liberal than those proposed earlier. States were to have 30,000, not 20,000, acres for each senator and representative. The smallest grant would thus be 90,000 acres, the amount received by Delaware, Florida, Kansas, Nebraska, and Nevada. New York, Pennsylvania, Ohio, and Illinois received respectively 990,000, 780,000, 630,000 and 480,000 acres.[7]

With the agricultural college scrip which was given to the Eastern states exchangeable for land held for $1.25 an acre, and the lands which were given to the Western states certain to be held for the same price, the grants seemed to promise a substantial sum for the institutions to which they would be assigned. Morrill even thought in 1862 that the proceeds from the scrip and lands "with some little outside aid, will be sufficient at no remote period to offer instruction free of any charge for tuition."[8] With such optimistic expectations an unseemly scramble for the grants set in. Near-bankrupt and down-at-heels sectarian institutions and meagerly supported state colleges and universities actively participated. With their alumni, clerical leaders and officers, local real estate interests, lawyers, and business elements combined into lobbies, they each urged their claims before the state legislatures. They offered sites, additional bounties, and other perquisites—indeed, some intimately personal rewards, it was stated. They competed in much the same way as many other communities have fought to secure county seats, territorial and state capitals, termini of railroads, the location of Federal and state institutions, and defense contracts.[9]

Those who had labored for the Morrill Act feared that this scramble might lead to division of the proceeds among two or

---

[7] 12 *U.S. Stat.*, 503.
[8] *Cong. Globe*, Appendix, 37 Cong., 2 Sess., June 6, 1862, p. 256.
[9] Evan Pugh, president of the Pennsylvania Farmers' College, was highly critical of the "scramble for a portion of the spoils" which he felt was a "melancholy illustration of the terrible extrem-ities to which" numerous poorly financed institutions "are driven in the struggle for existence." Copied in California State Agricultural Society: *Transactions*, 1865–6, p. 88. See also *Prairie Farmer* XIV (Sept. 10, 1864), 162, and XV (Feb. 11, 25, 1865), 88, 117.

more colleges, or that the scrip might fall into the hands of sectarian interests or existing colleges which had no real interest in agricultural education. The histories of some of the agricultural colleges show that the danger to the program was great and was avoided only by a series of fortuitous circumstances and the able leadership of men like Ezra Cornell, Andrew D. White, and Jonathan Baldwin Turner, who were strong advocates of secular education in a society predominantly sectarian.[1]

Meantime, the Eastern non-public-land states were selling their scrip, which the Morrill Act barred them from exchanging for land in Western states. Unfortunately, 1863 and the years immediately following were not a good time for selling. Homeseekers in the West now could homestead their claims and acquire ownership without cost, save for modest fees, at the conclusion of five years' settlement. Furthermore the market contained nearly nine million acres of military bounty scrip and other miscellaneous scrip, which could be acquired at less than a dollar an acre and which had less restrictions on its use than the college scrip. After Homestead was adopted, the market for all such forms of land-office money was limited mostly to lumbermen wishing to acquire large tracts and speculators buying for future appreciation in value. Notwithstanding the weak market for land scrip, the Eastern states offered their holdings promptly, as the Morrill Act had intended they should. Vermont, which moved the fastest, sold its scrip before other states had taken action, and received an average of 81 cents an acre. Other Northern states, moving more slowly, found that they could get little more than 50 cents an acre. Southern states were delayed in obtaining their scrip until 1867–73. By this time the amount of scrip on the market was small and they were able to sell their

[1] Carl Becker shows the bitterness of the sectarian institutions in New York at their failure to share in the land grant and the campaign of villification to which they resorted in his *Cornell University. Founders and Founding* (Ithaca, N.Y., 1943). See also B. E. Powell: *The Movement for Industrial Education and the Establishment of the University, 1840–1870 (Semi-* *Centennial History of the University of Illinois*, 2 vols., Urbana, Ill., 1918), I, 178 ff.; Alexis Cope: *History of the Ohio State University* (2 vols, Columbus, Ohio, 1920), I, 16 ff.; Ross: *History of Iowa State College*, pp. 40 ff.; W. H. Glover: *Farm and College. The College of Agriculture of the University of Wisconsin* (Madison, Wis.; 1952), pp. 28 ff.

holdings for 90 cents to $1 an acre. With good luck, Western states receiving land instead of scrip sold soon after location for $1.25 an acre, as Wisconsin did. Most of them, however, had to hold their selections for years; some still hold them and rent them for small sums.[2]

The returns from the sale of scrip or land in most instances were meager and the interest on their capitalization proved disappointing. Because of the small endowments thus secured and the failure of the state legislatures to adopt annual grants, over-optimistic plans for the new institutions could not be carried out. Historians of the new colleges in these initial years have few triumphs to relate; retrenchments, resignations, and failures were the norm.

Notwithstanding the small returns from the sale of the scrip and lands and the battles between advocates of sectarian schools for the government's bounty, the various agricultural and educational leaders in the Northern states gave thoughtful attention to the new institution they were engaged in developing. Though the scientists assembled at Yale, Harvard, and Rensselaer were not called on for aid, other distinguished men played a major part in the planning stage. Evan Pugh, head of Farmers' High School, which was shortly to become Pennsylvania State College of Agriculture, and Henry F. French, destined to be president of Massachusetts Agricultural College, were familiar with scientific developments abroad in agriculture and exercised a marked influence in the beginning stages of the movement.

Ohio, somewhat slower to get its plans under way, wisely sent John H. Klippart, its chief agricultural authority and secretary of its Board of Agriculture, on a three-month tour of Germany and France to study agriculture and agricultural schools. Klippart

---

[2] For the management and sale of the Agricultural College Scrip, as it was called, see Gates: *Wisconsin Pine Lands*, pp. 27 ff.; Thomas LeDuc: "State Disposal of the Agricultural College Land Scrip," in Vernon Carstensen, (ed.), *The Public Lands. Studies in the History of the Public Domain* (Madison, Wis., 1963), pp. 395 ff.; A. E. Martin: "Pennsylvania's Land Grant under the Morrill Act of 1862," *Pennsylvania History*, IX (April 1942), 85 ff.; W. H. Glover: "The Agricultural College Lands in Wisconsin," *Wisconsin Magazine of History*, XXX (March 1947), 261 ff.; Agnes Horton: "Nebraska's Agricultural-College Land Grant," *Nebraska History*, XXX (March 1949), 50 ff.

sought out Justus von Liebig, who warned against emphasis upon practical agriculture associated with manual training. The lecture method should be used, Liebig maintained, with intensive study of the theoretical side of chemistry accompanied by demonstrations and experimentation. Large farm tracts were not essential, nor should model farms be established; experiment stations were needed in which the theoretical should be applied and the results presented in demonstrations and lectures. Liebig deplored extravagant spending upon college buildings "and then starving teachers and professors" and urged that able men be secured and be well compensated for the use of their talents.

Klippart was deeply influenced by his visit with Liebig and greatly impressed with the type of training provided at the leading agricultural school at Hohenheim. In his report he discussed at length the courses offered in mechanical engineering and in chemistry as it applied to beet sugar refining, brewing, distilling, and starch making. The school's dissemination of good seeds and the annual sale of "bulls and bucks for the improvement of cattle and sheep" seemed good policy to him. In Klippart's report was much sound advice that might well have aided not only Ohio but all other states then planning their A & M institutions, but it was to take a generation before this report was fully appreciated.[3]

Michigan, Pennsylvania, New York, Maryland, and Iowa had chartered their agricultural colleges before the adoption of the Morrill Act. Michigan's college was already functioning in 1860, though its control by "politicians, lawyers, doctors and merchants, instead of practical farmers," was said to assure failure. By 1862 instruction was being given at Lansing by textbook and lectures on agricultural chemistry, noxious weeds, and the principles of stock breeding. Classes had limited opportunity for the dissection and examination of domestic animals but did have access to a museum of natural history, and a few hundred dollars were being spent on books. Stress was laid also on the

---

[3] Ohio State Board of Agriculture: *Twentieth Annual Report,* 1866, part 1, pp. 17–280, especially 63 ff., 170 ff., and part 2, pp. 11–50. According to the *Cultivator,* XIII (July 1865), 221, Klippart also represented the U.S. Department of Agriculture while he was in Germany.

older fields of learning and on manual labor in the fields. Both Michigan and Iowa took pains to have high-quality stock to teach the advantages of careful breeding. Iowa could boast in 1865 that it had Durham, Ayrshire, and Devon cattle, Essex and Suffolk hogs, and Merino and Southdown sheep. It also had a museum, a herbarium, a mineral cabinet, and a laboratory, but instruction was to be delayed for some years.[4]

In New York two institutions received some state aid in the fifties and had fairly promising beginnings, but they withered because of the war and loss of support. Efforts to secure the grant of nearly a million acres for People's College failed. The school was too feeble to survive and the grant was conveyed to a new institution at Ithaca. Ezra Cornell, made wealthy by the spectacular success of the telegraph business, became a patron of agriculture, to which he devoted much time and money. As president of the New York State Agricultural Society in 1862 he contributed much to its discussions, especially by his survey of Tompkins County agriculture. He purchased purebred Devon and Shorthorn stock which he displayed at state and county fairs, and he built up a promising farm at Ithaca, New York, on the heights above Cayuga Lake. His promise of a half million dollars to aid in creating a university at Ithaca if the land grant were turned over to it secured New York's scrip for Cornell University. Ezra Cornell was to live for some seven years after the founding of the new institution and was to have an important share in making plans for it, but he must have been sorely disappointed at the de-emphasizing, not to say neglect, of agriculture. However, the $5,000,000 which came to Cornell through investing the land scrip in Wisconsin pinelands enabled the university to pioneer in many educational fields in the nineteenth and early twentieth centuries.[5]

Elsewhere the states moved to beat the deadline established in the Morrill Act, which required the acceptance of the grant in

---

[4] *Country Gentleman*, XIV (Dec. 22, 1859), 401, and XV (Jan. 5, Apr. 26, 1860), 13, 272; Michigan State Board of Agriculture: *Annual Reports*, 1862, 1863, 1864; *Prairie Farmer*, XV (Feb. 11, 1865), 82.
[5] Gates: *Wisconsin Pine lands*, pp.

49 ff.; Becker: *Cornell University: Founders and Founding, passim;* G. P. Colman: *Education & Agriculture. A History of the New York State College of Agriculture at Cornell University* (Ithaca, N.Y., 1963), p. 44.

two years and the creation of a college of agriculture in five. Connecticut, Rhode Island, and New Jersey took the easy course of turning their share of scrip over to existing private institutions—Yale, Brown, and Rutgers—and Massachusetts gave one third of its grant to what is now Massachusetts Institute of Technology. These grants were made with the understanding that the schools would either establish an affiliated college of agriculture and mechanic arts or would enlarge their course offering to cover these fields. Yale, Brown, and M.I.T. ultimately gave up their grant to state institutions. With these exceptions, the policy of the states was to create public institutions. Thus Maine, New Hampshire, Kentucky, Ohio, and Illinois were moving toward the establishment of universities; Kansas, Indiana, most Southern states, and the new states admitted after 1865 mostly created A & M colleges. In the twentieth century these institutions were to blossom out in name, if not in fact, as full-fledged universities.[6]

What must have seemed to some as one of the most promising developments took place when Connecticut decided to appropriate its land endowment for the Sheffield Scientific School, which was associated with Yale. At the outset the newly founded institution had a strong orientation toward agriculture, with Samuel W. Johnson, William H. Brewer, and an able botanist and a zoologist on its staff.

Rutgers College, to which the New Jersey grant was transferred, planned a well-designed and comprehensive program of studies which, if it had been carried out, might have been a model for the faltering efforts elsewhere. Agriculture, chemistry, and civil and mechanical engineering were to be emphasized, and in the agricultural portion stress was to be laid on soils, theories of manure, farm machinery, drainage, irrigation, farm buildings, crops, what is now called animal husbandry, dairy management, fruit, and garden vegetables. Farm accounting, botany, and entomology were also to have attention.[7] Action on behalf of these plans came to little and agricultural studies soon disappeared at Rutgers, though engineering did flourish.

---

[6] Commissioner of Agriculture: *Report*, 1867, pp. 317 ff.
[7] *Country Gentleman*, XXV (Feb. 23, Mar. 16, 1865), 129, 176–7;

W. H. S. Demarest: *A History of Rutgers College, 1766–1924* (New Brunswick, N.J., 1924), p. 412.

Despite involvement in its greatest war, the drain of its manpower, and the concentration of responsible government officials on war objectives, the American people took time out to adopt the Morrill Act, and some twenty or twenty-two states began to plan and erect colleges of agriculture and mechanic arts either as separate institutions or as part of universities, new or old. The country seemed alive with discussions about practical college education, the role of science—particularly chemistry, botany, entomology, geology, and zoology—the place religion and manual training should have in the new institutions, the role of the state in providing support, and the position of "dead" languages and the liberal arts in the curriculum. The state agricultural societies and progressive farm journals such as the *Rural New Yorker, The Country Gentleman, The American Agriculturist,* and the *Prairie Farmer* gave much attention to the movement for agricultural education and developments that were occurring in agricultural sciences. Students, attracted by the combination of the practical, theoretical, and classical education which was open to all at little cost, flocked to these new institutions and for a time seemed to show great interest. In 1865 and 1866 Michigan State had 88 students, Pennsylvania State College of Agriculture 114 students, Kansas College of Agriculture 133 students, and Kentucky Agricultural and Mechanical Arts College 120 students.[8]

Turner, Klippart, French, Pugh, and many other early advocates of vocational training in agriculture and engineering had high hopes for the new schools and the older colleges and universities which were taking on new life with the prospect of aid from the land grants. All these hopes were to be fulfilled a thou-

[8] The liberal or classical side of education which was assured by the terms of the Morrill Act is stressed by H. F. French, president of Massachusetts State College, in his "Agricultural Colleges," in Commissioner of Agriculture, *Report,* 1865, pp. 137 ff. The enrollment figures are from French: loc. cit.; Dunaway: *History of Pennsylvania State College,* p. 67; *Prairie Farmer,* XV (Feb. 11, 1865), p. 88; Vivian Wiser: "Maryland in the Early Land Grant College Movement," *Agricultural History,* XXXVI (October 1962), 194; J. F. Hopkins: *The University of Kentucky* (Lexington, K.Y., 1951), p. 84. Of the 412 students at Cornell in its first year, only 30 were in agriculture, and most of the 30 were city boys. Colman: *Education & Agriculture,* p. 27.

sand times over in the future, but for the time being the story was different. Legislative investigations showed poor planning and failure to draw upon the best available knowledge provided by Pugh, French, and Klippart of the methods of teaching agriculture abroad. Moreover, the returns from the land grants and the supplementary funds appropriated by the states were too small to accomplish much.

The honeymoon of the new institutions lasted only a short time before disillusionment set in. Instruction in agriculture was woefully conducted—if, indeed, it existed at all in the new institutions. At Cornell there were professors of agricultural chemistry, botany, and veterinary medicine from the outset, and surely this was progress as contemplated in the Morrill Act, but there was no effective instruction in agriculture. At Kentucky there were no courses in agriculture or mechanics because, as a recent historian has said, these were new fields in American education and qualified teachers were not available. At Vermont there was an agricultural department but no staff. Elsewhere the record was similar; sciences relating to agriculture were taught, as they were coming to be in some of the older classical institutions, but practical instruction in agriculture was either nonexistent or ineffective. Small wonder that farmers and their representatives were distressed at the slight benefits agriculture was deriving from the A & M colleges and that they showed their disapproval by numerous attacks upon the colleges, their curricula, their reversion to the neoclassical emphasis.[9] However, the groundwork for the development of higher education in agriculture and engineering had been laid in the creation of many new institutions, and awareness of state responsibility had been partly accepted, a few able administrators were emerging, and some young, enthusiastic, and gifted scientists were shortly to come from these colleges. The promise was there but the fulfillment was yet to come.

---

[9] Jonas Viles: *The University of Missouri* (Columbia, Mo., 1939), p. 160 ff.; James Gray: *The University of Minnesota* (Minneapolis, 1951), pp. 97 ff., in addition to previous works cited.

Achievement of Homestead

IT HAS BEEN CHARACTERISTIC of settlers in the New World, whether on the first frontier in the Virginia and Plymouth colonies or on the last in the high plains, to take up more land than they could utilize efficiently in a lifetime. Whether or not they had the means to improve even a small part of their holdings, farmers all wanted to engross as large a tract as possible either in the hope of obtaining a speculative profit from the sale of the surplus or to make sure of land for their children as the country filled up. This land grabbing had the effect of scattering settlement in newly developing areas, thus making the building and maintenance of roads and other public improvements more difficult. It also kept the owners poor because of the burden of carrying their surplus and unproductive investment in land. As Horace Greeley put it, thousands "who were grabbing all the land within sight of their log cabins . . . and fondly expecting to become speedily rich by land speculation have suddenly awakened to the realization that their land grabbing has ruined them."[1] Indeed, it may be said that their speculative operations tended to slow down the growth of land values, which was just what the farmer-speculators did not want to do. Although farm papers continued to point out that a small well-cultivated farm in a compactly settled area was more desirable than a large block of wild land which was little improved, the desire to possess extensive acres,

---

[1] Greeley wrote this from Davenport, Iowa, Jan. 29, 1860. *New York Tribune,* Feb. 7, 1860.

which some thought gave a man a higher social status, never seemed to abate.

The first generation of farmers invested a lifetime of work in making a farm. Aside from housing, their immediate need was to prepare a small cleared or broken tract for wheat or corn to carry them over the first or second year. A crude cabin was constructed, and clearing and even fencing were hastily done without thought of durability but only to meet the pressing needs of the moment. Thereafter, farmers could be more deliberate in carrying out their improvements, but the task was no less hard or time-consuming. Girdling or cutting the trees, burning the logs, grubbing out brush and removing the stumps, clearing off the rocks, "laying up the stone fences" or splitting rails for worm or post and rail fences, draining wet areas, building the frame house, and making such enlargements as conditions required—these continued to absorb whatever time was not devoted to caring for the crops and the livestock, attending to marketing, performing the usual community obligations of road work, and school and church activities.

The seemingly everlasting process of farm making went on both on the outer edge of settlement and in the older areas, where farmers were continuing to clear and cultivate larger portions of their holdings. As the son of a northern Michigan pioneer said, they began "to clear land the first summer and kept doggedly at it month in and month out until the sons grew up and the father grew old. . . ." As the rate of clearing might average five acres a year, a lifetime was none too much to make a farm in a wooded area. In long-settled states such as New York and Pennsylvania, it has been seen that expansion of the area in cultivation was proceeding as late as the Civil War. Farther west in Indiana and Illinois, where the frontier stage had passed more recently, wild land was being subjected to cultivation more rapidly both by the creation of new farms on land previously held by speculators and by farmers fencing, breaking, and seeding larger portions of their tracts.[2]

---

[2] U. P. Hedrick: *The Land of the Crooked Tree* (New York, 1948), p. 63. The statistics are from *Ninth Census of the United States, 1870, Industry and Wealth,* pp. 81, 86. M. L. Primack: "Land Clearing under Nineteenth Century Techniques," *Journal of Economic History,* XXII (December 1962), 484.

Some pioneer farm makers who spent the best part of a lifetime in their task found at the end of their days that their farm was worn out and worth little. This was often the fate of farmers in the hill sections of New England, New York, and other portions of the country where slopes, soil, weather, and the concentration upon marketable crops made for erosion and diminishing fertility. The years of unremitting labor which farmers invested in their farms did not deter many of them from selling out and striking west for what they thought was the land of opportunity. Perhaps they were pessimistic about ridding themselves of the demands of their mortgage, were disillusioned with the yields their soil returned after all their labor, were troubled by the competition of crops produced on freshly cultivated land elsewhere, were tenants finally despairing of ever gaining ownership, or were attracted by accounts of fertile but cheap lands available and the rapid rise of land values in the West. Perhaps it was the restlessness so characteristic of American life which sent them on.

The high turnover of farming properties generally throughout the country can be seen in the many advertisements of farms for sale and in the census data. It has been emphasized that in 1860 42 per cent of the Vermont-born people had left their native state for opportunities elsewhere, mostly in communities farther west. South Carolina was similar, with 41 per cent of its native-born people living in other states. Then came Tennessee (35%), Connecticut (33%), New Hampshire (33%), and Kentucky (32%). This mobility of the farm population led an English agricultural authority who toured the Northern states to declare that "Every farm from Eastport, Maine, to Buffalo on Lake Erie is for sale."[3]

Farming was a most demanding occupation and its returns were frequently slight, or at least appeared slight to its participants in comparison with the advantages urban residents enjoyed. Progress toward the ten-hour day for workingmen made

---

[3] J. F. W. Johnston: *Notes on North America: Agricultural, Economical and Social* (2 vols., Edinburgh, 1851), I, 162. The percentages of the native-born living outside their state of birth are computed from *Eighth Census of the United States, 1860, Population*, pp. 616–17.

farmers contrast that with the much longer hours and exhausting work their occupation required. The flight to the city was under way. Many tried to reverse this disillusionment with farming and to divert the unrest that led to farm abandonment in poorer areas and the high turnover of farms elsewhere. Editors of farm journals, orators at state and county fairs, and politicians appealing for rural votes glorified the farmer's life, his independence and freedom, his healthy outdoor occupation, his importance in making America "great." Yet the migration westward of farmers from the older states and the high turnover of farms in newer regions continued.

In the public-land states certain marked tendencies were coming to light that caused concern. Large quantities of the better lands in the West were passing into the control of land companies, banks, and individual speculators. Agrarian leaders charged that land monopoly and the emergence of tenancy was imminent, and that there was a large class of landless farm laborers. What, they asked, had happened to the Jeffersonian dream of so molding the public-land system as to make America a land of small farm owners? The question was well put.

Long before 1860, westward-moving land seekers had reached the oak openings in Michigan, the small prairies in Ohio, and the larger prairies of northern Indiana, central and eastern Illinois, and eastern Iowa. Here they were to experiment with the process of adapting their farm-making techniques to treeless areas distant from timber for fencing, housing, and fuel, to prairie sod extremely difficult to break up for cultivation, and to tracts poorly drained. By 1860 they had overcome their suspicion of the prairies as being infertile because they had no growing trees. They had learned how to break the prairie sod with steel-tipped plows and were becoming aware of the richness of its soil. So also had capitalists come to realize how productive prairie soil could be and how profitable speculation in the public lands of the prairie states might be.

By 1860 the speculative excitement over public lands in Michigan, Illinois, Mississippi, Alabama, Iowa, and Wisconsin had led to the transfer of many million acres to institutions and individuals who planned only to hold them for resale at a higher price. In Iowa and Illinois alone a very conservative estimate

would place the amount of speculatively owned land at 12,000,-
000 and 8,000,000 acres respectively. In Minnesota less than half
the land in private ownership was in farms in 1860, most of the
balance being held by investors. Horace Greeley estimated in
1860 that this intrusion of the speculator between the government
and the settler had already cost the actual improvers of land between $500,000,000 and $600,000,000 in increased prices, interest payments, sheriff's fees, and losses from foreclosed mortgages.
Also, some 23,000,000 acres in Illinois, Iowa, Missouri, Wisconsin, and other states of the Mississippi Valley had been granted
to aid in the construction of railroads and the most successful
of these railroads was selling its land at prices ranging from six
to fifteen dollars an acre. Again, these grants were raising the
costs of land and thereby lengthening the time it would take a
settler to acquire full ownership of his farm.[4]

The amount of speculative and unimproved land held by
farmers themselves should not be overlooked. In 1860 farmers in
Iowa had 3,792,702 acres of improved land and 6,277,115 acres
of unimproved land, or 65 per cent more land unimproved than
was improved. This was in the state boasting the highest proportion of land suitable for improvement. In Indiana, Michigan,
and Wisconsin, only half the land in farms was improved. The
only states of the upper Mississippi Valley which had well over
half the land in farms improved were Ohio and Illinois, and even
there large amounts of land were still reported as unimproved.
Many farmers in these states remained in the farm-making stage
almost a lifetime because, as the statistics suggest, they had
undertaken to own and develop more land than they had the
energy and resources to master.

Much the same situation existed in all the Southern states
save Maryland and Delaware. A combination of planters and
speculators had bought up large amounts of land which were not
to be utilized in any substantial way until well after the 1860's.
Eleven states had a ratio greater than two to one of unimproved
to improved land in farms. In Louisiana the ratio was three to
one, in Arkansas four to one, and in Texas eight to one. In addi-

---

[4] P. W. Gates: *The Farmer's Age* (New York, 1960), p. 80; *New York Tribune*, Jan. 26, 1860.

tion a great deal of land in Arkansas, Alabama, Louisiana, Mississippi, and Texas was held by speculators without any development. As events were to show, after the Civil War the Southern states were capable of greatly expanding their cultivated area. The notion that the South had about reached its ultimate capacity in the use of land for cotton was without any foundation.

Costs of farm making were increasing as settlers moved into the prairies of Illinois, Iowa, Kansas, Minnesota, or Texas. More important was the fact that initial capital requirements to commence operations were heavier. Lumber for housing and fencing and expensive breaking plows hauled by a number of pairs of oxen or horses were required. One could hire custom prairie breakers to do the initial plowing but that was also expensive. Pioneers could no longer expect to subsist on game for a time. Furthermore, with corn or wheat almost the sole crops of the pioneer, he needed some financial reserve to carry him through till the first harvest. It is not too much to estimate that between $750 and $1,500 was required to bring a prairie farm into partial production.[5]

The increasing capital costs of farm making and the engrossment of much of the better lands by speculators and land companies made the West no longer a refuge open to distressed and impecunious people. Of the hundreds of thousands of immigrants pouring into Illinois, Iowa, Kansas, and Minnesota, many lacked the means to develop the raw prairie. They first turned to construction jobs on canals, on railroads, or in the developing towns and cities, or they accepted employment offered by established farmers. The census of 1860 showed that between 20 and 30 per cent of the people engaged in agriculture in the upper Mississippi Valley were farm laborers. Though a considerable portion of the laborers were farmers' sons who had not come of age and were working at home, many others were migratory and more or less permanent farm laborers.[6]

---

[5] C. H. Danhof: "Farm-Making Costs and the 'Safety Valve': 1850–1860," *Journal of Political Economy*, XLIX (June 1941), 317 ff.
[6] P. W. Gates: "Frontier Estate Builders and Farm Laborers," in

W. D. Wyman and C. B. Kroeber (eds.): *The Frontier in Perspective* (Madison, Wis., 1957), pp. 143 ff. Cf. Merle Curti: *The Making of an American Community* (Stanford, Calif., 1959), pp. 141 ff.

ACREAGE IN FARMS, 1860

NORTHERN STATES

	IMPROVED	UNIMPROVED
California	2,468,034	6,262,000
Connecticut	1,830,807	673,457
Illinois	13,096,374	7,815,615
Indiana	8,242,183	8,146,109
Iowa	3,792,792	6,277,715
Kansas	405,468	1,372,932
Maine	2,704,133	3,023,538
Massachusetts	2,155,512	1,183,212
Michigan	3,476,296	3,554,538
Minnesota	556,250	2,155,718
New Hampshire	2,367,034	1,377,519
New Jersey	1,944,441	1,039,084
New York	14,358,403	6,616,555
Ohio	12,625,394	7,840,747
Oregon	864,414	1,164,125
Pennsylvania	10,463,296	6,548,844
Rhode Island	335,128	186,096
Vermont	2,823,157	1,451,257
Wisconsin	3,740,167	4,147,420
Total	88,281,283	70,835,453

SOUTHERN STATES

	IMPROVED	UNIMPROVED
Alabama	6,385,724	12,718,891
Arkansas	1,983,313	7,590,393
Delaware	637,065	367,230
Florida	654,213	2,266,015
Georgia	8,062,758	18,587,732
Kentucky	7,644,208	11,519,053
Louisiana	2,707,108	6,591,468
Maryland	3,002,267	1,833,304
Mississippi	5,065,755	10,773,929
Missouri	6,246,871	13,737,939
N. Carolina	6,517,284	17,245,685
S. Carolina	4,572,000	11,623,859
Tennessee	6,795,337	13,873,828
Texas	2,650,781	22,693,247
Virginia	11,437,821	19,679,215
Total	69,462,565	171,181,988

SOURCE: *Eighth Census of the United States, 1860, Agriculture,*
p. 184.

Some Western immigrants, anxious to have a stake in the land, preferred to become tenants on the land of speculators or bonanza farmers, hoping that in the future they might be able to acquire sufficient livestock and equipment so that, with a little capital and a big mortgage they could set up as independent farmers. At the same time owners of extensive tracts found that it was sometimes more profitable to rent portions of their holdings to tenants on a share or cash rent basis than to hire laborers who, without a direct interest in the land, were not good workers. Tenancy was becoming so common that few people in the newer states could have been ignorant of its existence, although the Census Bureau did not take cognizance of it until 1880.

As early as 1854 *The Independent* of La Salle, Illinois, said in its price current section that country farms were renting for $1.50 to $2.00 per acre and cultivated land with housing for $3 per acre. If the tenant provided seeds, equipment, and working cattle, he paid one third of the crops to the landlord. By 1860 most of the great landlord estates of Illinois that were to last into the twentieth century were established, and settlers who did not wish to go farther west were drawn to them when the land available for purchase was held at prices beyond their means. Among these great estates were the 55,000-acre holding of the family of Matthew T. Scott, William Scully's 38,000 acres, Isaac Funk's 26,000 acres, and John Dean Gillett's 16,000 acres. Scott sold portions of his land to aid in carrying the balance, on which he was constructing homes, breaking the prairie, and encouraging tenants to take up farms by promising them deeds if they would pay him one half of six or eight crops of corn. Scully insisted that tenants should make their own improvements, which they could sell to successor tenants with the landlord's permission. Funk and Gillett, who were cattlemen, had ready use for all the corn their tenants could produce.

Between the Wabash and the Kankakee Valleys in northwestern Indiana and extending across into Illinois, there is a rich black-soiled prairie region where large holdings were acquired early and developed into great cattle ranches. Some of these ranches were to survive into the seventies, but others were in part divided into tenant holdings, with the tenants' share of the grain being sold to the landlord for his cattle-feeding operations.

The tenants seemed to be somewhat shiftless, their equipment was poor, the fields were not well cultivated, and the land was kept in corn year after year. Years later such continued abuse of rich soil was reflected in declining yields.[7]

Tenancy in the antebellum South is even harder to quantify but scattered bits of information in the original census schedules are informative. Since the printed schedules did not call for facts concerning tenancy, there are no systematic tabulations of them. Yet for Dallas County, a rich cotton county of central Alabama, 41 tenants are listed as living on holdings ranging from 20 to 1,000 acres and producing cotton, where these figures are given, of 4 to 147 bales. In Greene County evidence of 141 tenants was found.[8]

We may generalize that tenancy was not unknown in any part of the country, that it was becoming increasingly common in the newer states, and that permanent tenancy, where there was no prospect of the tenant acquiring ownership, was being established.

Many immigrants coming into the older public-land states were deterred from settling there by the large speculative ownerships, the extensive acreage in farms that was undeveloped, the great landlord estates operated by tenants, the high price for which undeveloped land was held, and the heavy mortgages they would have to take on. Other persons who had struggled to become farm owners by commencing as hired laborers or tenants or by buying on long-term credits from speculators, land companies, and the land-grant railroads also became discouraged, especially after the panic of 1857 set in and during the hard times

---

[7] *The Independent* (La Salle, Ill.), Mar. 4, 1854; Fred Gerhard: *Illinois as It Is* (Chicago, 1857), p. 404; M. B. Bogue: *Patterns from the Sod. Land Use and Tenure in the Grand Prairie, 1850–1900 (Collections of the Illinois State Historical Library,* XXXIV, Springfield, Ill., 1959), pp. 89 ff.; P. W. Gates: *Frontier Landlords and Pioneer Tenants* (Ithaca, N.Y., 1945), pp. 28 ff.; *idem:* "Cattle Kings in the Prairies," *Mississippi Valley Historical Review,* XXXV (December 1948), 379 ff.; *idem:* "Hoosier Cattle Kings," *Indiana Magazine of History,* XLIV (March 1948), 1 ff.; H. M. Cavanagh: *Funk of Funk's Grove. Farmer, Legislator, and Cattle King of the Old Northwest, 1797–1865* (Bloomington, Ill., 1952), *passim;* Danhof: "Farm-Making Costs," p. 323.

[8] Original Census Schedules of 1860, Alabama State Department of Archives and History.

which followed and lasted until 1862. Many of them gave up the struggle and set out again for the frontier, where they might try again to become farm owners. The census of 1860 revealed the strength of the migration from newer states to the frontier. For example, 30 per cent of the free population born in Alabama and 26 per cent of the free people born in Mississippi were living outside these states, mostly in Arkansas and Louisiana. Similarly, Indiana and Illinois had 22 and 16 per cent respectively of their native-born living outside, mostly in Iowa, Missouri, Kansas, and Wisconsin. Even Iowa, first opened to settlement in 1838 and admitted as a state in 1846, had 16 per cent of its native-born living farther out on frontiers before its own public lands were gone. As early as 1860 the Hannibal and St. Joseph Railroad recognized the possibility of obtaining settlers from Illinois for its lands in northern Missouri by advertising in the *Prairie Farmer*. Within a few years most of the trans-Missouri railroads with lands for sale, being aware of the unrest and discontent among farm laborers, tenants, and farm operators oppressed with heavy debts, were to undertake advertising campaigns in Illinois and even in the first tier of states west of the Mississippi.[9]

Those who clung to the hope of purchasing good lands from the government proceeded farther west to the outer edge of settlement, well away from railroads and other transportation facilities, from church and school, and, indeed, from other white folks. It was the elusive cheap or free land that drew them on, but to find it they had to precede the speculator into western Iowa, Minnesota, the newly opened eastern portions of Kansas and Nebraska, and Texas, leaving behind them speculators' deserts in Illinois and central Iowa where landlords were advertising for tenants and prospective tenants were advertising for land to rent.[1]

[9] *Eighth Census of the United States, 1860, Population*, pp. 616–617; *Prairie Farmer*, V (Feb. 18, 1860), 111.

[1] *Bloomington Pantagraph* (Bloomington, Ill.), Nov. 5, 1856; *Middleport Weekly Press* (Middleport, Ill.), Feb. 13, Mar. 20, 1861; *Kansas News* (Emporia, Kans.), Jan. 15, 22, Mar. 19, 1859, Aug. 24, 1861; *Neosho Valley Register* (Burlington, Kans.), Feb. 21, 1860; "Biographical Sketch of G. M. Dodge," Grenville Dodge MSS., Iowa State Historical Department, Des Moines, CXXII, 97. Edward Eggleston pictures in his perceptive but highly romantic *Mystery of Metropolisville* (New York, 1873), p. 106, the blighting effect of a land company on a portion of Minnesota in 1856.

Would-be settlers and speculators alike by 1860 were brought up against the permanent Indian country out of which present-day Kansas, Nebraska, and Oklahoma have been created. Through a combination of events, political and otherwise, Congress was induced to throw open the first two areas to settlement before the Indian title had been surrendered and the Indians removed to a more remote frontier. Land seekers swept over the eastern portions of the new territories, disregarding the Indians' rights, and established their preemption claims with little or no evidence of actual improvement. Much of the marching and counter-marching of the pro- and anti-slavery elements in Kansas, when carefully examined, appears to have been rooted in land speculation schemes. Few of the claim owners, whether they were actual settlers or bogus ones crossing the Missouri border to vote and control land, had the means to buy their lands when these finally came on the market; many were ready to sell their claims for a small profit, using their preemption rights contrary to the spirit of the law.

The road to land ownership for persons with limited means was becoming increasingly difficult and uncertain as settlers thrust westward into the prairies. The panic of 1857 halted railroad construction and urban development, tumbled the prices of farm commodities, made jobs and money scarce, and produced a Federal deficit which, in turn, induced President Buchanan to order many million acres of public land to be sold in Kansas, Nebraska, Minnesota, Wisconsin, and California. Because much of the land was good or even choice for agriculture and portions were certain to be selected for new territorial capitals, county seats, land-office towns, and termini of railroads, it would be in keen demand.

Squatters anxious to purchase and develop their claims were obliged to preempt and pay for them at $1.25 an acre before the land auction; otherwise the improved claim would be subject to purchase by others. In this instance the lands were put up for sale before the settlers had had a chance to accumulate the purchase money. Credit was always available under such circumstances to enable the settler to enter his tract, but at a high price. In the years just before the Civil War interest rates ranged from

20 to 120 per cent on the outer edge of the frontier, the more common rate being 30 to 50 per cent. Moneylenders at government sales reaped a great harvest in this period. Business conditions did not improve until 1862 and in the meantime most of the debtors were unable to prevent their creditors from foreclosing on their improved claims. One Shylock in Fillmore County, Minnesota, foreclosed 30 of 58 mortgages, and there is no reason to think him unusual. He estimated that there were liens on three fourths of the farms of Minnesota.[2]

For a decade land reformers had been deploring the existence of great landlord-owned estates, the increasing numbers of farm tenants and farm laborers, the concentrated ownership of land by railroads and speculators, the increased cost of farm making, and the burden of mortgage indebtedness. They argued that the government, in selling at $1.25 an acre land which it would take an abundance of capital and years of hard labor to transform into sucessful farms, was placing an additional, at times an impossible, hurdle in the way of ownership. They held that wild land on the frontier had no value until it was improved by the labor of the settlers, by the taxes paid by residents for roads, schools, and town and county government, and by the construction of railroads, paid for in part out of the high freight rates. Since it was the investment of the farmer's labor and the public's money that made land valuable, it seemed to these reformers double taxation to make settlers pay for government land. Andrew Jackson, George W. Julian, and Horace Greeley were precursors of Henry George in maintaining that wild land on the frontier had no value, that its value came from the improvements made upon it and in its vicinity. Jackson in his annual message to Congress of December 4, 1832, urged that "the public lands shall cease as soon as practicable to be a source of revenue." It is the labor of the adventurous and hardy population of the West "alone which gives value to the lands." In the *New York Weekly Tribune* of June 14, 1862, Greeley said that the settler who "trans-

---

[2] P. W. Gates: *Fifty Million Acres. Conflicts over Kansas Land Policy, 1854–1890* (Ithaca, N.Y., 1954), pp. 72 ff.; Margaret Snyder: *The Chosen Valley. The Story of a Pioneer Town* (New York, 1948), pp. 158, 301.

forms by his labor a patch of rugged forest or bleak prairie into a fruitful, productive farm, pays for his land all that we think he ought to pay."[3]

It was in the severe times following the panic of 1857 that the West's demand for free lands reached its peak. Congressional views on homestead were influenced by sectional controversies over slavery, Kansas, immigration, and the role of the foreigner in politics, as well as by the South's fear that free lands would make for more rapid growth of the upper Mississippi Valley and thereby further disturb the balance between the two sections. Greeley predicted that free homesteads would discourage land speculation and would make settlers less dependent on Eastern credit with its high interest rates. On the other hand, speculators in Western lands, including a number of influential Southern members of Congress, feared that free government land would ruin their investment. From the angry discussions of 1859 and 1860 finally emerged an emasculated homestead bill that postponed any further sales of public lands for two years but did not provide for free lands. Even this crumb of relief was denied settlers, for Buchanan, who had earlier led them to believe that sales would be postponed until the public lands were covered with preemption claims, vetoed the measure and insisted that the sales be held.[4]

The Republican Party, meantime, was firmly committed to a free-land policy, though its leadership refused to follow Greeley, Julian, and other advanced reformers in supporting the thoroughgoing pro-settler law they advocated. A free-homestead bill could

---

[3] J. D. Richardson (ed.): *Messages and Papers of the Presidents* (9 vols., New York, 1904), III, 1164; *Country Gentleman*, XIX (May 22, 1863), 338. The writer in this journal disparaged the Homestead Act because it offered land of no value to settlers.
[4] G. M. Stephenson: *Political History of the Public Lands from 1840 to 1862* (Boston, 1917), p. 132 ff.; Gates: *Fifty Million Acres*, p. 89; P. S. Klein: *President James Buchanan* (University Park, Pa., 1962), p. 346; Cyrus Woodman, March 31, 1852, to B. C. Eastman, Woodman MSS., and P. W. Ellsworth, Jan. 30, 1860, to M. M. Strong, Strong MSS., Wisconsin State Historical Society; J. S. Easley, July 6, 1860, to George Weare, Easley MSS., University of Virginia Library. John Slidell, R. M. T. Hunter, W. B. Stokes, and Eli Shorter were substantial investors in Northern land and opposed the Homestead bill. *Cong. Globe*, 36 Cong., 1 Sess., May 10, 1860, p. 2043, and 36 Cong., 2 Sess., Dec. 5, 1860, p. 16; *Buffalo County Journal* (Alma, Wis.), Mar. 13, 1862.

only pass if there was weakening of Southern opposition, which seemed unlikely, or if Southern opposition was stilled by secession. When the South withdrew, homestead was adopted with only token opposition from Democratic holdovers representing the border states and from Justin Smith Morrill and one or two other Republicans. Morrill, who showed vision and statesmanship in pushing through the Agricultural College Act, here questioned the wisdom of giving land away when the revenue needs of the government required that it be sold. His doubts were overcome by Julian, who assured him that the public lands had long since ceased to be an important source of revenue, since land warrants and land scrip, issued to veterans and others for aid or as compensation, were commonly purchased at a discount and used to enter government land.[5]

It is surprising that so little consideration was given in the press to Congress's major change in land policy. The *Prairie Farmer*, for example, merely mentioned the measure, as it did Morrill's Agricultural College Act likewise. Excitement over war news tended to displace concern about these and other economic measures.[6]

A long series of measures, adopted under Western pressure, had gradually reduced the price of public land and the size of the unit of sale. The Homestead law was the culmination of this development. To summarize briefly: The Homestead Act applied to any person who was twenty-one years old or older, or who was head of a family; who was a citizen, or who had filed his intention of becoming a citizen; and who had never been disloyal to the United States. The act offered him the right to settle on a quarter section of public land (or 80 acres, if the tract was within the primary area of railroad land grants) upon which there was no other claim and which was open to preemption. He could make his improvements and at the end of five years "prove up" and have a patent for his tract. On their final entry persons taking advantage of the act were required to affirm that they were not making the entry for others and that no part of the 160 or 80 acres had been conveyed to others, mortgaged, or in any way

---

[5] *Cong. Globe*, 37 Cong. 2 Sess., Dec. 18, 1861, p. 136.
[6] *Prairie Farmer*, IX (June 14, 1862), 371, and X (July 5, 1862), 8.

become liable for debt. Small fees were required for services rendered by land officers in handling the homestead entries.[7]

Free homesteads were criticized by people other than speculators in 1862. Some held that the law was partial and discriminatory in that the donation would only benefit persons who went to the West. Others held that it would drain off population from high-priced land and thereby lower land values in Eastern communities, that it would deprive older states of their share in the lands, and that it would reduce the value of soldiers' land bounties and of railroad land grants. Thurlow Weed, the millionaire lobbyist of the Republican Party, thought the public lands should have been used to "ballast the Treasury" by meeting the cost of the war and paying off the debt. But these were the cries of conservatives who feared the elevating effect that free land would have on the propertyless poor, the day laborer, the immigrant.[8]

If conservatives viewed with alarm the social results they foresaw from Homestead, the land reformers were disappointed that the thoroughgoing reconstruction of American land policies they had favored was not achieved. Homesteads were to be alienable, and the safeguards to prevent abuse of the law and the accumulation of settlers' rights by capitalists were weak and inadequate. The privilege of buying at $1.25 an acre unlimited quantities of public land which had once been offered at auction, a privilege which Galusha Grow and George W. Julian had tried to end, was retained, though, it should be noted, it was not to be the practice after 1862 to offer additional land at auction and thereby make it open to unlimited entry. However, at the time the Homestead law went into operation, there were approximately 135,000,000 acres of public land extending from Michigan to California that were surveyed and open to settlement. Of this amount 53,000,000 had been "offered" at auction and were therefore subject to sale in unlimited amounts. During the war additional land, mostly timbered, was offered in Wisconsin, Oregon, and Washington Territory, on the excuse that the timber would be lost to the government through pilfering or would be homesteaded improperly, even though the land was not suited for farm-

---

[7] 12 *U.S. Stat.*, p. 392.
[8] Thurlow Weed, Jan. 29, 1864, to Gov. E. D. Morgan, *National* *Intelligencer*, Feb. 24, 1864. Weed advocated the repeal of the Homestead Act.

ing. Surveying was continued, though at a much slower rate than in the past. Only 13,236,000 acres were surveyed between 1861 and 1865.

There were important provisions in previously enacted laws and in some enacted after 1862 which limited the areas where homesteaders could take advantage of the free lands the government was offering. Between 1862 and 1871 Congress granted to railroads, in alternate sections on the checkerboard plan of government surveys, land from ten to forty miles on each side of the lines thus being subsidized. If all the place grants had been available and earned, they would have totaled 155,000,000 acres, but since many tracts were already alienated the actual acreage received was 94,000,000 acres. To this should be added the 38,-000,000 given to the states to aid in the building of railroads. Railroads thus received an area five times as great as that of Ohio. An even larger limitation on the area open to homestead was the 140,000,000 acres given to states and territories to aid them in establishing common schools and universities and to construct public buildings. At least half of this large acreage was given after the adoption of the Homestead Act; a portion of the balance had been given before 1862 but was still held for sale and development. To the railroad and state grants thus withdrawn from homestead should be added 140,000,000 acres in Indian reservations that were in part to be allotted and sold, and great quantities of speculatively owned land, bringing the total of undeveloped land that would never be free to settlers to between 400,000,000 and 500,000,000 acres. In fact, the area not open to homestead, though undeveloped, was much greater than the total acreage that homesteaders were finally to win as free grants.[9]

Free-land policy as embodied in the Homestead law was grafted, then, upon a land system to which it was ill-fitted and incongruous. The two systems existed side by side for the next twenty-eight years—indeed, longer—during which time the

---

[9] The statistics are compiled from the *Annual Reports* of the Commissioner of the General Land Office; from Thomas Donaldson: *The Public Domain* (Washington, 1884); and from *Report of the Public Land Commission, Senate Documents*, 48 Cong., 3 Sess., 1905, no. 189.

choicer selections of the railroads, states, and speculators were being sold. Hence the amount of homesteading was smaller than it surely would have been otherwise.[1]

Contrary to the alarmist view of some that Homestead would lower land values in older areas and strike hard at land-grant railroads and other investors in land in the West, the measure had no such effect. Neither were Greeley and the *New York Tribune* correct in assuming that it would "greatly diminish if not entirely arrest that pernicious monopoly of the Public Lands" which past policy had permitted.[2] Throughout the war, speculators continued to pick up tracts that seemed to be good investments and land accumulation proceeded, though at a somewhat slower rate. In 1864 and 1865 lumbermen, speculator-promoters of town sites along the projected railroads, and other men of capital began the fourth great onslaught on the public lands. The remaining pinelands of the Lake states, much of the prairie land of east-central Kansas and eastern Nebraska, and most of the valley lands in California passed into their hands. The depression following the panic of 1873 slowed this movement for a time but after 1880 it began again in even greater volume. It may be roughly estimated that between forty and fifty million acres of public lands were thus acquired by speculators, lumbermen, town and colony promoters, and land companies between 1864 and 1869, when virtually all sales of large tracts were ended. These figures do not include the land they acquired through commutation and perversion of the settlement laws. Clearly capitalist investors were not deterred from investing in the public lands by the adoption of free homesteads.[3]

The retarding effect of land speculation upon the development of Iowa induced John A. Kasson, member of the House of Representatives, to propose a measure to allow Iowa to tax absentee-owned land more heavily than that which was locally owned. Congressmen may well have been amused at his efforts, for the no-discrimination feature had been basic in public-land

---

[1] P. W. Gates: "The Homestead Law in an Incongruous Land System," *American Historical Review*, XII (July, 1936), 652 ff.
[2] *New York Tribune*, May 6, 14, 1862.
[3] For large acquisitions of public lands between 1865 and 1869 see Gates: "Homestead Law," pp. 665 ff.

policy since the days of Hamilton and few would have dreamed of changing it. Kasson's proposal was buried in committee.[4]

By anticipating the actual settler or small stockman, these capitalist investors made it more difficult for the small man to acquire a stake in the land and to develop it. Added to other costs, it forced him to rely more heavily than his Eastern counterpart on borrowed funds, and it made his economic status less stable as the tide of prosperity rolled in and out. Thus it contributed to reduce many landowners to tenants and tenants to laborers, and increased the rate of turnover of farm properties. For permitting the right of unrestricted purchase of public lands until 1889 and tolerating the abuse of the settlement laws, Congress and the General Land Office share responsibility.

In the years immediately after 1862 both the wisdom of Congress in enacting the Homestead law and the many errors it had committed in the past in shaping land policies became obvious. In Illinois, although only 21,000,000 of its 35,000,000 acres were in farms, the public lands were gone. A large part of the land not in farms was in the hands of speculators or was held by the Illinois Central Railroad. In the first five months of the operation of the Homestead law the railroad sold 60,000 acres for an average price of better than $11 an acre on long-term credit. The risks involved in buying unimproved land at such prices are evidenced by the large number of sales that had to be canceled and extensions of time that had to be granted by the railroad to delinquent debtors. In other states the story was the same. In Missouri the Hannibal and St. Joseph Railroad was trying to draw settlers to its half million acres. In Iowa, numerous speculators and the American Emigrant Company, which had bought the swamplands of one of the counties; in Michigan, William T. Carroll and other absentee capitalists; in Minnesota, the state, wishing to dispose of its school lands; and in Wisconsin, combinations of speculators and railroads—all were anxious to attract immigrants, particularly immigrants with capital who could purchase land.[5]

---

[4] *Cong. Globe*, 39 Cong., 1 Sess., Dec. 11, 1865, p. 20.
[5] *Genesee Farmer*, XXIV (April 1863), 132; *Frankfort Tri-Weekly Commonwealth* (Frankfort, Ky.), May 4, 1863; *The Crisis*, (Columbus, Ohio), June 18, 1862; *National Intelligencer*, Feb. 20, 1862; *St. Paul Pioneer & Democrat*, July 7, 1862.

Where then were prospective settlers to look for the elusive free lands? The answer was given by a farmer in Blue Earth County, Minnesota, who had proceeded well beyond transportation facilities by railroad or river: he must go where land was remote, where he could not easily get his crops out and the cost of raising and hauling them to market would be greater than the return.[6] Though it was the prairie lands near timber that increasingly attracted settlers, those land seekers who did not care to go so far into the West as central Kansas, eastern Nebraska, or southeastern Dakota could find great areas that had hurriedly been passed over by land buyers in the past, such as parts of Trempealeau County, Wisconsin, portions of Michigan, considerable portions of Missouri, and the more remote prairie land of Minnesota. It was to these areas that homesteaders first turned.

Applications for filing homesteads were not to be accepted in the local land offices until January 1, 1863, to give the officers time to prepare for the expected rush. On New Year's Day, in thirty different land offices in the public-land states, anxious people were waiting to file their homestead applications when the offices opened. Because he was the most persistent in asserting that he filed the first claim, Daniel Freeman's homestead near Beatrice, Nebraska, was selected for the honor and his claim has been made the Homestead National Monument. The location is not inappropriate, for Nebraska ranks with Montana, North Dakota, and Colorado in the number of homestead filings carried to patent.[7]

It was in Minnesota that the greatest activity occurred in homesteading between 1863 and 1870. Even before Homestead became law, settlers attracted by the excellent wheat harvests of the last three years began a rush across the Mississippi into Minnesota. The *St. Paul Pioneer and Democrat* of June 29, 1862, described one group of families with twelve emigrant wagons on

---

[6] *Country Gentleman*, XVII (Apr. 18, 1861), 251; St. Paul *Pioneer & Democrat*, July 10, 1862; *Rural New Yorker*, XVI (June 27, 1865), 166.
[7] Ray N. Mattison: "Homestead National Monument: Its Establishment and Administration," *Nebraska History*, XLIV (March 1962), 1 ff.; Charles Plante and R. H. Mattison: "The 'First' Homestead," *Agricultural History*, XXXVI (October 1862), 183.

their way from Wisconsin to the free lands beyond. All ferries were crowded daily with emigrants who planned to select land and file their entries before the big rush occurred. At the Winnebago office fifty filings were being made every day, and at the St. Cloud office in the Sauk Valley not less than two hundred families had settled and filed for homesteads, according to dispatches in the *Pioneer and Democrat* of June 25, 1863. Actually filings for homestead could not be registered until January 1, 1863; these early entries were declaratory statements made under the provisions of the Preemption Law and could be changed to homestead filings after the first of the year.[8] In the first two and a half years of the operation of the act, 9,529 homestead entries were filed in Minnesota out of 26,552 for the entire country. Between January 1, 1863, and June 30, 1870, 25,663 entries were made in Minnesota, and the number of farms, as given in the census reports for 1860 and 1870, increased from 18,181 to 45,600. Oliver Hudson Kelley, later to be a founder of the Grange, in 1863 compared the homesteaders who were making farms on the public domain, which in five years they would own, with the absentee speculators who had patched "up the country with land warrants [and] entailed upon some portions of our State a curse not yet removed." Fortunately, he said, they had selected inferior lands and were not able to find customers for them.[9]

Wisconsin, too, had its rush of settlers eager to take up the free lands, with Trempealeau County, which Merle Curti has studied so usefully, being the center of activity. The *Galesville Transcript* reported on July 18, 1862, that many immigrants were coming in and already had made numerous excellent locations. During the first six months the Homestead Act was in

---

[8] J. M. Edmunds, Commissioner of the General Land Office, held that declaratory filings of intentions to preempt land could not be changed to homestead entries if made after May 20, 1862, the date of the enactment of the Homestead law. A check of a number of preemption entries filed after May 20 in the Winnebago and St. Cloud offices (in records in the National Archives), however, shows that they were successfully changed to homestead entries. There seem to have been no grounds for the arbitrary action of Edmunds. The *New York Tribune*, June 6, 1862, had assured interested enquirers that preemptions made after May 20 could be changed to homestead entries.
[9] Commissioner of Agriculture: *Report*, 1863, p. 35; *Census of 1880, Productions of Agriculture*, p. 25.

operation, the La Crosse land district had more homestead entries than any other. Unfortunately, of the homesteaders who filed their claims in Wisconsin in the first year under the act, a smaller proportion succeeded in proving up and making their final entries five years later than was the case in any other state save California.[1]

Homesteading was actively carried on during the war years in Michigan, Kansas, and Nebraska, and somewhat less actively in Iowa, Missouri, Washington, Oregon, Colorado, and Dakota. In California, where one would expect the continued heavy immigration to result in active homesteading, the number of original entries filed was small because the best undeveloped land was claimed under Mexican grants. There were frequent clashes between squatters and the Mexican grantees or their assignees. Because many of these claims had not been surveyed and patented, large areas in their vicinity were temporarily outside the public domain and not subject to homestead until exact boundaries had been determined. Furthermore, the state had grabbed as swampland well over two million acres, mostly in the San Joaquin Valley, which were to pass to large owners.[2]

Homesteading was slower to get under way in Missouri, the only slave state in which it applied, because of the turmoil there at the onset of war. In 1863 and 1864 only 236 filings were made, mostly north of the Missouri River; but in 1865 the rush to Missouri increased, with 3,193 homestead entries being made.[3]

The homestead claims of the sixties, seventies, and even eighties were made in the humid portions of Minnesota, Kansas,

[1] Curti: *Making of an American Community*, p. 212; *Galesville* (Wis.) *Transcript*, July 18, 1862.
[2] I have dealt with homesteading in Iowa in "The Homestead Law in Iowa," *Agricultural History*, XXXVIII (April 1964), 67 ff. Some of the difficulties of settlers in California are described in my "California's Embattled Settlers," *California Historical Society Quarterly*, XLI (June 1962), 99 ff. Thomas Donaldson's table differs somewhat from the figures in the

Annual Reports of the Commissioners of the General Land Office for 1863, 1864, and 1865. The total for the United States includes a few scattered entries in Ohio, Illinois, and Nevada.
[3] The Bureau of Land Management brought out in 1962 a valuable booklet entitled *Homesteads* which shows by tables and charts the number and acreage of homestead entries that were carried to patent from 1868 to 1961.

ORIGINAL HOMESTEAD ENTRIES, CIVIL WAR YEARS

STATE	1863		1864		1865		Total
	no.	acres	no.	acres	no.	acres	no.
California	343	52,289	494	75,919	279	41,822	1,116
Colorado	—	—	304	45,306	157	24,284	461
Dakota	75	11,829	111	17,660	64	10,107	250
Iowa	184	18,978	284	29,546	578	64,540	1,046
Kansas	1,149	173,725	678	96,258	383	51,544	2,210
Missouri	20	1,400	216	22,408	786	66,488	1,022
Michigan	1,531	185,939	1,572	207,879	741	94,659	2,844
Minnesota	2,299	277,526	3,258	428,487	3,972	531,707	9,529
Nebraska	349	50,775	769	114,649	812	114,875	1,930
Oregon	200	28,813	144	21,092	203	20,051	547
Wisconsin	1,677	164,643	1,079	111,058	733	77,929	3,489
Washington T.	341	53,183	447	69,998	211	33,227	999
United States	8,223	1,032,871	9,405	1,247,170	8,924	1,141,443	26,552

SOURCE: Thomas Donaldson: *The Public Domain* (Washington, 1884), p. 351.

Nebraska, and California, and on some fair agricultural land in Michigan and Wisconsin. In Minnesota, Kansas, and Nebraska, 56, 58, and 60 per cent respectively of the homesteaders filing their entries between 1863 and 1870 had proved up and taken title at the end of five years. These percentages, which are substantially greater than for later years, show that the Homestead law worked well in these states in the early years of its operation despite the restlessness of the frontiersmen, the long droughts, and the destructive grasshopper plagues of the sixties.[4]

Historians who have belittled the significance of the Homestead Act need to take another look at the part it played in the development of areas both east and west of the Mississippi. Despite its shortcomings, the act cannot be called a distressing disappointment. True, homesteading on rangeland unsuited for farming units of 160 or 320 acres did not work well and there

[4] Cf. J. C. Malin: "The Turnover of Farm Population in Kansas," *Kansas Historical Quarterly*, IV (November 1935), 339 ff., and A. G. Bogue: *Money at Interest. The Farm Mortgage on the Middle Border* (Ithaca, N.Y., 1955), pp. 209 ff.

was much abuse of the law. But at least until 1880 the privilege the act provided was made good use of by actual settlers. Recent scholarship suggests that the Homestead Act was, as its framers expected, constructive and far-reaching in its results.[5]

By the conclusion of the Civil War the Homestead Act was contributing to the rapid development of the West and the division of the arable lands into family farms. But the other side of the picture must not be forgotten. Along with the homesteaders taking advantage of the government's bounty were the speculators, engrossing their thousands of acres, and the cattlemen, building their great ranches with capital provided from abroad.

Without railroads to bring in settlers and to link them with markets for their crops and livestock, homestead would have been an empty promise, as was well understood by all true advocates of Western growth. All the benefits that Stephen A. Douglas had predicted from railroad land grants came swiftly with the construction of the first land-grant railroad, the Illinois Central. Its immediate and spectacular success and its effect on the growth of Chicago induced the city fathers of Minneapolis, Milwaukee, St. Louis, Rock Island, Burlington, Memphis, and New Orleans to ask for aid to railroads then being planned from these points. Southerners, no matter how rigid they were on interpreting the Constitution, could scarcely oppose aid to railroads for their states, and numerous grants were voted by Congress to the five Southern public-land states (six, if Missouri is included) and the five Northern public-land states and territories. These grants, and the confidence they gave to promoters of railroads, made possible the spreading of the railroad network in the two tiers of states east and west of the Mississippi River and the opening up of great new areas to settlement and agricultural development.

Major beneficiaries of this government aid program were the five Northern states of Michigan, Illinois, Wisconsin, Minnesota, and Iowa, in which 4,501 miles of railroad were built

---

[5] L. B. Lee: "Homesteading in Zion," *Utah Historical Quarterly,* XXVIII (January 1960), 215 ff.; P. W. Gates: "The Homestead Act: Free Land Policy in Operation, 1862–1935" in Howard Ottoson (ed.), *Land Use Policy and Problems in the United States* (Lincoln, Nebr., 1963), pp. 3 ff.

between 1850 and 1860. These states added 209,910 new farms and increased the amount of improved land by 15,925,008 acres. The increases were to be of major importance during the war in enabling that section to meet military requirements for corn and wheat and also to ship abroad the huge surpluses of grain and flour that were exchanged for munitions and other instruments of war.

In the five states of the Confederacy which received land-grant aid for railroads—Alabama, Arkansas, Florida, Louisiana, and Mississippi—1,631 miles of railroad were built, 49,460 new farms were established, and 6,195,537 acres of new land were improved in the fifties. Missouri, the sixth slave state to receive railroad land grants, built 1,948 miles of railroad and added 38,334 new farms and 3,308,446 acres of improved land. Only Illinois exceeded Missouri's agricultural growth. The South desperately needed the food and manpower of Missouri, as well as of Kentucky, and made every effort to win their support, only to be outfoxed by Lincoln.[6]

The connection between land grants, railroad construction, growth of population, expansion of agriculture, and rising land values was apparent to most progressive politicians. Support for government aid was halted only by the outmoded constitutional views of the element in control of the Democratic Party, which questioned the power of the Federal government to make land grants. Projects for a Pacific railroad to tie California to the Mississippi Valley, which Douglas was anxious to aid, therefore had to wait. Moreover, the jealous South feared that the growing states of the upper Mississippi Valley would diminish its influence in American affairs. Lincoln and the Republicans had no such scruples or fears and on July 1, 1862, the Pacific railroad bill, as important for agriculture as the Homestead Act and the Morrill Agricultural College Act, was signed. The main line of the Pacific railroad extending from Omaha, Nebraska, to the Pacific was granted ten alternate sections of public land for each

---

[6] Statistics of annual construction of railroads are found in H. V. Poor: *Manual of the Railroads of the United States, 1869–70* (New York, 1869), pp. xxvi–xxvii, and the data on the number of farms and the improved acres are from *Eighth Census of the United States, 1860, Agriculture*, pp. 184–188, 222.

mile of its line within a twenty-mile strip. Generous government credit to aid in construction was also provided.[7]

Conscription and the demands of war, accompanied by active recruiting for labor and inflated wages, all made it difficult to enlist large numbers of workers on construction jobs in 1861–5. Furthermore, immigration had not yet fully recovered from the depression of 1857–62. Also, capital was drawn into other more profitable ventures where the returns would be immediate. Yet the westward progress of the iron rails was notable, particularly in states in which active homesteading was being done. Minnesota led with 213 miles, followed by California with 191, Nebraska with 122, Missouri with 108, and Wisconsin with 105.[8]

During the war years, with the Republicans in control in Washington, Congress overrode all constitutional doubts about the government's power to give land to farm makers, to make grants for railroad construction and for the endowment of agricultural colleges, to create a department of agriculture, and, one should add, to provide for a national banking system. With these steps taken and the Union restored, the country was set in 1865 for a great period of economic expansion in which railroad building, the westward movement of population, and the creation of farms and new commonwealths were to proceed at a rate that outdid all previous records.

In the Confederacy there was some uncertainty concerning responsibility for the public lands previously administered by the Federal government. Article 44, section 3, paragraph 2 of the Confederate Constitution stated: "Congress shall have power to dispose of and make all needful rules and regulations concerning the property of the Confederate States, including the lands thereof."[9] This was not to be, however, because the five Southern public-land states proceeded to extend their administration over the lands.

Alabama in its state convention created a State Land Office with a commissioner as its head, reenacted the preemption and

---

[7] 12 *U.S. Stat.*, p. 489.
[8] *Poor's Railroad Manual*, 1869–70, p. xxvii; P. W. Gates: "The Railroads of Missouri," *Missouri Historical Review*, XXVI (January 1932), 138–39.

[9] *Provisional and Permanent Constitutions of the Confederate States* (Richmond, 1861), p. 29; C. R. Lee, Jr.: *The Confederate Constitutions* (Chapel Hill, N.C., 1963), p. 195.

graduation acts of the United States, retained the $1.25 an acre for lands outside the primary areas of railroad land grants and $2.50 an acre for the reserved lands within the primary areas, declared that the military bounty warrants were to be accepted as before, and, what is startling, offered every non-landowning citizen eighty acres, free of all costs and charges, provided he resided upon and improved the land in the year following the entry. The size of the free homestead was half that which the United States was to offer in 1863, but there were to be no fees. The offer of free homesteads in Alabama, restricted to its own citizens, involved no danger to the plantation class, but the possibility of free homesteads in Kansas or Minnesota in 1859 and 1860 had been opposed by Alabamians in Congress who, with other Southerners, were then trying to shackle the West and delay its growth. Later the Alabama Graduation Act was repealed. In 1862, when inflation had changed currency values considerably, the state worked out a rough classification system for land pricing, with swamplands and tracts within 6 miles of a navigable river or a railroad to be held at $10 an acre, land between 6 and 15 miles of a river or railroad to be held at $3, and land beyond 15 miles to be held at $1.50. Mineral lands were finally priced at $100 an acre.[1]

The abstracts of entries of the Alabama land offices reveal that people made very little effort during the war to acquire land from the government. The fact was that in Alabama, as in the four other public-land states, the remaining lands were mostly sandy soil covered with longleaf pine. At the time such land did not attract farmers and was not to do so for many years after 1865. The most active land office was at St. Stephens, where in 1861 219 entries were made for 20,000 acres, most of it in 80-acre homesteads or tracts bought under the Graduation Act. Elsewhere the entries were few and for small acreages. Total sales from November 1, 1862, to November 1, 1863, were $51,-421. None of these transactions were to have any validity when

---

[1] *Clarke County Democrat* (Grove Hill, Ala.), June 27, 1861. There was some sentiment in the Convention for "ceding" the public lands to the Confederacy on the ground that each state had an equal interest in them. Acts of Dec. 8, 1862, and Dec. 4, 1863, *Laws of Alabama*, 1862, p. 80, and 1863, p. 80.

the Federal government again took over management of the public lands of Alabama.[2]

In Mississippi the best of the remaining public lands were withdrawn until the railroads to which alternate sections had been granted had completed construction and selected their tracts. Officials of the Gulf & Ship Island Railroad in the piney-woods area of southern Mississippi made their selections, though they had laid no track, and urged that the withdrawn sections be restored to market, as there were many people wishing to purchase them. At the same time the Southern Railroad (the Vicksburg & Meridian), with a land grant west of Meridian, offered its lands to "planters anxious to move their familes and Negroes from exposed locations to a desirable place of security" for $2 to $10 an acre. The Alabama & Tennessee Railroad offered its 300,000 acres in eastern Alabama for sale, and was willing to sell 40 acres for $1.25 an acre to soldiers or widows in occupancy of land before 1863. It is probable there were few takers of any of these offers during the war.[3]

Louisiana established a General Land Office on March 1, 1861, and adopted most of the features of the Federal system, including the $1.25 an acre price, preemption, graduation, and the reservation of section 16 for schools. On June 18, 1863, in order to secure homesteads for the families of wounded and dead soldiers, the state withdrew all public lands from entry save those on which preemption rights had been established.[4] Arkansas at first allowed persons to make entries of the public lands but in 1862 withdrew all public lands from entry to safeguard equities that might have been established by settlers who had not filed for their tracts.[5]

Florida realistically appraised the 7,653,000 acres it took over from the Federal government at 10 cents to a dollar an acre, and, through the issue of bonds, made them the basis for the

[2] Register of Cash Receipts, St. Stephens and Elba Offices, Alabama State Archives. Copy of letter from U.S. Department of the Interior, Nov. 8, 1924, to J. W. Neal, makes this clear. *Selma Morning Reporter*, Jan. 7, 1864.

[3] J. M. Bradley, Land Office, Paulding, Miss., Apr. 16, 1863, to Gov.

Pettus, Gov. Corr., Miss. Arch.; Vicksburg *Daily Whig*, Jan. 13, 1863; *Selma Morning Reporter*, Sept. 26, 1863.

[4] Acts of Mar. 1, 1861, and June 18, 1863, *Laws of Louisiana*, 1861, p. 205, and 1863, p. 21.

[5] Act of Mar. 21, 1862, *Laws of Arkansas*, 1862, pp. 6–7.

expansion of its credit. In 1862 it suspended all land entries made by men in the army to protect their rights while they were away, but provided that other land on which there were no preemption rights might be sold—for $2 an acre if it was hummock and for $1 an acre if it was ordinary land. Soldiers might have land within six miles of a navigable river or railroad for 50 cents an acre and, if it was more remote, for 25 cents an acre. Land acquired at these prices was not to be subject to sale or execution during the lifetime of the holder, provided he continued to occupy it. Some $88,824 was received by the state from the sale of lands. Here, as elsewhere in the five public-land states, no acts of the seceded states in administering the lands were to be recognized when the Union was restored.[6]

Texas had long disposed of its public lands in a free and easy manner to colony promoters, to settlers with preemption rights, and, for a short time in the fifties, to homesteaders as free grants. In 1856 it repealed its homestead act, thereby making its position consistent with its opposition in Washington to homesteads on the national public domain. Texas continued preemption but tried to get enough revenue from its public lands for its ordinary expenses and for the war. It raised the price of its lands to 55 cents in 1862 and to $2 in 1863, but without profiting much from these increases. Not until 1869 and 1870 did Texas limit purchases to 160 acres. It should be added that the United States was not to enact such restrictive legislation until 1888, except that it applied restrictions to the five Southern public-land states between 1866 and 1876.[7]

In summary, the 37th and 38th Congresses pushed to conclusion the concept of free lands for settlers toward which reformers had long worked, but did not end the revenue feature of public-land policy or establish any limitation upon the right of

---

[6] Act of Dec. 13, 1862, *Laws of Florida*, 1862, pp. 45–6; J. E. Johns: *Florida during the Civil War* (Gainesville, Fla., 1963), pp. 99, 106.

[7] A modern history of the administration and disposal of the public lands of Texas is much needed. Of limited value for these phases

are Reuben McKitrick: *The Public Land System of Texas, 1823–1910, Bulletin of the University of Wisconsin, Economics and Political Science Series*, IX (Madison, Wis., 1918), and A. S. Lang: *Financial History of the Public Lands in Texas, The Baylor Bulletin*, XXXV, no. 3 (Waco, Tex., 1932).

ownership. They lavishly granted lands to aid in the building of four "transcontinental" railroads to extend from the Mississippi Valley to the Pacific, as well as numerous other lines in the Valley, and agreed to lend on generous terms many millions of dollars to the Pacific Railroad (Central Pacific, Union Pacific, and their eastern prongs). Free homesteads and the promise of railroad construction were to be the major influences in directing to the new territory the great flood of settlers that swiftly peopled the last American frontier from the Missouri and Red River Valleys to the Sierras and Cascades.

Congress, in further limiting the revenue policy and in making imperial grants to the railroads during a war that was producing huge deficits, displayed vision and statesmanship in discarding the timid ideas of the budget balancers and the fears of those concerned primarily with minority rights and limitations of governmental powers. Henceforth, growth, progress, and development were to be effected, indeed charted, not by private enterprise alone but by private enterprise assisted by the policies, favors, and funds of the Federal government.

12

Government Patronage of Agriculture

F ARMING, though the major occupation of the American people in the early days of the republic, was given little attention
in Congress. "Husbandry seemed to be viewed as a natural bless-
ing that needs no aid from legislation," said Henry L. Ellsworth.
"Like the air we breath, and the . . . water which sustains life,
the productions of the soil are regarded by too many as common
bounties of Providence, to be gratefully enjoyed, but without
further thought or reflection."[1] Influential agricultural interests,
such as the rice, tobacco, and cotton planters, might express concern about competition in foreign markets, but they needed little
or no government aid. At a time when parasites and animal diseases were responsible for enormous losses to potato growers,
cattle and hog raisers, and wheat producers in the North, there
were few who thought that government aid might solve such problems. In the absence of demand, government had done little for
farmers, but other economic interests had long since learned
that through tariffs, charters, grants of land, and transportation
improvements their welfare could be advanced. Notwithstanding
the failure of farmers to bring their problems to its attention, the
Federal government had begun to assist them in small ways before 1860.

---

[1] Commissioner of Patents: *Report, Sen. Doc.*, 25 Cong., 2 Sess., 1838,
II, no. 105, p. 4.

From his appointment in 1836 as Commissioner of Patents, Henry L. Ellsworth, landlord of acreage in Indiana exceeding four townships, agricultural experimenter, and pioneer protagonist of prairie agriculture, did what he could to assist farmers. He secured a small appropriation from Congress to begin the free distribution of seeds and cuttings and the collection of agricultural statistics. Under his enthusiastic direction, the government collected information concerning crops, weather, rainfall, plant diseases, exports, farm machinery, and experiments with imported species of plants. At first modestly, then more boldly, this data was published in his annual report as Commissioner of Patents and supplemented by accounts from farmers of their experiences. By 1844 the agricultural portion of the report had grown into a substantial volume by itself which, along with free distribution of seeds, constituted important constructive aid to the agricultural interests, all at small expense. After 1845, politics intruded increasingly into the agricultural work of the Patent Office, the quality of the material in the report of the agricultural branch declined, and, unfortunately, the free seeds which were imported from abroad brought new diseases and harmful insects with them to plague American farmers.[2]

Agricultural leaders came to deplore the meager interest the government was taking in farm matters. They disliked the subordinate position which the agricultural branch had in the Patent Office, dependent as the latter was for support on fees paid by inventors. Northern authorities felt that the agricultural branch was devoting too much of its attention to problems relating to Southern agriculture, such as replacing diseased sugar cane with disease-free cane from other countries. Southern leaders, on the other hand, were concerned at the attention given to sorghum, which might become a substitute for cane sugar and molasses.

The superintendent of the agricultural branch throughout the greater part of the Buchanan administration was the highly unpopular and bitterly criticized Daniel Jay Browne. Browne had many counts against him, including charges that he assumed credit for the work of subordinates in his agency, even of scientists whose work he seems not to have understood, and that he was

---

[2] P. W. Gates: *The Farmer's Age* (New York, 1960), pp. 320 ff.

responsible for dismissal of the most eminent scientist in the division, the entomologist Townend Glover. It was said that he included in the annual volume on agriculture much stale information which had been in the farm journals over and over again, that he was competing with farm journals and even newspapers in the publication of materials, and, finally, that the seeds he was distributing, which cost the government a considerable sum, not only were inferior and full of weed seeds, but were commonly known throughout the country, so that their distribution did nothing to diversify and improve crops.[3]

Perhaps in answer to criticism that much of the material in the earlier reports of the Patent Office was stale, Browne initiated the practice of paying contributors for original articles. Most of the effusions that resulted were hackneyed compilations which had been compressed from other accounts. For example, three essays dealt with the horses of New England in considerable and repetitious detail, and all drew their information from Daniel C. Lindley's *Morgan Horses*, published in 1857. Also, the six authors who prepared essays on grape culture wasted useful space in repetition. Less than a fourth of the articles were written by men of standing in their field.

In the latter part of the Buchanan administration Browne was replaced by Thomas G. Clemson, who took the more imposing title of Superintendent of the Agricultural Affairs of the United States. Clemson was a man with substantial political connections, a prolific writer for the *American Farmer*, and somewhat of a scientist, though he seems to have clung to certain scientific notions long after they had been questioned and discredited by his contemporaries. From the outset he took a stand in behalf of the use of Federal powers to advance agriculture that did not wholly comport with the view of his deceased father-in-law, John

---

[3] Manuscript report of the Agricultural Committee of the House of Representatives on the agricultural branch of the Patent Office, Jan. 10, 1859, Patent Office, Agriculture Files, National Archives; statement of Sen. Edgar Cowan, May 8, 1862, *Cong. Globe*, 37 Cong., 2 Sess., p. 2015; *Prairie Farmer*, V (June 7, 1860), 360.

Payments for the articles in the *Reports* for 1861 and 1863 are found in *House Ex. Doc.*, 37 Cong. 2, Sess., 1862, IV, no. 5, p. 1, and no. 14, pp. 2 ff.; *House Ex. Doc.*, 37 Cong., 3 Sess., 1863, VII, no. 66, pp. 2–3; *House Ex. Doc.*, 39 Cong., 1 Sess., 1866, VII, no. 49, pp. 21 ff.

C. Calhoun, or with those of many of the leading Southerners of the day. He agreed with friendly critics of the agricultural branch that its affiliation with and subordination to the Patent Office was unwise and that it should be given independent status. He wanted generous appropriations for the importation of foreign plants and experiments with them in the government propagating garden and in many nursery gardens throughout the country. Specifically, Clemson favored extensive efforts to domesticate the buffalo, greater diffusion of agricultural knowledge through close co-operation with the state agricultural societies, detailed examinations of agricultural operations in all parts of the country, and the introduction of new plants, animals, birds, and fish. He advocated "entomological investigations into the nature and history of the predatory insects . . . injurious to our crops," trials with irrigation and with rehabilitation of wasted land, and the stocking of rivers with fish. He recognized that for research in agriculture, chemists were needed, together with a chemical laboratory where they might conduct their studies. Clemson maintained that only through the establishment of a new department in which the agricultural work of the government might be centered could all such activities be made to function efficiently and effectively.[4]

Clemson's report for 1860 was received more favorably than previous volumes had been but the praise was tempered with criticism. Charles T. Jackson, the distinguished chemist and geologist of Boston, declared that it exceeded any other book in existence in new matter of real scientific value for agriculture. He citied especially Clemson's article on fertilizer and others on grapes and fish breeding. Another critic thought it better than any that had preceeded it, but he found its contents haphazardly selected from agricultural journals and annuals and said that many parts had no practical value. No publisher, he added, would for a moment think of bringing it out on a commercial basis. Complaints were made that none of the information provided was based on experiments, that the division's propagating garden of five acres for testing plants of native and foreign origin was not being effectively used, and that agents sent abroad to collect seeds

---

[4] Commissioner of Patents: *Report, 1860, Agriculture*, pp. 5–26; A. G. Holmes and G. R. Sherrill: *Thomas Green Clemson* (Richmond, 1937), *passim*.

for distribution were political hacks, not skilled seedsmen. More important was the fact that the branch had quite neglected a major purpose for which Congress supported it: the "collection of agricultural statistics." No statistics were included in the volumes for 1859–61.[5]

When the Southern states seceeded, Clemson felt the pull of South Carolina too strong to resist and resigned his postion, though not until he had completed his final report, with his introduction and his detailed eclectic analysis of fertilizers. He gave no indication of losing interest in the problems of agriculture and the way government powers should be utilized to solve them. He found it strange that the Confederacy included no provision in its Constitution for a department of agriculture. "Of all the departments of the Government, the most useful, the most essential, that which would command all others and should receive the first and most earnest attention, has been entirely ignored." Some leaders had feebly attempted to graft an agricultural branch upon the patent office of the Confederacy, but their action met scurrilous attacks. The *Southern Confederacy* of Atlanta, for example, said the bureau in Washington was a "stench in the nostrils of all good men in the South." It was expensive, its benefits, if any, were shared by few, it used tax revenues for the benefit of few, its annual report as well as its seeds and plants were distributed for political effect, and the bill to provide for a similar bureau in the Confederacy was an entering wedge for all the corruption and worthless expense of the Washington agency.[6]

In contrast to the generous support most Northern states had given to agricultural education through appropriations for agricultural colleges, fairs, societies, and bureaus, the Southern states had done practically nothing. In 1860 the *Southern Cultivator* expressed regret that the South had done so little and compared the generous assistance provided by the Northern and Middle Western states with that of Kentucky and Tennessee, whose aid to agricultural education was small, and Virginia and Georgia, who gave nothing. Mississippi had appropriated funds for an

---

[5] C. T. Jackson, June 18, to Clemson, Patent Office Correspondence, Agriculture, National Archives; *Rural New Yorker*, XII (Nov. 1,

15, 1861), 357, 365.
[6] *Southern Confederacy*, May 9, 1861.

agricultural bureau in 1857 in addition to small sums for county agricultural societies, but in 1861 it suspended all such aid for the duration of the war.[7]

Again, in opposition to prevailing opinion in his section, Clemson warmly advocated the establishment of a Confederate university with facilities free to both rich and poor. At such an institution science should be stressed in its relation to the use of the soil for agricultural purposes and the use of minerals for industrial development. Clemson borrowed from his own report to the Commissioner of Patents of 1860 many ideas concerning government patronage of agriculture. His plan for a university was well in advance of public opinion in the South, though the time was soon to come when his views were to prevail and great colleges of agriculture were to be created in states that earlier had looked disdainfully upon proposals to establish them.[8]

Separation of the agricultural branch from the Patent Office and the establishment of a bureau or department wholly independent of other agencies, though perhaps associated with the Department of the Interior, had long been ably supported by the United States Agricultural Society, farm journals, and local societies, and had been recommended by Abraham Lincoln in his first message to Congress. Not until the withdrawal of Southern representatives and senators, however, was it possible for Congress to elevate the branch to higher rank. In the House Owen Lovejoy initiated the move to create a department of agriculture and Senator James F. Simmons, a more conservative type of Republican, assumed the leadership in the Senate.

Opposition came from conservative anti-bureaucrats, small-government men, budget balancers, and the very few who did not feel it necessary to pay lip service to farm interests. Discussion centered on whether to create a department or bureau of agriculture. The former idea was accepted, though essentially the new agency remained little more than an independent bureau for

---

[7] *Southern Cultivator*, XVIII (February 1860), 67; C. S. Sydnor: *A Gentleman of the Old Natchez Region. Benjamin L. C. Wailes* (Durham, N.C., 1938), 168; Act of Aug. 2, 1861, *Laws of Mississippi*, 1861, p. 42.

[8] *De Bow's Review*, new ser., VII (January 1862), 92; *New York Tribune*, June 14, 1862.

years. Critics feared that the supporters of the new department would push it up to Cabinet status and that it would "grow and become exorbitant in its demands upon the Treasury." Aside from those conservatives who almost invariably fled to the Constitution when anything new was proposed, the senators voting against the bill included Fessenden of Maine, Hale of New Hampshire, Collamer of Vermont, Harlan of Iowa, and Lane of Kansas, all from states largely agricultural. Disregarding the fact that the ablest agricultural and horticultural leaders, including leaders in the move for agricultural education, supported the creation of an independent department of agriculture, these men insisted that few or no actual farmers had any knowledge of the move or would support the measure.

A strongly worded report of the Committee on Agriculture, of which Owen Lovejoy of Illinois was chairman, recommended the creation of a department with a commissioner at its head. The committee had no difficulty in disposing of the argument that other aspects of the American economy had no department to represent their interests, saying it was painfully evident that New York and Lowell have more influence "in directing and moulding national legislation than all the farming interests in the country." By an overwhelming vote—122 to 7—the House passed the bill to create a Department of Agriculture on February 17, and the Senate took similar action on May 10, 1862, by a vote of 25 to 13, thus opening the way for what many hoped would be a new departure in government aid to agriculture, but which others thought of as another agency for the distribution of patronage.[9]

The act of May 15, 1862, provided for the establishment of a Department of Agriculture over which a Commissioner of Agriculture should preside with a salary of $3,000, which was the same as the salary paid to less influential bureau chiefs. Other than its independence, there was no material change in the responsibility or obligation of the office, though the act did authorize the appointment of "chemists, botanists, entomologists,

---

[9] *House Reports,* 37 Cong., 2 Sess., 1861–2, III, no. 21; *Cong. Globe,* 37 Cong., 2 Sess., 1861–2, Feb. 17, May 2, 8, 10, 1862, pp. 857, 2014, 2017.

and other persons skilled in the natural sciences pertaining to agriculture" as Congress might from time to time authorize. Though the difference in salary of an ordinary bureau chief and a department head of Cabinet rank was extraordinarily large— $3,000 as compared with $8,000—the new office and its emoluments were sufficient to attract an able and outstanding man.[1]

There were many distinguished leaders who deserved consideration for the new position because of their activity in state and national agricultural societies and their own experimental work and extensive writings. Most outstanding was Marshall Pinckney Wilder, famous as a nurseryman, plant breeder, hybridizer, and fruit specialist, whose achievements were known throughout the United States and abroad. As president of the Massachusetts Horticultural Society, the American Pomological Society, and the United States Agricultural Society, in all of which he was an active and influential leader, he had done much for the fruit industry and the nursery business and had played a significant part in the movement for the adoption of the Morrill Act of 1862 and the act for the establishment of the Department of Agriculture. Jonathan Baldwin Turner was a well-known nurseryman and frequent writer on agricultural matters who had played a major role in the movement for Federal aid to establish agricultural colleges and who, like Dr. John F. Kennicott, also a nurseryman from Illinois, had strong support for the position in the West. John Hancock Klippart, secretary of the Ohio State Board of Agriculture, had made the annual reports of that board among the best in the country, with numerous articles of his own on wheat, sheep rearing, land drainage, the history of corn, and agricultural colleges abroad, together with translations of articles from German and French farm journals. Either Klippart or Benjamin Pierce Johnson, secretary of the New York State Agricultural Society and a perceptive writer on agricultural problems, would have been an excellent choice. Finally, Amos Brown, teacher and president of People's College of New York, had shown much initiative in inaugurating his institution and in supporting the adoption of the Morrill Act. Any of these men,

---

[1] 12 *U.S. Stat.*, p. 387.

all of whose names were suggested to Lincoln, would have brought prestige, honor, leadership, and experience to the office.[2]

To replace Clemson, President Lincoln, in his vigorous pursuit of the spoils system, selected not a prominent leader in agricultural matters but a man quite unknown to all but his political associates, Isaac Newton of Pennsylvania, and when the new department was created he pushed Newton up to the commissionership. The choice was unfortunate, for about all that could be said for Newton was that he had had farming experience, had peddled butter, came from Pennsylvania, was an ardent Republican, had been strongly recommended for the position by a Philadelphia seedsman, and had some slight influence with Lincoln and his wife, Mary. His education was meager, his knowledge of other parts of the United States slight, and his acquaintance with leaders in agriculture so limited as to lead a writer in the *Rural New Yorker* to enquire: "Who is Isaac Newton?" The *Ohio Farmer*, like most agricultural journals, disliked Newton, whom it called weak, illiterate, and ignorant, a dunce and a "great lubberly old Quaker." It concluded that his appointment was a "gross outrage on the farmers of the country." On the other hand, the *Country Gentleman*, no admirer of Newton, reported a statement that his farm in Delaware County was one of the best to be seen.[3]

The unpopular onetime superintendent of the agricultural branch of the Patent Office, D. J. Browne, who had vainly hoped to be reappointed to that post by Lincoln, subsequently threw his support to Newton. In return, Newton employed him to go abroad to investigate the production and manufacture of flax and wines and to secure seeds and cuttings. Newton could have done nothing that was so certain to create resentment in Congress and in the agricultural press as to make this appointment, and the

---

[2] *California Farmer*, XVII (July 18, 1862), 132. Dr. Kennicott was unanimously recommended by the Illinois legislature. *Rural New Yorker*, XIV (June 20, 1863), 197.
[3] *Magazine of Horticulture*, XXVI (March 1860), 1377; H. J. Car-

man and R. H. Luthin: *Lincoln and the Patronage* (New York, 1943), *passim; Rural New Yorker*, XIII (July 12, 1862), 223; *Ohio Farmer*, XI (July 5, 1862), 214; *Country Gentleman*, XIX (Apr. 10, 1862), 241.

recall of Browne was angrily demanded. To make matters worse, the seed wheat that was imported in 1862 and distributed in small bags was infested with the destructive grain weevil and proved to be wholly unadapted to American growing conditions. The *Rural New Yorker* said that "as long as charlatans and plagiarists are pensioned by government to collect seeds abroad the danger of importing pests" would continue. Browne was ordered to return and his connection with the agricultural work of the government was finally terminated. His essay, resulting from his trip, on the "History, Industry and Commerce of Flax" is a mishmash of geography, history, and statistics, with some information about growing and processing flax that was doubtless useful at a time when the North was trying to find substitutes for cotton.[4]

Newton's reports show some improvement over those of Browne, not because he was more careful in selecting contributors, for he was not, but rather because he was assembling a staff of scientists and statisticians whose contributions were to be distinguished. Newton followed the practice begun by Browne of hiring outside writers to contribute articles, and the same hodgepodge of topics is to be found in his reports as in the earlier ones. By good fortune, he was able to publish in the 1864 report a rare article on Holstein cattle, which were then largely unknown in America. On the whole the reports dealt with well-known subjects, offered time-tried advice, and broke little new ground. From the correspondence of the agricultural branch we may generalize that farmers receiving them read and appreciated much of the material, no matter how stale, for they found it informative and filled with useful advice.[5]

Some vital questions that went to the heart of many farmers'

---

[4] *Rural New Yorker*, XII (Aug. 24, 1861), 271, and XIII (Mar. 8, Sept. 20, 1862), 77, 302; *American Agriculturist*, XXI (April 1862), 104; *National Intelligencer*, Aug. 25, 1863. A peremptory resolution of the House of Representatives calling for an accounting of Browne's expenditures while abroad convinced Holloway that Browne's employment would no longer be tolerated. His final draft was refused and he was ordered to return forthwith. *Cong. Globe*, 37 Cong., 3 Sess., Jan. 12, 1863, p. 281; *House Ex. Doc.*, 37 Cong. 3 Sess., VI, no. 53; Commissioner of Patents: *Reports, 1861, Agriculture*, pp. 21–83.

[5] W. W. Chenery: "Holstein Cattle," in Commissioner of Agriculture, *Report*, 1864, pp. 161–7.

problems were not given attention. There is nothing in the reports concerning marketing of either wood or hay, two important cash crops for many farmers in the North. There are, however, two articles on forests, one of which discusses the depletion of timber resources. This article is a forerunner of the concern which the department showed in later years for farmers' woodlots and which in turn led to the National Forest Service of today. The sale of fluid milk, which was becoming increasingly important to many farmers as the milksheds of major cities extended, was touched on in only one article, and that planned by Browne, not Newton.[6] The reports ignored controversial questions such as the grading of wheat at the elevators (a practice which created much resentment against the warehousemen), adulteration of milk by both farmers and distributors, the sale of milk from swill-fed cows and of meat from diseased livestock, false claims for commercial fertilizers, railroad rates, road labor that was required of tenants but not of absentee owners, the spread between farmers' prices and retail prices, and the fluctuation of the currency. True, the same criticism can be made of most farm journals of the time. Issues with political overtones were taboo in the department's annual volume.[7]

Newton's reports contain nonsense that anyone familiar with the various sections of the country and with previous efforts to introduce exotic plants might have avoided. In planning for recovery of the South after the conclusion of the war, Newton averred that the introduction and adaptation of the following might save the country the expenditure of millions of dollars: tea and coffee plants, the opium poppy, the vanilla bean, ginger root, castor bean, silkworms, and camphor, cork, and olive trees. Farmers were told the silkworm had been successfully introduced and acclimated and that its silk was strong and of good quality.[8] Other useless articles disparaged the use of wallpaper and carpets in farmers' dwellings, declared that hard water is harmful to man

---

[6] Frederick Starr, Jr.: "American Forests; Their Destruction and Preservation," in Commissioner of Agriculture, *Report*, 1865, pp. 210 ff.; S. L. Loomis: "The Consumption of Milk," in *Report*, 1861, pp. 209 ff.

[7] Gates: *The Farmer's Age*, pp. 351 ff.
[8] *Reports*, 1863, pp. 6, 313–37, and 1865, p. 6.

and beast, and discoursed on such topics as "Fresh and Salt Water Aquaria."

Newton lacked a delicate sense of propriety, for he encouraged and indeed paid for articles by livestock salesmen and breeders who used the opportunity to plug their favorite breeds. This was much the same as the practice of proprietors of farm journals in promoting the sale of agricultural machinery and fertilizer in which they had a financial interest. Francis Rotch of Morris, New York, called by Henry S. Randall "one of the most eminent and skillful cattle and sheep breeders in the United States," prepared an article on "Select Breeds of Cattle, and Their Adaptation to the United States" which reproduced the standard information about Shorthorns, Devons, Ayrshires, Herefords, and Jerseys, but contained disparaging remarks about Dutch or Holstein cattle, in which he had no interest. In at least eight other instances, favored livestock breeders were given the opportunity to advertise their stock at no cost to themselves.[9]

Fruit, especially grapes, wine making, and other horticultural subjects were given disproportionate attention in the reports in relation to their part in the farmers' economy. Yet the treatment given to these subjects doubtless added much to the enjoyment of readers and to their plans for diversifying their farms and adorning their lawns and homes. Nurserymen naturally were pleased with Newton's reports and at the meeting of the Illinois State Horticultural Society in 1862 they declared that they had nothing to condemn and much to commend "in the energy and intelligence which seems to characterize" the management of the Department of Agriculture. They extended "their hearty sympathy and co-operation" to Newton but gently suggested that some "prominent able agriculturist from the great North-West" be associated with the department.[1]

Notwithstanding their many defects, the Newton reports

---

[9] Articles on sheep by Henry Boynton, D. C. M'Cann, W. R. Sanford, and H. S. Randall, on cavalry horses by Francis Morris, on mules by J. T. Warder, and on White Chester hogs by Paschall Morris, Philadelphia seedsman and proprietor of an agricultural warehouse, appear in the *Reports* for 1863–5. Seedsmen seem to have been among Newton's closest supporters.

[1] *Prairie Farmer*, X (Dec. 13, 20, 1862), 374, 391.

contained much of value to ordinary farmers and a few articles that no historian of agriculture should neglect. Sheep and cattle, their various breeds and advantages and disadvantages, appear prominently in every volume. The cultivation of sorghum, flax, and hemp, and substitutes for Southern molasses, sugar, and cotton were described. Poultry raising was presented not as a rich man's fancy but as a commercial enterprise. Cheese making, increasingly the center of the dairy industry in parts of New York and Ohio, was twice described in detail, once by X. A. Willard, the country's unrivaled expert on dairy products and problems. The 1865 report was distinguished not only for the Willard essay but also for a remarkable analysis of the problems found and the progress achieved in setting up agricultural colleges in the various states.[2]

The Reports were much in demand, though not always for the purpose for which they were prepared. The *Sorgo Journal and Farm Machinist* reported that of the 150,000 copies printed of the 1864 report, nine tenths were appropriated by members of Congress, and only through them could farmers hope to secure a copy. This number would allow only one copy of the report for every ten farmers in the loyal states.[3]

It is interesting to compare Newton's reports with the transactions of the New York State Agricultural Society prepared by the secretary, Benjamin P. Johnson, a widely traveled and extensive writer on farm matters. The society's volume for 1862 contains the presidential address delivered to it by Ezra Cornell. The speech was full of sound advice and raised questions that called for careful consideration. Cornell was in advance of his time in condemning hedge fences as a result of his study of agriculture in England. Articles by Dr. Asa Fitch, state entomologist, on insects infecting gardens, by X. A. Willard, later to be lecturer at Cornell, on dairies and cheese manufactures of New York, by Henry S. Randall, the foremost expert on sheep, and

---

[2] *Report*, 1865, pp. 137–86. An article by Jonathan Baldwin Turner, sometimes called the "father of the Agricultural College Act," on industrial colleges was rejected by Newton but later published as a pamphlet. *Prairie Farmer*, XIII (May 21, 1864), 364.

[3] *Sorgo Journal and Farm Machinist*, III (March 1865), 48.

by Johnson on the great International Exhibition in London in 1862 still are useful and read well. So also does the 100-page "Agricultural Survey of the County of Orange," which was a model of description and analysis. Material taken from other journals or annuals was confined to 60 pages out of 712, and no self-advertising was permitted to intrude.

Free seed distribution was one of the oddest features of the patronage system. It brought the government into competition with seed companies and with agricultural periodicals which offered free seeds to attract and retain subscribers. This partly explains why the department was constantly attacked in the agricultural press. But to members of Congress looking for ways to do favors to their constituents at no cost to themselves, the 3,000 packages of small vegetable seeds and the several bushels of larger seeds, such as beans, peas, oats, and barley to which each was entitled were a godsend. In one year over 1,200,000 packets of seeds were sent out, and of these, 40,000 held a quart of wheat or other cereal grain. At another time 25,000 cuttings and plants were distributed.

No small part of the funds appropriated for the benefit of agriculture was expended in purchasing, packaging, and mailing these annual handouts which the secretary of the Iowa State Agricultural Society called a "vast amount of trash." The *Rural New Yorker* cautioned its readers about the use of Patent Office seeds, lest they be infested with the grain weevil or other insects, and reminded them that the Hessian fly, the wheat midge, and the bark louse all had come in from abroad.[4]

Newton conceded in July 1863 that the large shipment of spring wheat which had been carefully acquired in England for distribution among American farmers had "entirely failed," proving that it was not adapted to conditions in this country. The following year an official of the department expressed his belief that the "want of selection and defective cultivation," which resulted

---

[4] *Homestead,* VII (May, August 1861), 448, 575; *National Intelligencer,* Jan. 25, 30, 1862; *Rural New Yorker,* XIII (Mar. 8, 1862), 66; Iowa State Agricultural Society: *Eighth Report,* p. 5; Commissioner of Agriculture: *Report,* 1863, p. 10; *Prairie Farmer,* VIII (Sept. 26, 1861), XI (Feb. 14, 1863), 98, and XIII (Jan. 16, 1864), 37.

from improper instructions concerning planting, care, and harvesting, were responsible for the poor showing of the free seeds. Free seed distribution grew into a "fungus, of little value in itself," said Horace Capron, successor to Newton, "while it absorbed largely of the nutrient to sustain the vital functions of the Department."[5]

Notwithstanding the many complaints concerning the poor adaptability of the seeds to American growing conditions or to the particular area to which they were sent, the defective varieties sometimes selected, the lack of instructions or advice accompanying them, and the competition they provided for the seed houses, which were commonly linked with the farm journals, the distribution of seeds continued throughout the nineteenth century and into the twentieth.[6]

If Newton did not endear himself to agricultural authorities, he did get along well with Congress. By popularizing the reports by including features not related to agriculture, thereby making them more attractive for Congressmen to distribute, and advocating an abundant supply of reports, Newton made himself sufficiently popular that Congress voted without opposition to raise his salary from $3,000 to $4,000 at the same time that it was quibbling over other appropriations. More important, Newton secured a continued expansion of his department's budget which brought the appropriation from $60,000 for the year ending June 30, 1861, to $155,000 for the year ending June 30, 1866. These increases made it possible to enlarge the staff from eight full-time employees to twenty-nine. Opponents of bureaucracy could well feel that their reluctance to create the new department had proved

---

[5] *Monthly Report on the Condition of the Crops*, July 1863, p. 2; *Bi-Monthly Report of the Agricultural Department*, November–December 1864, pp. 16–19; Commissioner of Agriculture: *Report*, 1867, p. 17.
[6] *Southern Cultivator*, XVIII (November 1860), 344; *American Agriculturist*, XXI (April 1862), 104, and XXII (February 1863), 40; *Oneida Weekly Herald*, Apr. 5, 1864; *New York Tribune*, Mar. 14, 1861. In discussing the bill for

the establishment of the Department of Agriculture, Sen. W. P. Fessenden said that few members of Congress could "muster the courage to vote against an appropriation" for free seed distribution. *Cong. Globe*, 37 Cong., 2 Sess., May 10, 1862, p. 2016. In 1865, 234,945 packets of seeds were delivered to senators and representatives, 119,683 went to agricultural societies, and 408,593 to individuals. *Report*, 1865, p. 5.

justified, the more so because most of the appointments were made for their political effect.[7]

All was not politics in the Department of Agriculture, however, Townend Glover, a well-known leader in the growing field of entomology, who had previously been in the agricultural branch of the Patent Office, was brought back and made head of his field, to the gratification of many. The first important result of Glover's work in his new position was an essay containing the best of current knowledge concerning destructive insects and ways to combat them. Here was scientific information being applied by a skilled practioner to the problems met every day by farmers. True, Glover was better at describing than combating insects, and he was slow to appreciate the effectiveness of pyrethrum. He was scooped by the New York State Agricultural Society on this insect destroyer; not until he attended the Entomological Exhibition in Paris in 1865 did he become acquainted with it.[8]

As part of his work Glover began collecting and mounting specimens which were made the nucleus of a museum for identification purposes and for stimulating popular interest in the work of the department. Insect-eating birds were studied in much the same way the modern ornithologist pursues his work: by examining the contents of the stomachs of birds. Though Glover was not the first to call attention to the danger of importing seeds and cuttings which might be infested, he went farther than others by recommending that all foreign seeds and plants brought into the country be carefully inspected. If they were found to contain "new and unknown insects," he urged that they be either fumi-

---

[7] *Cong. Globe,* 37 Cong., 3 Sess., 1863, part 1, pp. 667 ff. The salary increase was struck out in conference. 12 *U.S. Stat.,* p. 108, and 13 *U.S. Stat.,* p. 45; *Federal Register,* 1861, 1865; Carman and Luthin: *Lincoln and the Patronage, passim.* Newton's appointment of his son to have charge of the Department's seed room, though deplored by some as nepotism, was not uncommon in the Lincoln administration.

[8] *American Agriculturist,* XXII (May 1863), 138; "The Destruction of Noxious Insects by Means of the Pyrethrum (Persian Insect Powder)," New York State Agricultural Society, *Transactions,* XXIII, (1863), pp. 202 ff.; Townend Glover: "Entomological Exhibition in Paris," in Commissioner of Agriculture, *Report,* 1865, p. 88.

gated or destroyed. Gardeners, nurserymen, farmers, and timberland owners of a later date were to regret exceedingly that his advice was not adopted.

Glover's invitation to farmers to send in specimens of insects, birds, diseased grain, and other items for his rapidly growing museum caught the fancy of many people, particularly those who wanted identification of insects harmful to their crops and information on the best methods of combating them. Hundreds of letters poured in asking for information, and the replies took up much of his time. By the end of the 1860's it can be said that through his identification and description of harmful insects, and his proposals for controlling them, Glover had done much to make the science of entomolgy a practical one and had added greatly to the prestige of the Department of Agriculture.[9]

Charles M. Wetherill and Henry Erni, successively the department's chemists, could not expect their work to gain public support as quickly as that of the entomologist. Wetherill, who had studied under Liebig, was early taken out of the department by Lincoln to use his talents in producing a new form of gunpowder. Much of the chemists' time was devoted to making soil analyses for farmers in various parts of the country. Their reports were couched in technical language, and one may wonder how much real value they had for the laymen. Wetherill's report on sorghum, at a time when every effort was being made to find a substitute for the sugar and molasses previously supplied by Louisiana, was helpful and probably added to the excitement that induced many to turn to this crop in part in place of corn. Analysis of the process of wine making may have been of some aid to wine makers in New York, Ohio, and California, but for specialists one would assume that technical works would have been preferable. Critics might raise eyebrows that a chemist in the Department of Agriculture should devote his time to analyzing samples of coal, asphalt, oil rock, and copper ore for outside interests. There is little in Erni's reports during the war that made any great impact on agriculture, or that can even be regarded as

---

[9] *Ohio Farmer*, XV (Mar. 3, 1866), 66; L. O. Howard: *History of Applied Entomology (Smithsonian Miscellaneous Collections*, LXXXIV, Washington, D.C., 1931), 35 ff.

offering a service farmers might find valuable for the moment. What is important is that chemistry was recognized as a science that must be utilized in the development of modern agriculture. Like the good bureaucrat that he was, Erni urged that more space be allotted for the mineral and geological cabinet, that a special room be provided for the analytical work, that new equipment be authorized and additional staff appointed.[1]

William Saunders, the new superintendent of the experimental garden, found little to encourage him when he undertook an inventory of the plants previously established. No books or records of previous operations were to be found and it was impossible to determine when, whence, and why the thousands of plants such as the candleberry myrtle, Japanese cedar, Christ's-thorn, indian shot, or *bryophyllum calycinum* had been imported and propagated. Of the 120 varieties of grapes in the garden it was possible to identify only a few and the work devoted to the others was lost. Under the new dispensation it was proposed to make the garden less a collection of oddities from various parts of the world and more a true experimental garden in which testing of the merits of seeds and cuttings, hybridizing to produce superior plants, and investigating the diseases and insects which retarded their growth would be conducted. Special attention was given to grapes, berries, and other fruit, in accordance with their growing importance in the agricultural economy. From Saunders's reports farmers and specialists in fruit production may have learned something of the varieties, requirements, and diseases of fruit, particularly grapes.

The experimental or propagating garden carried over from the Browne regime was much too small for the plans the department had under consideration. A larger tract situated between the present 12th and 14th Streets was secured in 1864 as an experimental farm. On this was begun a series of experiments and tests with "346 varieties of seeds, including 18 kinds of Indian corn, 34 of beans, 13 of peas, 77 of potatoes . . . 33 of

---

[1] R. V. Bruce: *Lincoln and the Tools of War* (Indianapolis, 1956), pp. 212 ff.; Commissioner of Agri- culture: *Reports*, 1862, p. 508, 1864, p. 514, and 1865, p. 46.

melons, and many varieties, respectively of tomatoes, beets, and other vegetables." There is no evidence that the department tried to determine what knowledge already existed about these many varieties, or what the seed houses and private nurseries had done with them. Instead, it pushed ahead as though no scientific testing or experimental work had been carried out, thus ignoring much that had been accomplished by such innovators as the firms of Ellwanger and Barry of Rochester, New York, William R. Prince of Long Island, or Marshall Pinckney Wilder of Massachusetts. Assembling and studying the catalogs of the major seed and nursery firms and close questioning of their leaders might have been more useful than one or more years of blind work. But what was important about the new experimental garden was not the immediate results, for they were few and slight, but rather that extensive and systematic experimental work was begun.[2]

The most valuable part of the work of the Department of Agriculture was statistical. The act creating the department provided for the collection of statistics and thereafter they constituted a major feature of its reports. At the outset the only data the department had available was that in the census of 1860, with all its errors. Real pioneering was undertaken in soliciting from more than two thousand generally well-chosen people located in all parts of the loyal states information on rainfall and temperature, the number of acres in and condition of the principal crops (estimated in fractional improvement of or decline from the yield of the previous year), the average yield per acre of various crops for the past year, and something about market conditions, including export and import figures for the principal crops. In addition Newton summarized information gained from the press and correspondence concerning crops abroad, particularly wheat. The information was tabulated as swiftly as the primitive means permitted and published in the monthly report, which was sent to newspapers, farm journals, and agricultural leaders and thus had a far wider circulation than the annual report

---

[2] *Reports*, 1862, p. 540, 1863, p. 547, 1864, p. 605, and 1865, pp. 5, 13, 25.

could achieve. Here was the beginning of what became one of the most important features of the modern Department of Agriculture, the crop reports.[3]

Illustrative of the practical information provided in the monthly reports is the information in the August 1863 number. It showed that the wheat and barley crops were well along, with threshing underway, and that they were the largest ever produced. Oats, on the other hand, had been somewhat damaged by the drought of May and June, though the late rains helped the crop. Corn was generally in a good condition, but it was expected that the crop in the corn belt would be 20 per cent less than the previous year. The drought had cut expected yields of cotton, tobacco, and sorghum. The hay crop was better than the June circular had deemed possible. The grape rot was serious, but the apple crop was encouraging. Information of this nature, when brought together by the statistician of the department and distributed throughout the country, provided some basis on which the more forward-looking farmers could plan their future planting and breeding operations as well as their marketing.[4]

The monthly reports were regarded by such vigorous administration organs as *Harper's Weekly* and the *National Intelligencer* as imaginative and progressive ventures that should tend to reduce speculation and wide swings in prices and give enterprising farmers information of material aid. Perennial critics of government activity in agriculture disliked the reports as further intruding on their activities and threatening their patronage.

Newton used the monthly report as his personal organ in which he could defend himself against attacks by farm organizations and journals and ride his hobbies. Protection to bar competition from foreign products, especially wool, was a favorite subject with him, but at the same time he advocated a vigorous fight for foreign markets for American agricultural exports.[5]

---

[3] The *Oneida Weekly Herald*, 1863–4, quoted frequently from the *Monthly Report*, but the farm journals used its information less regularly.

[4] *Harper's Weekly*, VII (Nov. 14, 1863), 722; *Rural New Yorker*, XV (Jan. 2, 1864), 5; *Cultivator*, XIII (March 1865), 96; *Prairie Farmer*, XII (Oct. 26, 1863), 216.

[5] *Monthly Report of the Department of Agriculture* for November 1863, pp. 2–3; ibid. for January 1865, p. 4, and February 1865, p. 4.

For the annual report the data collected for the monthly report was further processed, compared with that of past years, and presented in a useful fashion. These agricultural statistics now constitute a major source for the history of the period. However, when the Commissioner found it necessary, for one reason or other, to change in a subsequent report the figures he had once arrived at for a crop, he provided no explanation of the reason for the substitution, which leads one to question all his statistics.[6]

Despite his own meager education Newton seems to have had some insight into the future role of the agricultural colleges that were getting under way with the aid of the land grants provided in the Morrill Act. He held that the Department of Agriculture needed the help of the colleges in distributing the seeds and plants, in conducting experiments and reporting on them, and in assisting old systems of farming in various sections of the country and developing new ones. He favored a broad training program for future farmers that would include Latin, mathematics, natural philosophy, vegetable and animal physiology, meteorology, chemistry, geology, botany, zoology, and physical geography, interspersed with lectures on practical subjects such as manures, drainage, livestock and grain raising.[7]

Credit for the literate character of the reports, the selection of the better and more useful articles, and the management of the non-political affairs of the department was generally given James S. Grinnell, chief clerk of the department, who, as the *Prairie Farmer* said, "furnished the brains to run the institution." When he was discharged in 1865 to make a place for a nephew of Newton, the articulate element among agriculturists demanded Newton's dismissal.

The Department of Agriculture under Newton had accomplished much good in restoring Townend Glover to his position as entomologist, in enlarging the work of the propagating garden and beginning the experimental garden, in initiating chemical analysis of crops and soils, in reviving the statistical work, in getting out

---

[6] *Reports*, 1863, p. 3, and 1864, pp. 3 ff.

[7] *National Intelligencer*, Mar. 5, 1864.

the monthly and bimonthly reports, and in publishing meritorious and useful articles in the annual reports. But since it had failed to win the favor of the agricultural press and of leaders of agricultural societies, they had continued to criticize its activities and minimize the value of its constructive achievements. A writer in the *Rural New Yorker* called the expenses of the department a "great leak" and declared that the distribution of seeds was a worthless service. The *Working Farmer* called Newton "thoroughly incompetent" and maintained that the department was run to gratify his prejudices and advance his narrow-minded projects. His nepotism was not unusual for the time but was taken as another evidence of his small-mindedness. The discharge of Grinnell led to a concerted drive for his dismissal in which ten agricultural societies, the *Ohio Farmer,* the *Prairie Farmer,* and the *Rural New Yorker* joined. They maintained that he was unfit for the position he occupied and did great harm to the cause of agriculture. Even the conservative Farmer's Club of the American Institute of New York appointed a committee to consider calling for his resignation, and a majority report of this special committee so recommended. Their report was laid on the table after a member of the minority argued that Newton was no worse than other appointees of Lincoln and proposed instead that the entire Department of Agriculture be abolished.[8]

Heavy pressure for Newton's removal continued. President Johnson tried to replace him but was unsuccessful because Congress liked his nominee for the position no better. Despite the continued demand for his dismissal, Newton survived in office until his death in 1866. Whatever could be said of his "incompetence to the point of illiteracy, of waste and malfeasance in the purchase and distribution of seeds and plants, and intrigues with congressmen," Newton left his mark on the department, for the

---

[8] *Prairie Farmer,* XVI (Sept. 16, 1865), 208; *Rural New Yorker,* XVI (June 24, 1865), 198; *Country Gentleman,* XXVI (Sept. 14, Oct. 12, Dec. 21, 1865), 177, 241, 401; *Working Farmer,* XVIII (Feb. 1, Mar. 1, 1866), 32, 55, 63; *Ohio Farmer,* XV (Mar. 3, 1866), 66; Ohio State Board of Agriculture: *Twentieth Annual Report,* 1865, part 2, p. 54.

new lines of statistical enquiry, experimentation, and scientific activity which he had fostered were continued and developed by his successors.[9]

---

[9] E. D. Ross: "Lincoln and Agriculture," *Agricultural History*, III (April 1929), 62. For Oliver Hudson Kelley's guarded judgment of Newton see *Working Farmer*, XVIII (August 1866), 181.

13

Groundswells of Agrarianism

As FARMERS WATCHED the growth of manufacturing, commerce, transportation, and banking, and the rise of special-interest groups associated with these developments, and as they came to see that their own welfare was sometimes adversely affected, they resented this growth and feared the power it might ultimately concentrate in few hands. The sheep and wool raisers feared the wool manufacturers; debtor farmers feared the banks and the control of currency and credit they exercised. Western corn and wheat farmers were concerned over transportation costs and elevator practices, while Eastern farmers were troubled that the railroads were bringing Western wheat produced at low cost into their markets, which forced them to change the rotation patterns to which they were accustomed. In addition, land-hungry settlers, whether of old American stock from the East, second-generation Westerners, or new immigrants from abroad, all disliked the absentee land company and speculator whose major objective was to profit from these groups by the high retail prices at which they sold them land. Out of these and many other annoyances came the sparks that produced numerous little flare-ups that soon subsided, friction that led to a state of bitterness, and outright agrarian outbursts that were scattered, unintegrated, and not very productive. These outbursts mark the beginning of a movement that was to emerge in the postwar years as agrarian discontent and that was to take political form.

At the outbreak of the war, and even before hostilities commenced, a startling variety of stay laws, appraisement laws, stronger occupancy laws, and tender laws were adopted that seemed to some persons like a revolutionary wave threatening the destruction of American concepts of property rights. This radical legislation was in part a carryover from the panic of 1857, which had brought about drastic deflation and cessation of economic activity in the Middle West and which had led to the demand for moratoria and appraisement laws, particularly in Iowa, Wisconsin, and Texas. Cyrus McCormick, to whom farmers owed several hundred thousand dollars for reapers sold on credit, found it difficult to make collections because of stay laws and other impediments placed in the way of the execution of judgments, and he was compelled to exact larger down payments on sales. "Homesteads were everywhere beyond the grasp of the creditor, as well as an amount of personal property varying in value from state to state" says McCormick's biographer.[1]

With the opening of hostilities, the closing of the Mississippi, and the establishment of the blockade of Southern ports, cotton and sugar planters of the South and grain farmers of the upper Mississippi Valley could neither sell their produce nor make payments on their obligations. Indeed, the economic crisis was more severe than it had been in 1858 and 1859. Banks closed or suspended payments, court calendars were crowded with suits for payments, money was scarce and business at a standstill. In such desperate circumstances debtors again asked the state legislatures for relief.

Stay laws had a long history in America—a history by no means honorable, creditors would say, although others would maintain that the laws had been equitable and essential. They were intended to halt for a time legal proceedings for the recovery of debts and to prevent distress sales of property at a period when money was scarce, interest rates unusually high, and most debtors unable to meet the demands of their creditors.

---

[1] W. T. Hutchinson: *Cyrus Hall McCormick* (2 vols., New York, 1930–5), II, 73 ff.

First enacted along with currency and tender laws in the trying days of the Critical Period in the 1780's when distress was widespread, the stay laws, as they emerged from the two-house state legislatures, were more conservative than when first proposed. Some were struck down by state courts, but others accomplished their remedial objectives. The new Federal Constitution of 1787 with its prohibition on ex post facto laws and its impairment of contracts clause seemed to remove the possibility of making stay, tender, occupancy, and appraisement laws apply retroactively again.[2]

In later periods of economic distress following the Embargo of Jefferson's administration and the panics of 1819, 1837, and 1857, the states again enacted all the remedies of the Critical Period. Support of this legislation was by no means confined to small farmers. Indeed, at various times combinations of merchants, planters, bankers, speculators, and farmers worked for relief acts. The usual measures were bankruptcy acts, occupancy, appraisement, and stay laws, and acts to create new inflationary state banks and to end imprisonment for debt. From the rigidities of high Federalist interpretation of the impairment and ex post facto clauses of the Constitution, used by Justices Story, Washington, and, at times, Marshall, to strike down these measures, the Supreme Court moved to a greater degree of tolerance under Taney, but measures which clearly threatened the security of debts were commonly voided.[3]

After the firing on Fort Sumter, Lincoln's call to arms, and the withdrawal of the last of the eleven Confederate states, a burst of patriotic fervor swept over both the North and the South and people everywhere rushed to enlist. Prosperous merchants and businessmen made generous donations to aid in equipping regiments and lavishly feted the men going into the army. State legislatures hastened to vote generous funds and impose new taxes for the prosecution of the war and to adopt a series of protective measures to give security to the families of the soldiers.

---

[2] Merrill Jensen: *The New Nation* (New York, 1950), *passim.*
[3] M. N. Rothbard: *The Panic of 1819* (New York, 1962), J. B. McMaster: *History of the People of the United States* (8 vols., New York, 1883–1910), IV, and R. C. McGrane: *The Panic of 1837* (Chicago, 1924), for background.

The most important of these measures were stay laws, which were rushed through legislatures without much discussion at a time when normally conservative men were too timid to vote against proposals that the advocates of vigorous prosecution of the war supported.

Sugar and cotton planters of the Deep South were hard hit by the outbreak of war, the blockade, and the closing of the Mississippi River. Their cotton was no longer marketable and was shortly to be burned to keep it from the enemy. Their plight compelled them to turn to grain crops, which they were ill-prepared to produce and which brought them little return. They had pledged their cotton, and some their slaves and land, for the payment of debts they now could not meet. Merchants, brokers, factors, shippers, and a variety of other economic interests in Mobile, New Orleans, Galveston, Savannah, Memphis, and Charleston were overloaded with staples they had been holding for better prices and now found they could not ship. Neither could they make collections on debts due them or make payments on obligations they owed. Then, too, there were the small yeoman farmers, the younger men of army age, who produced a few bales of cotton or a surplus of corn, hogs, fuel wood, or other commodities, and who were, perhaps, in debt for past supplies or for the purchase of their farms. It was they who rushed to enlist and it was they whom the stay laws were ostensibly enacted to relieve. One may wonder, however, if these measures were not more useful to the planters, city merchants, and brokers.

Every Confederate State enacted a stay law in 1861 or early 1862, generally without the deliberate and careful examination that measures affecting property rights ordinarily received. But as soon as the emotional excitement and patriotic fervor of the first days of the war began to subside, the stay laws came in for critical examination in the newspapers and in the correspondence of the governors. These sources enable the present-day reader to see how forces lined up in support of or in opposition to the laws.

A flood of resolutions, memorials, and letters calling for the enactment of a stay law descended upon the legislature of Mississippi in 1861. Everyone was more or less in debt and with the closing of the ports would be unable to meet his obligations, declared a legislative committee. Soldiers rushing to arms were first given protection on January 22, 1861, by an act which forbade suits for debts against soldiers and levied fines up to five times the debt on any attorney or other person attempting to secure judgments. This was well enough so far as the men in the service were concerned, but it did not meet the needs of the moment. Business was at a standstill, planters were threatened with actions against their landed and personal estates, and the courts were demoralized by the movement to suspend civil trials. Finally, by a series of acts in 1861 and 1862, the state suspended all laws for the collection of past debts on bonds, promissory notes, bills of exchange, open accounts, and contracts until twelve months after the end of the war.[4]

The Mississippi statutes were among the tougher stay laws of the time, because they not only suspended all collections but prohibited persons from using the ordinary legal remedies, except in cases of fraud. Their effect was to confiscate bills receivable, said a critic, who had no doubt the measures were in violation of the impairment clause of the Confederate Constitution. Another critic calling himself "Equal Justice" attacked them because instead of merely assuring debtors that their property would not be sacrificed at a forced sale, they were so liberal to the debtor as to end his anxiety about his obligations. Persons who could have paid were taking advantage of the stay laws; indeed, debtors were using their funds for speculative purposes instead of paying their obligations. One man told the governor of Mississippi that he had sold his property in southern Alabama but could not collect from the purchaser because of the stay law; meantime he had to continue to pay the taxes and was compelled to borrow from his purchaser, who was speculating with money he owed on the plantation and who charged him 25 per cent interest, while his sale contract called for only 10 per cent. "Equal Justice" declared that Mississippi creditors were being brought to ruin by the stay laws. He approved of the law which was intended to benefit soldiers—for this he conceded there was justification— but he felt that the others, which applied more widely, should be amended to permit the courts to hear cases and to assess damages

---

[4] *Laws of Mississippi,* January 1861, pp. 37, 74; J. K. Bettersworth: *Confederate Mississippi* (Baton Rouge, La., 1943), pp. 21, 24, 28, 97; *Laws of Mississippi,* 1861–2, pp. 109, 235.

against delinquent debtors, though the debtors might be allowed to retain the property involved until the conclusion of the war.

On the other hand, a defender of stay laws in Mississippi argued that the other states of the Confederacy all raised more food crops, the price of which had been pushed up to prosperous levels, whereas Mississippi was entirely dependent on cotton which now had no market; therefore it needed an effective stay law, which did not involve repudiation. The argument went on in Mississippi throughout the war and waxed hot again at its conclusion. The wartime act was superseded by another stay law in December 1865, but this one was later declared to be in violation of the Federal Constitution.[5]

In neighboring Alabama early stay laws of February 8 and December 10, 1861, postponed actions against property but required that interest should be paid annually. They made notes of Alabama and the Confederacy acceptable for payments and freed the lien if they were not accepted. Except in cases already commenced, soldiers' property was declared not subject to attachments. The measures were criticized as being "pretended" stay laws, slanted too much on the side of the creditor, the money-lender, and the lawyer. Cotton planters who were barely able to meet their taxes and buy molasses for their slaves in place of scarce pork were finding that interest charges and court costs were piling up liens against their property and making it necessary for them to sacrifice some of their tangibles. A later act re-embodied some of the provisions of the earlier act and tightened the tender portion of the measure of December 10 by providing for forfeiture of liens or other judgments against debtors not in the service if currency was not accepted in payment of obligations. Efforts to make it a penal offence to refuse to receive Confederate currency failed.[6]

---

[5] Jackson *Weekly Mississippian*, Aug. 14, Nov. 20, Dec. 3, 1861; *Hinds County Gazette* (Raymond, Miss.), Feb. 5, 1826, Dec. 16, 23, 1865; Col. A. Proncewski, Oct. 29, 1862, to Gov. Pettus, Gov. Corr., Miss. Arch.; 40 *Mississippi Reports*, p. 39.
[6] *Laws of Alabama*, Called Session, 1861, p. 3, and Regular Session, 1861, p. 33; *Laws of Alabama*, 1863, p. 55; *Clarke County Democrat* (Grove Hill, Ala.), Jan. 2, 1862; Augusta *Chronicle & Sentinel*, Oct. 25, 1863; W. B. Modawell and J. J. Walker, Feb. 17, 1862, to Gov. Shorter, Gov. Corr., Ala. Arch.

North Carolina had experimented with stay laws in 1783 and 1812. On May 11, 1861, it adopted its third measure, "To provide against the Sacrifice of Property and to Suspend Proceedings in Certain Cases." Essentially, the measure barred creditors from using the courts to compel payments on contracts, bills of sale, or mortgages through levies upon the property of debtors. The constitutionality of the act was promptly challenged. In proceedings that were unusually rapid, the State Supreme Court, in the June term, declared the act void "because it is in violation of the *Constitution of the United States,* and of the Constitution of the Confederate States, which in this respect is the same, and also, of the Constitution of the State." The Court's argument was strongly reminiscent of Story and Marshall, since it went back to the case of Jones versus Crittenden, which had struck down the Suspension Act of 1812.[7]

The purpose, incidence, and fairness of stay laws came in for much discussion in North Carolina in 1861. The most telling argument advanced in their support was that the great bulk of the enlisted soldiers were small farmers in their twenties and early thirties, who had numerous young children, little property, and considerable debts. They were leaving their families facing dubious prospects; their homes must therefore be assured them while they were fighting for their country. One writer declared that a large majority of the people of North Carolina owed debts that had been incurred in normal times, and that if the sheriff and his deputies were turned loose on them, there would be a revolution. Another maintained that the men being recruited in the late summer of 1861 were mostly from the middle class which customarily bore much of the burden of the government, and that they, too, were in debt. If denied protection against the "ruthless band of money changers," how could they be induced to enlist? Failure to fill up the army would require the draft, which few wanted. Without the protection of the stay law, the soldier could not fight; he would desert to protect his family. If his home were taken from him, his children would be sent to the almshouse and his wife would have to go begging on the streets. Over and over

---

[7] Italics added. *Barnes v. Barnes, 53 North Carolina Reports,* p. 369; 4 *North Carolina Reports,* p. 55.

it was suggested that the volunteers came from the debtor class whose families needed the relief of the stay laws. Here one can see again the beginnings of the complaint heard on all sides in the later days of the war that it was a rich man's war and a poor man's fight.[8]

Opponents of the stay law held that it was unconstitutional because it would impair the obligations of contracts, destroy credit, and prevent sales of property except for cash, which was lacking. After its enactment they urged the people to avoid the law, "be honest," pay just debts, and, if "avaricious, hard-hearted, narrow souled, skin-flint, close-shaving people won't let you alone —if they will press you unmercifully and force you to it, only make a mortgage or a deed of trust for the benefit of, not yourself, but *for all your creditors.*" Other critics maintained that stay laws delayed justice, destroyed commerce except for cash, tempted debtors to defraud the poor, deprived the creditor in the army of the right to collect his just debts, and invited violence and crime. It was even charged that the stay law, by compelling the sale of properties for cash, prevented the breaking up of large plantations. One of the bitterest indictments was by a correspondent of Thomas Ruffin who declared:

> The stay law is a revolutionary measure, radical, unwise, demoralizing, disgraceful to the state, to the age and the Southern Confederacy. Its champions are the profligate, the spendthrifts, reckless, insolvents and especially such as have consideration because of the property around them for which they owe and are determined to keep upon no better principles than that which animates the bandit of the Alps.

Two weeks later the same correspondent wrote: "A heavier blow was never struck at our liberties than the stay law."[9]

---

[8] *North Carolina Standard*, Aug. 28, 31, Dec. 11, 1861, and Feb. 1, 1862.
[9] Various writers in *North Carolina Standard*, June 15, Oct. 2, Nov. 2, 1861; J. T. Trowbridge: *The South: A Tour of its Battlefields and Ruined Cities* (Hart-ford, Conn., 1866), p. 580; J. G. de Roulhac Hamilton (ed.): *The Papers of Thomas Ruffin; Publications of the North Carolina Historical Commission* (3 vols., Raleigh, N.C., 1918–20), III, 187, 189.

The Court's action in voiding the stay law was received with much satisfaction by its opponents and with equal displeasure by its advocates. After its invalidation one writer said, doubtless with exaggeration, that thousands of writs were being served against poor debtors whose families would be reduced to penury. He asked: "Are the rich fighting the battle of the South," men who are free of all debt, or is the army mostly filled with persons in debt who will now be deprived of their homes by the action of the court? It was the noteholders, other creditors, "and their barefoot children," he observed sarcastically, who were protected by the voiding of the stay law. A Person County upholder of stay legislation reported that between June, when the first stay law was invalidated, and September, when another was enacted, twenty-five executions were brought in his county against debtors, which was more than had been made in any four years in the last twenty. To avoid the loss of their homes some people were said to have sold their last cow and horse.[1]

When the state Supreme Court struck down the first stay law, North Carolina legislators were still in that period of deep patriotic fervor when most people were either offering their services in the army or aiding and encouraging others to make the plunge. To replace the stay law they rushed through on September 11 "An Act to Change the Jurisdiction of the Courts and the Rules of Pleading therein" which accomplished much the same end. The new measure was awkwardly drafted, complex and technical, disguised as a law to enforce the administration of justice, so that the Supreme Court could not judicially determine that it was a stay law. It postponed for twelve months all actions on collections, whether initially undertaken or in process of execution, suspended the statute of limitations, eliminated one of the two sessions of the county courts, transferred civil jury cases pending in county courts to superior courts and abolished their spring terms, and otherwise placed obstructions in the way of creditors using the courts to secure judgments. Subsequent amendments and extensions of this act in 1862 and 1863 prevented suits for debts from being tried, and maintained

---

[1] *North Carolina Standard*, Aug. 31, Oct. 16, Nov. 30, 1861, Feb. 1, 1862.

the equivalent of a stay law in operation for the duration of the war.[2]

As the original patriotic fervor subsided, men who had kept quiet about the alleged iniquities of this second suspension act of 1861 began to demand its repeal or drastic amendment, calling the act more objectionable than the stay law for its destruction of the rights of creditors, the long delay it assured debtors, its clear unconstitutionality, and its obvious disregard of the judiciary. Efforts were made to modify it in the North Carolina convention but were narrowly defeated.[3]

More than a year after the excitement over stay laws had somewhat subsided, Governor Vance expressed disapprobation of the second act of 1861 for suspending the normal operations of the courts, though he favored action to protect the property of soldiers from sacrifice. His difficulty, and that of other critics of stay legislation, was that they could seem to find no way to stay proceedings against soldiers without having them apply equally to other debtors who had no need for relief and who were using the relief measures to retain their capital for speculation. The obstruction of judicial proceedings by creditors against debtors continued throughout the war but with diminishing effect, as is shown by a letter to Governor Vance of December 28, 1863, wherein one J. B. Wallington stated that on a debt of $1,000, of which one half had been paid, he had offered the balance in Confederate notes, only to be refused and required to pay in gold or silver. Wallington, a soldier, had a wife, three children, and four Negroes but could not raise the specie to meet his debt and was threatened with sale. The governor, whom he asked for help, could only reply that if the creditor was heartless enough to force the property to sale, there was no power to stop him.[4]

During the trying days of Reconstruction North Carolina again tried to stay judicial proceedings involving the collections of debts by ordinances of its conventions of 1865-6 and 1868 and by a law of February 12, 1867. In 1869 these measures

---

[2] *Laws of North Carolina*, Second Extra Session, 1861, p. 14; *North Carolina Standard*, Jan. 22, 1864.
[3] *North Carolina Standard*, Sept. 18, 25, Nov. 2, 16, 30, Dec. 17,

25, 1861, Feb. 5, 1862.
[4] Report of Gov. Vance to the North Carolina Legislature, *O.R.*, ser. 4, II, 187. The Wallington letter is in Gov. Corr., N.C. Arch.

reached the North Carolina Supreme Court, which struck them down in Jacobs versus Smallwood. The statement of the Court that "eight years of stay laws have left a considerable indebtedness, with interest and cost accumulated, and creditors and sureties impoverished, without any corresponding benefit to the principal debtors" may have been quite gratuitous and without any empirical basis. Surely the members of the two conventions and of the legislature who had drafted the various suspension measures were as closely in touch with the facts of debtor-creditor relationships as the judges were in their ivory tower.[5]

Georgia had a less difficult experience with its stay laws, possibly because influential planters and merchants needed their protection as much as did the small farmers and homeowners. Possibly also, the fact that its first stay law, one of the earliest to be enacted in the crisis days of November 1860, was passed over the governor's veto by such large majorities—108 to 20 in the House and 95 to 13 in the Senate—deterred judges from looking askance at its provisions. The Georgia law declared that in the event of suspension of specie payments by the principal banks of Georgia, all actions by creditors against the property of debtors should be suspended until December 1, 1861, and all statutes of limitation should similarly be suspended. This measure was re-enacted in 1861, 1862, and 1863 and finally on March 9, 1865, for the duration of the war. Between January 1 and March 9, 1865, it had been allowed to lapse, but by that time civil government had become so demoralized in Georgia that few if any cases were brought.[6]

Governor Joseph E. Brown had opposed the stay law of 1860 but in November 1861 when Georgia was in the "midst of a revolution," with its ports blockaded so that planters could not get their cotton out and banks could not import specie, he called for the re-enactment of the measure he had previously vetoed. Without its re-enactment, said Brown, "a few heartless speculators who happened to have funds at their command would buy up property at nominal prices." To assure protection for soldiers against unfavorable court action, the legislature took two further

---

[5] *Laws of North Carolina*, 1866–1867, p. 23; 63 *North Carolina Reports*, p. 114.
[6] *Laws of Georgia*, 1860, p. 23.

steps. The first, "An Act for the Protection of Soldiers in the service, against judgments," adopted on December 14, declared that no judgment obtained in any state court against any soldier should be enforced until three months after his discharge. The second measure, adopted the same day, suspended all statutes of limitation for the duration of the war.

Georgia creditors were no more willing to accept stay laws than those of North Carolina or other states. Demands were made for repeal or modification of the laws. The Augusta *Chronicle & Sentinel* could see little reason or necessity for their enactment and maintained that they encouraged people to make no effort to meet their obligations. It conceded that at the outset there might have been some justification for them but that in 1863, with the country never more prosperous, goods greatly increased in value, and people well able to discharge their debts (as indeed many were); with farmers hoarding their corn, and with cotton molding in warehouses and ginhouses while the owners waited for high prices, it was time to repeal the laws. Many long-headed creditors, it declared, did not wish to collect their obligations since they might have to accept inflated currency. The *Chronicle & Sentinel* told of an acquaintance who offered to pay his debt, when due, in Confederate treasury notes, only to have them rejected by the creditor, who expressed his determination to hold the obligation. The *Chronicle & Sentinel* called this action dishonoring the currency and striking at the vital spot in the government and urged, on moral and patriotic grounds, that creditors should accept the currency, but it did not advocate compulsion in the form of a tender act. Another scribe, signing himself "A creditor," took a different position. It was the stay laws that had kept seven tenths of the people from having judgments levied against them and their property sold. He advocated an amendment to prevent suits for recovery until the conclusion of the war, as they caused extra expense for the debtor and put the judgment obligation in a state ready for immediate execution when the war was over without the debtor being able to interpose objections.[7]

---

[7] *Chronicle & Sentinel,* July 13, 1862, July 3, Dec. 28, 1863; Atlanta *Southern Confederacy,* Oct. 23, 1861.

Whatever the attitude of critics of its stay laws, most Georgians thought them necessary during the war and turned to them in somewhat different form in the bitter days of Reconstruction. Two acts of 1866 "for the relief of the people of Georgia and to prevent the levy and sale of property," were passed by very large majorities over the veto of the governor. The first granted ten months of exemption from payment and extended payments thereafter over four years; the second gave a longer exemption period but required that payment should be completed in the time provided in the first act.[8]

Students of legal history will find some amusement as well as some sound common sense in the conflicting views respecting a stay law of South Carolina. This act of January 1862, like other Southern statutes, prohibited any final process for forcing collection of debts through court action and suspended statutes of limitation. It was to be in effect only until the next session of the legislature but was re-enacted regularly thereafter. Charleston merchants, a commercial group second in importance only to those of New Orleans, may not have liked the measure, but the South Carolina planters doubtless did. The suspension or stay laws remained in effect in South Carolina throughout the war and apparently were not seriously challenged.

In 1866, however, a case involving the stay laws did reach the Supreme Court. It first came before A. P. Aldrich, a circuit judge and a man of eminence in South Carolina affairs. In his delightful and charmingly written decision the justice expressed regret that the attorneys had not argued the case with precedents, since Sherman's bummers had destroyed his entire legal library and friends had been able to round up for him only a case or two together with Chancellor Kent's *Commentaries*, which he had never considered a very high authority. Though he had access to no other law books, Aldrich's learning as well as his appreciation of social and economic forces shows in his decision. In his opinion the state's stay law said, and rightly, "You may not add to the calamity which overwhelms the land by harassing with law-suits and Sheriff's sales those who happen to be in your debt."

---

[8] Acts of Mar. 8, 1866, and Dec. 12, 1866, *Laws of Georgia*, 1865–6, p. 241, and 1866, p. 157.

He pointed out numerous instances in which the courts had sanctioned legislation abridging property and contractual rights notwithstanding the impairment clause of the Constitution. To permit judgments and executions would bring "widespread ruin and distress," he was convinced. "On the one hand is a multitude of debtors praying for mercy and for time . . . on the other is a company of creditors clamoring for their constitutional right, as they are pleased to call it." The stay law was intended to protect the property and family of those who were fighting. On this ground and the Lockian notion of the greatest good for the greatest number, and finally with the legal aphorism "Let justice be done, though the heavens fall," Aldrich upheld the law.

On appeal to the full court, the chief justice, B. F. Dunkin, disregarded all of Aldrich's points, searched the records of the United States Supreme Court and of the supreme courts of states, selected his cases well, including a very questionable decision—Green versus Bibble—that even John Marshall had not cared to join in, and rendered, quite in contrast to the light and sympathetic decision of Aldrich, a dull legalistic decision which struck down the legislation. Justice Aldrich had the last word in a long and breezy dissent which, if it did not become the basis of reversal at a later time, was full of common sense. Aldrich declared that reflection and subsequent investigation into other works than Chancellor Kent had convinced him that his original conclusion was sound. He showed that South Carolina had enacted seven or eight stay laws, that the convention of 1865 had sanctioned and approved the act of 1865, and that seven of the present judges of the Supreme Court which was hearing the case had sat in the convention. How, he asked, can a law which merely hastens or retards the remedy, impair the obligation? Essentially, Aldrich argued, "the remedy is not a part of the contract." Aldrich's ablest point was made when he showed that he could match decisions by John Marshall and Langdon Cheves which would justify the stay laws with the decisions of Kent and Story upon which the Chief Justice relied.[9]

Nearly a fourth of the population of Louisiana was centered in New Orleans, the principal commercial center of the South.

---

[9] 13 *South Carolina Reports*, p. 507; *Charleston Courier*, Jan. 18, 1862.

The merchants, brokers, and factors of this city handled most of the sugar and almost two fifths of the cotton of the South. Banking, insurance, shipping, exporting, and importing houses serving the South had their headquarters there. A creditor element existed in Louisiana that was much stronger than in states like Alabama, Mississippi, and Georgia. This is not to minimize the influence of the planters in Louisiana, who were the politically dominant element. Being in debt to the amount of $8,000,000 and fearful that their creditors would push them to the wall while their economic position was weak, the planters demanded a stay law. To the conservatively minded commercial class in New Orleans stay laws were "wild, revolutionary and iniquitous." They would be a disgrace to Louisiana, would subvert confidence, and would aid only the unworthy. A writer calling himself a conservative pointed out that Tennessee, Arkansas, and Mississippi, whose planters also were in debt to the New Orleans factors, had adopted stay laws, and that failure of Louisiana to do likewise would lead to the bankruptcy of the very class on which the welfare of New Orleans depended.

After excited discussion, the Louisiana legislature on January 17, 1863, adopted a moratorium law somewhat different from the stay laws of other states. It provided that in a forced sale of property the minimum acceptable price must be its value as of April 1, 1861, and if no bid was offered at that level, the sale was to be postponed until twelve months after the end of the war. A critic of the law pointed out that since both slaves and real property had greatly appreciated in terms of Confederate currency, appraisements of that date would be well below current values, and the sheriffs would be able to sell almost any property. He stated that a large majority of the legislature had wanted an effective stay law and had regarded the act as satisfactory at the time, but that they had been duped into enacting one that would do little to protect hard-pressed debtors.

Unsatisfactory as the Louisiana stay law was, it called down upon the legislature a long and bitter attack by the New Orleans *True Delta* in which this "agrarian legislation" was denounced as destructive of property rights and of constitutional guarantees. Unless New Orleans were separated permanently from the rest of Louisiana financially, politically, and territorially, said the *Delta*, it would have to submit to a "more insupportable tyranny than any ignorance, vindictiveness and malevolence ever framed." Though opponents continued to say that such legislation was not the result of popular will, the overwhelming support which stay laws received in the various state legislatures suggests the contrary.

When Union forces captured many of the river parishes of Louisiana, the military authorities had to face the stay law problem. An early order forbade foreclosures of mortages and sales against loyal citizens, whether owners or mortgagors. Later, on February 18, 1864, this order was modified to permit executions except where they were against equity and justice and where the parties were entitled to the favor and protection of the authorities.[1]

A quick summary of the stay laws of other states to show the differences in approach may be useful. Tennessee statutes barred the collection of debts by persons in non-slave-holding states, postponed magistrates' courts till January 1, 1862, extended the period of redemption to three years, and stayed all judgments a year. In 1862 Texas suspended all statutes of limitations until January 1, 1864, or six months after the close of the war, so far as they related to debts, claims due on bills, bonds, promissory notes, and contracts for payment of money. The next year it suspended all actions involving debts affecting real or personal property until a year after the conclusion of the war. Arkansas postponed civil and criminal cases of persons in military service. Virginia combined appraisement with stay by forbidding any sale on execution unless the property brought what the assessors thought to be a fair price. Florida stayed judgments and executions at common law or decrees in chancery until twelve months after peace had been restored. Kentucky banned all actions after thirty days upon which there was no limitation and in 1865 suspended all laws for the collection of debts. Both acts

---

[1] New Orleans *True Delta*, Jan. 26, 1862; *New Orleans Picayune*, Nov. 14, 1861; *Laws of Louisiana*, 1861–2, p. 49; *Charleston Courier*, Jan. 11, 1862; *Carrollton Times*, Oct. 29, Nov. 5, 1864.

were voided by the state Supreme Court. Military operations forced the suspension of most local and state courts.[2]

In the North the demand for stay legislation was less extensive, being confined to the public-land states, where settlers were still engaged in making farms on government land and where many, if not most, of the more recently arrived farm makers were heavily in debt. Nor was there in the North a body of influential businessmen such as the planters and dealers in cotton who were suddenly cut off from their source of income by the outbreak of the war and threatened with the loss of their property. Consequently, the pressure for stay laws was directed toward the enactment of special legislation applicable only to men in the armed forces, not the general type which was common in the South.

The Northern measures varied from state to state, but all were to apply for the duration of the war or until the soldiers were released from service. For example, the Iowa stay law of May 29, 1861, postponed all actions pending or thereafter brought against soldiers until they were released from the army. Ohio stayed all proceedings against the real or personal property of anyone in the armed service until two months after his release. Michigan gave the purchasers of its swamplands a full year's extension of payments after discharge in addition to exempting them from arrest and from all processes, attachments, and executions.

Missouri, whose stay laws of 1822 and 1835 had been struck down by the state Supreme Court, tried again in 1861, passing an act which postponed all executions of any judgment of any court for nearly two years, thereby stopping all legal action in foreclosures. The state court again gagged at the application of the law retroactively, thereby making it of little consequence.

Wisconsin had been hard hit by the panic of 1857 and much farm property was threatened with foreclosure. Horace Greeley's

---

[2] Acts of Jan. 28, May 8, June 27, 28, 1861, *Laws of Tennessee, 1861*, pp. 18, 35, 40, 46; *Laws of Texas*, 1861–2, p. 40; Austin *State Gazette*, Mar. 4, 1863; *Hunt's Merchants Magazine*, XLIV (May 1861), 663; 4 *Kentucky Reports*, p. 292; 13 *South Carolina Reports*, p. 518; *North Carolina Standard*, Nov. 23, 1861; *Laws of Florida*, 1861, p. 17; J. E. Johns: *Florida during the Civil War* (Gainesville, Fla., 1963), p. 78.

advice to mortgage-ridden farmers, to let their land go for sale and to try elsewhere on cheaper land, contributed to the movement for an appraisement law which would delay forced sales. An angry writer in the *Wisconsin Farmer* spoke about the "rapacious and heartless creditors" who "have mouths as large as the whale that swallowed Jonah . . . who crunch down small fry without the least compunction." It may have been fear of the courts which kept the appraisement measure from adoption, but the state did enact a measure on April 17, 1861, which declared that all persons in military service were exempt from civil process and required that all actions against them be stricken from the calendar until the defendants were discharged from the army.[3]

Much angry feeling, expensive litigation, and anti-rent warfare occurred during the Civil War years as the unexpected result of a series of measures affecting the public lands which had been adopted earlier. For example, when in 1846 Congress granted land on the alternate section pattern to aid in improving the Des Moines River, it could not foresee that this grant, under conflicting interpretations of the Department of the Interior, would bring about one of the longest and bitterest conflicts between various contenders for title to well over a hundred thousand acres of valuable farmland in Iowa. Responsibility for this unfortunate embroglio rested on careless members of Congress who drafted legislation without regard to previous acts, on administrators in the General Land Office who were inept if not corrupt, and on greedy capitalists who seized upon public errors of fact as well as of judgment and who were supported by a line of judicial decisions. More than one thousand settler families moved upon the land in question, made their improvements over many years, got title from the government, and then were ejected on the ground that the government had erred. Almost a generation before the Des Moines River lands controversy was finally settled, an Iowa State Commission reported on the losses settlers had suffered by improving lands for which they had either United

[3] *Laws of Iowa*, 1861, p. 6; *Laws of Ohio*, 1861, p. 113; *Laws of Michigan*, Extra Session, 1862, p. 45; *Hunt's Merchants Magazine*, XLIV (May 1861), 630; *Stevens v. Andrews*, 31 *Missouri Reports*, p. 205; *Wisconsin Farmer*, XII (Apr. 1, 1860), 125, 127; *Laws of Wisconsin*, 1861, p. 319.

States patents, warrantee deeds of railroads, deeds of the state government, or quitclaim deeds, or for which they had taken preliminary steps toward title under the Preemption or Homestead Acts. The number of claimants was 1,032, the value of their improvements was $758,031, and their losses were then estimated at $800,000. Many of these settlers had taken up their land before the Civil War when it was thought title questions had been settled. They organized their settlers' protective association and spent years in unsuccessfully fighting the absentee owners who gained title to their homes.[4]

In California land-hungry settlers moved upon and began improving the hitherto largely undeveloped, unfenced, unsurveyed Mexican grants. In some cases the titles to these grants were fabricated, in others incomplete and uncertain under Mexican law. In still others, the titleholder had satisfied all requirements for ownership. Few of the grants had clear boundaries; some were floating grants which could be located within broad areas. When California was transferred to the United States, Congress had made the mistake of not giving its landless residents a homestead, as it had done for the landless in the Old Northwest, Louisiana, Florida, and the Oregon country. Consequently, Californians looking for land, and the thousands who rushed into the new state after the discovery of gold, settled upon these boundless wastes where there were no improvements and no indication of ownership. Soon the Mexican claimants or their assignees learned of their activity and went to law to have them ejected. Between the claimants and the squatters hoping to preempt and later to homestead the land on which they resided, warfare soon developed which kept California in an uproar for years, cost both settlers and claimants huge sums for prolonged litigation, absorbed the attention of the District Court and the Supreme Court of the United States more than any other kind of issue, and contributed to the disrespect for law which has been

---

[4] *Report of the Commission Appointed under the Provisions of Chapter Seven of the Private Local and Temporary Laws of the Fourteenth General Assembly of the State of Iowa to Ascertain the Extent of Losses of Settlers upon Des Moines River Lands by Reason of Failure of Title* (Des Moines, 1872); C. H. Gatch: "The Des Moines River Land Grant," *Annals of Iowa*, I (April, July, October 1894), 354 ff.

too characteristic of the West. Squatters organized, had their organs of opinion, entered politics, and showed a tendency to distrust not only the courts and the administrative officials but also the Republican Party and conservative leadership in the Democratic Party. They developed a markedly agrarian program of their own.

In their search for methods of financing railroads in Kansas, promoters thought of the Indian reserves which remained after the territory was opened to settlement. If a reserve could be obtained intact by a railroad, it would be worth much more than alternate section grants, for the increased value which construction would give to all the land, not merely half of it, would come to the railroad. In Iowa, Illinois, and, later, Colorado, railroad promoters tried to obtain the reserved sections within the primary area of the land grant to secure for themselves the full return which construction would bring, but they were never able to get all the good locations. In Kansas, the opportunity of controlling all the adjacent land seemed available if the Office of Indian Affairs could be pursuaded to sell the Indian reserves through which the lines were projected. Lincoln's Commissioner of Indian Affairs and his Secretary of the Interior were quite willing to enter into such arrangements, provided they were given an interest in the lands to be thus transferred. Six treaties for the sale of reserves direct to the railroads were negotiated with the respective Indians, and five were carried to completion. Nearly a million and a half acres were thus acquired without the land becoming a part of the public domain. The sixth treaty, which provided for the sale of 8,000,000 acres, was defeated by an uprising in the House of Representatives.

All these treaties disregarded the fact that several thousand settlers had already established themselves on the tracts. True, they were intruders and had gained no rights as squatters on Indian reserves, but now that railroads had obtained control of the reserves, the settlers would have to pay the railroads' high prices for the land instead of being able to acquire it as a homestead or preemption from the Federal government. Land warfare developed, settlers' associations were organized, and representatives were sent to Washington to lobby in their behalf. They did finally defeat the Osage "steal," as they called it. But on the better-developed tracts of the Delawares, the Kickapoos, the Cherokees, and the Pottawatomies, the squatters were unsuccessful.[5]

Borrowing from the experience of the South, where planters organized currency-issuing banks by exchanging cotton or mortgages on their land for stock in the new institutions, railroad promoters in Wisconsin in the fifties exchanged railroad stock for mortgages on farms along their right of way. Some 6,000 farmers were thus induced to participate in financing railroads on the understanding that the stock would pay more than the interest their mortgages carried. The mortgages, amounting to $4,500,000 to $5,000,000, were peddled to Eastern institutions and investors, and when the railroads collapsed and their stock became valueless these mortgages fell into default. Interest running at 8 per cent accumulated rapidly and legal action was taken by the absentee investors to safeguard their rights through foreclosure proceedings. The farmers now realized how badly they had been bilked, for in most instances the railroads had not been built, the farmers' equity in stock was worthless, and their farms were threatened. From the state legislature they secured, between 1858 and 1863, fourteen relief measures which either tried to make corruption a proper plea for voiding the mortgages or consisted of some form of stay law to delay foreclosure. All these statutes were struck down by the courts; the farmers paid or foreclosure followed. Frederick Merk summarizes the results of this unfortunate method of financing railroads: "Many sturdy Wisconsin pioneers had been evicted from their homesteads, larger numbers had suffered serious losses, and all had for years endured agonies of uncertainty as to their ultimate fate. Nothing could persuade such men that railroad officials were not elementally and thoroughly villainous."[6]

---

[5] P. W. Gates: "California's Embattled Settlers," *California Historical Society Quarterly*, XLI (June 1962), 99 ff.; *idem:* "Adjudication of Spanish-Mexican Land Claims in California," *The Huntington Library Quarterly*, XXI (May 1958), 213 ff.; *idem: Fifty Million Acres. Conflicts over Kansas Land Policy, 1854–1890* (Ithaca, N.Y., 1954).

[6] *American Railroad Journal*, XXXIV (Feb. 2, 1867), 93; Frederick Merk: *Economic History of Wisconsin during the Civil War Decade* (Madison, Wis., 1916), p. 269.

The policy of granting land to aid in the construction of railroads produced an enormous amount of litigation and criticisms of the railroads over the selection of their lands, the prices they charged, and their refusal to pay taxes on their lands. In Iowa, for example, people who had bought swampland from the state were later told that the land belonged to the Burlington Railroad and that they must purchase their title a second time. Nothing could exacerbate the feelings of the people more, particularly when railroad freight rates were beginning to arouse hostility. Nor did it help matters when the Burlington officials threatened to change the route of their line if the counties through which it was projected insisted on maintaining their right to swamplands claimed by the railroad. The threat to change the route produced a counterthreat in the Iowa legislature to resume control over the lands granted to the railroad.[7]

By the sixties criticisms of the administration of railroad land grants were being voiced, although not stridently at first. But they were to swell to a concerted roar and to lead not only to the decision to make no more land grants but to the movement for the forfeiture of unearned, unsold, and unpatented land given to the railroads. The easy credit terms allowed by the railroads encouraged some to buy their high-priced land who had insufficient capital to begin farming; the result was continued bickering with the railroads over payments, extensions, compound interest, and foreefeiture of contracts. Others who found the high-priced land beyond their means went farther afield in the search for free or cheap land. The railroads were thus both contributing to development and at the same time slowing it down and scattering settlement.

First of the railroads to receive land grants and to be completed was the Illinois Central, whose line extended through the mostly undeveloped prairie region of central Illinois. The railroad sold its alternate sections for high prices, which did not deter purchasers, since they were allowed to buy on extended credit.

---

[7] J. N. King, June 21, 1865, to C. E. Perkins, Land Letters, C.B.&Q.R.R., Newberry Library; R. C. Overton: *Burlington West. A Colonization* *History of the Burlington Railroad* (Cambridge, Mass., 1941), pp. 202 ff.

Unfortunately, the panic of 1857 and the four years of depression which followed made it necessary to grant extensions of payments and finally to cancel numerous contracts, so that little of the land had been conveyed to purchasers before 1863. Furthermore, the railroad was anxious to retain the good will of the settlers lest it lose special charter privileges and be forced to sell its remaining lands for whatever they might bring; consequently it was lenient to delinquents if they seemed to be making improvements. As long as the title to the lands was in the railroad, the lands were free of taxes, which explains why many settlers were reluctant to make the final payment. Settlers on the odd-numbered sections, whose lands became taxable the year they acquired them from the government, naturally disliked the exemption of their neighbors' property, for it compelled them to carry a double portion of the cost of local government, schools, and roads.

The slowness with which the Illinois Central conveyed title and the belief that it connived with its settlers to keep the lands off the tax roll as long as possible aroused angry feelings against the company and led in 1865 to the passing of an act which required railroad land that had been sold on contract to be assessed on the date of the last due payment. But the half million acres of unsold land, and another half million on which the final payment was not yet due, still remained, and these were not contributing to the support of local government. Later efforts to compel the officials to sell the remaining tracts failed, and it was not until 1905 that the Illinois Central's land business was finally closed out. Tax exemption for well-developed land, or for land that might have been developed had the price been right, created a favored group of non-tax-paying farmers and dealers and left in its wake a marked feeling of resentment.

This same tax exemption feature cropped up in Wisconsin, Kansas, and Nebraska and in other new commonwealths at a later time and became the object of wrathful denunciation by Grangers and Populists. A joint resolution of the Nebraska legislature of February 13, 1867, urged that all railroad companies having land grants be required by Federal law to obtain patents for their land. The failure of the Union Pacific to take title to the 3,900,000 acres it had earned was seriously retarding development, the resolution declared.[8]

Railroad land was sold to speculators and bonanza farmers as well as to settlers, despite public pronouncements that none but actual settlers would be encouraged to buy. Tenancy, a product of the heavy cost of farm making on the treeless prairies and plains, was in part a product of railroad land-grant policy. The always latent anti-monopoly feelings of the West were expressed in objections to sales to speculators, criticism of the large bonanza farms, which were held to be bad for the community, and resentment at the emergence of tenancy.

Illinois was blighted by large speculative holdings and a score of successful bonanza farms which at first attracted much approving attention. Among the best-advertised of the bonanza farms was Isaac Funk's 26,000-acre holding in central Illinois, which a neighbor declared delayed development and settlement, retarded the establishment of schools, and was "no benefit to any body; though he is a right good neighbor." As early as December 1862, the complaint began to be heard that tenant houses on the bonanza farms were "miserable sheds, not fit for beasts to live in." Mean tenant houses attracted poor tenants. Tenancy, though well under way in Illinois and Indiana and getting started in Iowa, had not yet caused alarm, but the great amount of speculatively held land and the rising price of good prairie soil were setting forces in motion that were making for the rapid emergence of tenant-operated farms and a class of landless laborers in the corn belt.

Tenants and hired hands rarely came in for favorable attention in the farm journals, but one "Hired-Hand" with some literary skill and a grievance was awarded space for a two-column statement of his trouble. As a farm worker in Logan County, Illinois, where tenancy and landlordism were well under way,

---

[8] *Laws of Illinois*, 1865, p. 80; *Laws of Nebraska*, 1867, p. 142; P. W. Gates: *The Illinois Central Railroad and Its Colonization Work* (Cambridge, Mass., 1934), pp. 303 ff.; L. E. Decker: "The Railroads and the Land Office, Administrative Policy and the Land Patent Controversy, 1846–1896," *Mississippi Valley Historical Review*, XLVI (March 1960), 679 ff.

he had to give five days to road work though he had no property, not even a horse. Since he only had 200 days' work a year—and less, if he were ill—this five days of road work took one fortieth of his income. The work was partly done on the road bounding his employer's farm on which he hauled his grain to market; the balance of the time was spent on a road along the property of a non-resident speculator, whose land was being made more valuable as a result but who did no road work himself. The law taxed only residents under fifty. Such bonanza farmers as "the Jake Strawn's, the Ike Funk's, the Mike Sullivan's, the Sol. Sturges's, and the Ould Sculley's . . . are exempt from road work, while every poor devil at work for them by the month, must turn out and work his five days along side of their large tracts of land." He favored a poll tax of two days' work from every man and a property tax to be levied on residents and non-residents alike and spent on road work.[9]

Farmers everywhere deplored their dependence on the middleman, the buyer who determined price, quality, weights, and measures. Southern planters complained that the deductions made by their factors for trash in bales of cotton and for poor ginning and baling were unreasonable. Similarly, dairy farmers complained that the New York milk dealers bought by beer measure and sold by wine measure, and prairie farmers felt that the grain merchants, warehousemen, and millers bilked them in weighing and grading the grain assigned to them as well as by the charges they levied. It was as absurd for the grain buyer to insist on measuring oats as weighing 34 pounds and corn as 60 pounds when the state law had set other weights, as for the farmers to insist on 38 inches of cloth, 210 pounds of flour in a barrel, and 18 ounces for the pound. An investigation by the Chicago Board of Trade revealed that "many gross and inexcusable irregularities" existed in the delivery and shipment of grain, especially in the downgrading of wheat when it came into the elevators and the upgrading of it when it was sold. To eliminate the irregularities, the "Withering tax" of elevator and commission men, and the dependence upon railroads, it was proposed to

[9] *Rural New Yorker,* XII (July 27, 1861), 237; *Prairie Farmer,* VIII (July 25, 1861), 49, and X (Dec. 13, 1862), 372.

build in Chicago a People's Warehouse with a capacity of a million bushels, to buy boats and freighting equipment to transport grain to the East, and to set up farmers' stores. Warehousemen always worked hand in glove with the railroads, the farmers were convinced. One railroad gave a monopoly on grain shipment from a prairie town to a buyer who levied an extra charge of one cent a bushel on all grain sent over the line. As a result angry farmers hauled their grain some distance to a competing line rather than pay this tribute, and one hundred and fifty farmers agreed not to patronize merchants or other businesses that shipped or received goods over the offending railroad.[1]

Railroad rates were becoming increasingly burdensome, particularly between communities where there was no competition from rival lines. It was charged that transportation costs absorbed 80 per cent of the value of wheat, 30 per cent of the value of pork, and 20 per cent of the value of beef and that it took six bushels of grain to pay the cost of shipping one. Richard Yates, Governor of Illinois, took up the issue of rates in his message to the legislature in January 1863. No Illinois resident, he declared, could be unaware of the upsetting effect of the loss of Southern markets, which had been supplied by water transportation, or of the current high costs of transporting produce by rail to the East. Two projects were under consideration to provide competition in rates and to destroy the monopoly of the railroads. One was to deepen the Illinois and Lake Michigan Canal to make it navigable by steam-powered vessels, and the other was to improve water transportation to the East by the enlargement of the Erie Canal. Both were recommended by the governor, though neither could be undertaken by the state alone.

William H. Osborn, president of the Illinois Central Railroad, one of the heaviest carriers of grain to Chicago, actively supported making a ship canal of the already outmoded Erie, possibly to the discomfiture of his fellow railroad executives. He emphasized that the heavy flow of grain East by lake, canal, and

---

[1] *Prairie Farmer*, old series, IX (September 1849); new series, V (Feb. 16, 1860), 98, VIII (Oct. 31, 1861), 294; IX (Apr. 5, 1862), 216; *Dairy Farmer*, I (June 1860), 38; *Rural New Yorker*, XIII (Oct. 4, 18, 1862), 317, 334; B. L. Pierce: *History of Chicago* (3 vols., New York, 1937–1957), II, 77 ff.

railroad so choked facilities as to cause delay and losses and he acknowledged that high transportation costs had almost rendered agriculture unprofitable. He stirred up the Illinois State Agricultural Society to take a strong stand in behalf of the enlargement of the Erie Canal and through his access to influential journals of opinion focused wide attention on it.

A "Great Canal Convention" met in Chicago with a distinguished list of delegates to consider various plans for improved water transportation. The one project for which there was the most support and which seemed at the time to offer the most promise to Middle Western farmers was Osborn's proposed Niagara Ship Canal. A canal on the American side around the Falls at Niagara, together with improvement of the Erie Canal so that grain could be carried to tidewater without breaking bulk, would surely lead to lower freight rates, it was held. A bill to authorize the expenditure of $3,500,000 for the construction of the Niagara Ship Canal by the State of New York and $13,346,824 for the improvement of the Illinois and Michigan Canal by the Federal government was acrimoniously debated in the House of Representatives. It was finally defeated by the votes of representatives whose states would draw little benefit from either. The issue would not die, however, and continued to excite attention through the war. At a farmers' convention in Morris, Illinois, in November 1865, the Niagara Ship Canal was strongly urged upon the national government as a means of protecting farmers against excessive freight rates.

Not all farmers were taken in by President Osborn's campaign to induce the government to spend millions of dollars on improving transportation from Chicago eastward. One hard-bitten critic in the *Prairie Farmer* expressed the view that farmers would profit much more from a reduction in the excessively high rates the Illinois Central charged than from such an impractical scheme as improving the outmoded canals of New York. He pointed out that the I.C. charged 14 cents to ship a bushel of corn from Champaign to Chicago, a distance of 128 miles, whereas the cost of shipping from Chicago to Buffalo was only 11 cents. He urged that farmers should not be misled by the grain dealers, speculators, and railroad officials and warned that it was the corrupt use of passes by the railroads that gave them their immense political influence.[2]

At the conclusion of the war, grain rates came under concerted attack and shipments down the Mississippi again flourished. The *Prairie Farmer* noted this transfer of business from the railroads and warned that their rate structure was "a great wrong." It quoted a resolution of the Ogle County Board of Supervisors protesting against the "excessive tariffs" of the railroads and urged farmers to meet and lay plans for securing relief from the high costs of marketing their produce. Spokesmen for farmers demanded the establishment of railroad commissions which should hear complaints about high and discriminatory rates, accidents and their causes, and the use of passes and hush money, and which should have power to order the elimination of all such abuses. Meetings and conventions were held and an anti-monopoly league was organized in Illinois to focus demands upon the legislature. In Ohio a convention of farmers declared that "combinations of carriers, for the purposes of maintaining or increasing rates for transportation of property . . . are oppressive to producers and consumers, and should be prohibited by law." Throughout the Middle West farmers were becoming sensitive about freight rates and showed a growing inclination to resort to drastic action to force reductions.[3]

Wisconsin farmers, already incensed against the railroads by their farm mortgage scheme, were further angered by the high transportation rates charged on carrying wheat to Milwaukee or Chicago, the secret tariff cutting and rebates given to influential

---

[2] *Nashville Dispatch,* Dec. 10, 1863; *Illinois Senate Journal,* 1863, pp. 15–21; Frederick Merk: "Eastern Antecedents of the Grangers," *Agricultural History,* XXIII (January 1949), 1 ff.; letter of W. H. Osborn in *Rural New Yorker,* XVI (Jan. 10, 1863), 13; *Prairie Farmer,* XI (Jan. 17, Apr. 4, 1863), 33, 209, and XVI (Nov. 11, Dec. 2, 1865), 349, 398; Report of Ezra Cornell, "The Great Canal Convention," in New York State Agricultural Society, *Journal,* XIII (June, July 1863), 47; *Cong. Globe,* 37 Cong.,

3 Sess., Feb. 2, 7, 9, 1863, pp. 766, 806, 826.
[3] *Ohio Cultivator,* XVI (Feb. 15, 1860); *Prairie Farmer,* VI (Aug. 2, 1860), 72, XIII (Apr. 2, 1864), 225, XV (Jan. 7, 21, 1865), 3, 52; *Rural New Yorker,* XIV (Oct. 3, 1863), 317; H. K. Beale: *The Critical Year. A Study of Andrew Johnson and Reconstruction* (New York, 1930), pp. 256 ff.; G. H. Miller: "Origins of the Iowa Granger Law," *Mississippi Valley Historical Review,* XL (March 1954), 657 ff.

shippers, and the dominant influence the railroads acquired in a shipping combination on the upper Mississippi. With rates two and three times as high as formerly on the transportation of their principal commodity, the farmers were driven to desperation, especially in 1865 when wheat was declining in price. Numerous mass meetings were held to denounce the railroads' practices, the Chicago Board of Trade and the Chicago Mercantile Association were persuaded to protest against the rates and the discrimination against independent steamboats on the Mississippi, and the Milwaukee Chamber of Commerce was induced to urge the Wisconsin legislature "to correct these abuses." Some adjustments were made in rates, but the most important result of this early anti-monopoly movement was the laying of the groundwork for a much greater protest against railroad rates and other abuses in the seventies.[4]

Although the rate structures, land policies, and transportation schedules of the prairie railroads were coming in for attack, other railroad practices were watched with approval. Above all, their construction into new territory was applauded, as were their sincere efforts to bring in settlers and to aid in the development of both their land and surrounding areas. The land-grant railroads gave liberal extensions of credit when low prices and poor crops made payments on land contracts difficult, as in 1860–1. The Illinois Central agreed to take corn in payment, allowing 18 cents for 75 pounds of corn in the ear delivered at the railroad grounds near Chicago. It gave generous aid to the state fair, offered inducements that might speed up the drainage of wet land, of which it had an abundance, conducted experimental farms on which purebred stock, sugar beets, and crop rotation schemes were tried, aided in setting up a sugar beet factory, and provided financial assistance to J. W. Fawkes' efforts to harness the steam engine to the plow. After a trial of steam-operated plows, which were only partially successful, the I.C. made a subscription to a steam plow manufacturing company. Officials of land-grant railroads, particularly those of the I.C., truly cultivated public opinion.[5]

---

[4] Merk: *Economic History of Wisconsin*, pp. 308 ff.
[5] *Prairie Farmer*, XI (Apr. 4, 1863), 216; Gates: *The Illinois Central Railroad*, pp. 280 ff.

The feeling against the farm machinery manufacturers, particularly the reaper manufacturers, for their failure to maintain spare parts in the hands of local dealers, for the frailness of their machines, for the fact that no one machine included all the desirable features, and for their high prices, has already been seen.[6]

Currency policies, like railroad rates, public and railroad land policies, patent monopolies, and interest rates, were criticized during the war by farmers. The enactment of the National Bank Act, the issuing of greenbacks, the abandonment of the gold standard, and the high premium the government paid in gold on bonds for which it had received depreciated greenbacks—all enabled capitalists to make large returns from banking and investing in government bonds. Farmers, whose tax vulnerability was high because their investments were in real and personal property, could easily be persuaded that the banking, currency, and fiscal measures of the Lincoln administration were harmful to them. At farmers' conventions in Ottawa and Dixon, Illinois, in 1862, they listened to Alexander Campbell—a well-known currency reformer, pamphleteer, and congressman—discourse on the slight influence farmers had in government, the overwhelming power of Wall Street, and the monopolistic position and rate structure of the railroads. They were exhorted to combine for mutual protection, because it was through combinations that the Eastern merchants, bankers, and speculators were able to dominate matters affecting them. Campbell advocated a direct tax on wealth, a reflective—not subservient—press, payment of government bonds in greenbacks instead of specie, interest rates at 3 per cent, and currency convertible into bonds and acceptable for all debts, duties, and taxes.

The Ottawa convention adopted a memorial to Congress criticizing the "Chase system" of selling bonds, which gave the banks the power to expand or contract the currency, advanced the rate of interest, and thus plundered the wealth-producing classes and taxed the industrial interests for the benefit of the

---

[6] *Prairie Farmer*, VI (Dec. 20, 1860), 392, VII (Feb. 21, 1861), 23, X (Nov. 1, 1862), 280, XIV (Aug. 6, 20, 1864), 83, 113; *New York Tribune*, Nov. 9, 1861; *Rural New Yorker*, XVI (Apr. 8, June 10, 1865), 110, 181; *Sorgo Journal*, II (April 1864), 59.

bankers and usurers. It urged the establishment of a uniform currency acceptable for all debts, duties, and taxes and convertible into government bonds. Here were enunciated some of the basic reforms later taken up by the Democrats in 1868 and by the Greenbackers in the seventies. The Illinois State Agricultural Society unanimously endorsed the resolutions of the Ottawa convention, which were given wide publicity in the *Rural New Yorker* by Charles D. Bragdon, its reforming editor. Because of good crops and favorable prices, however, radical agrarianism was not widespread in 1862 and 1863.[7]

During most of the war period Bragdon was a crusading contributor to the *Rural New Yorker,* one of the most widely read farm journals. He attended the farmers' conventions in Ottawa and Dixon and gave full accounts of them. He seems to have been much influenced by the views of Campbell and in his columns thereafter continued to urge farmers to be more alert politically and to elect legislators who knew their problems, not people who worked for the monopolies. Farmers should meet combinations with combinations, urged Bragdon, by organizing by special interests, as the sheepmen were doing in wool growers' associations. The cheese makers, the butter makers, the cattle breeders, and the hog producers should be organized and prepared to push for their interests at the state capitals and in Washington. He drafted a platform which included a tight dog-licensing law to protect sheep, laws to control the practices of railroads and warehouses, and laws for protection against fruit thieves, bird killers and melon marauders. He also advocated provisions for the annual collection of agricultural statistics and for the publication of the transactions of state agricultural and horticultural societies, the exemption from taxation of all machinery used in the manufacture of sorghum, flax, hemp, cotton, and beet sugar, and protection for wool producers. He recognized the need for an independent press, uninfluenced by the patronage of the railroads and farm machinery manufacturers. His editorial and news

---

[7] *Rural New Yorker,* XII (Dec. 6, 20, 1862), 390, 405, and XIV (Jan. 10, 31, 1863), 14, 37. For Campbell's part in the movement for currency reform and the views of Edward Kellogg on which it was based, see C. M. Destler: *American Radicalism, 1865–1901* (New London, Conn., 1946), *passim.*

columns, the liveliest in the *Rural New Yorker*, brought credit to agricultural journalism, which previously had had little to boast about in the matter of political and economic criticism.[8]

---

[8] *Rural New Yorker*, XIV (Nov. 7, 1863), 358, and XV (Feb. 20, Nov. 5, 1864), 61, 357.

14

War's Aftermath

THE RE-ELECTION of Lincoln in November 1864 and the surrender of Lee in April 1865 assured the preservation of the
Union and the supremacy of the Federal government. For Southern planters, however, there were many unanswered questions.
What, for example, were the rights, privileges, and protection the
freedmen could enjoy? How far would the South go in accepting
freedom and economic and political rights for its ex-slaves? How
serious was the talk (and half-hearted action already taken)
concerning the forfeiture of estates of the planters who had participated in the rebellion and the division of their holdings among
the freedmen? How could Southern agriculture be revived without using force on the Negroes, who were the only important
source of labor, and who, many Southerners thought, could never
be made useful hands again without compulsion? These questions make it necessary to consider congressional policy toward
the ownership of land in the South and toward the prospect of
rural rehabilitation.[1]

Thousands of Negroes had left the plantations and joined
the invading armies marching through Georgia, Mississippi, and
Alabama; thousands had been taken from the plantations to
engage in defense work for the Confederates; still other thou-

---

[1] The most recent treatment of Reconstruction is E. L. McKitrick:
*Andrew Johnson and Reconstruc-
tion* (Chicago, 1960).

356

sands had gone with their refugee masters to Texas, Florida, lower Georgia, and elsewhere to escape the advancing Union troops. Those who attached themselves to the Union forces or who were on the Sea Islands, in the cane-producing parishes of Louisiana, or in the Delta counties of Mississippi when the Federals arrived heard of plans for redistribution of the land among the freedmen. They took the stories seriously and looked forward to receiving allotments of land.

On the other hand, the slave-owning planters of the antebellum period knew that though their former slaves were now free, there was no other place for them to earn a living than as workers on the plantations. Two hundred years of dependence upon and exploitation of the slaves in field work had created a relationship and an attitude toward them that had been intensified as the peculiar institution came under attack by abolitionists. This attitude of the master toward the slave could not easily be shaken off by emancipation and defeat in war. When the defeated soldiers returned to their homes and began to pick up the threads of their lives in their home communities, it soon became apparent that their attitudes toward the black folk had not changed. They were resolved to put them in their place again, which was to be one of servile obedience to a predominantly white society. When the human kindness of any employer to his servant did not yield satisfactory results, threats, punishment, whipping, mutilation, and worse were to be employed and supported by black codes, the chain gang, and white judicial tyranny. It was against the almost certain resort to such practices that Northern radicals favored measures to deprive the aristocracy of their wealth in land, thinking that in so doing they could create a society in which the freedman could flourish. Had they read more carefully a book they had used to political advantage in an earlier day—Hinton Rowan Helper's *Impending Crisis*—or made themselves better acquainted with the views of Andrew Johnson, they might have discovered that the greatest enemy of the freedman was not the aristocratic planter but the poor white.

Abolitionists like Charles Sumner, George W. Julian, and Thaddeus Stevens were righteously indignant that the slave owners of the South had tried to break up the Union by secession and had brought about a long and terribly costly war because they, a minority in the republic, could not have their way. As punishment, nothing less than outright confiscation of the property of the leaders and supporters of the rebellion would satisfy these and other radicals. Retribution was not, however, their sole or perhaps even their first motive for this drastic proposal. Seizure of the property of the planters and its distribution among the freedmen and possibly the landless whites would permit a far-reaching reconstruction of the social fabric of the South. Retribution had many advocates during the war, though their emotions subsided fairly soon after its conclusion, but the number who favored sweeping social reorganization was much fewer. These two attitudes were voiced in both houses of Congress during debates on the confiscation bill of 1862 and the measures to provide for the establishment of the Freedmen's Bureau in 1864 and 1865.

Julian, the most forthright and radical of the three leaders, favored the outright confiscation of the property of all persons participating in or aiding the rebellion. War emotions led men who were anything but radical, like Doolittle of Wisconsin, for example, to work with Julian and Stevens in advocating confiscation. As adopted by Congress the Confiscation Act of 1862 provided, or seemed to provide, for permanent confiscation of the property belonging to the guilty parties. Lincoln was troubled about this and other aspects of the bill and prepared a veto message, but Congress, anticipating him, rushed through a joint resolution explaining that the measure was only intended to provide for confiscation for the lifetime of the rebels. Lincoln then signed the bill but sent his veto message along to Congress.[2]

With emotions still running high against rebel leaders in 1864 and 1865, confiscation was again taken up when the House of Representatives moved to amend the explanatory resolution of 1862 to provide for permanent confiscation. The Senate did not approve the House move but instead went further by amending the bill to create the Freedmen's Bureau so as to repeal the explanatory resolution. The amendment was finally lost in con-

---

[2] H. R. Helper: *The Impending Crisis* (New York, 1860); J. G. Randall: *Constitutional Problems under Lincoln* (Urbana, Ill., 1951), p. 276; P. W. Gates: "Federal Land Policy in the South, 1866–1888," *Journal of Southern History,* VI (August, 1940), 303 ff.

ference committee, at which point the House rushed through a separate bill to repeal the explanatory resolution. Thus a majority in both houses had tried to repeal the resolution or make it nugatory and had shown their desire to carry through permanent confiscation of the property of those who had participated in the rebellion. LaWanda Cox believes that in passing the Confiscation Act of 1862 and the Southern Homestead Act of 1866, and in attempting to provide for outright confiscation, Congress was motivated to a considerable degree by a desire to break up the large sugar, rice, cotton, and tobacco plantations of the South into small holdings for freedmen and white refugees.[3]

Another measure which passed the House but did not come to a vote in the Senate likewise shows the anxiety of a majority of the Republican leaders, stimulated by Julian's egalitarian and reformist ideas, to assure the Negroes an opportunity to own land in the South. This was a bill that would secure to persons in the armed service, including labor forces employed by them, without distinction of color or race, the right to establish homesteads of forty and eighty acres on the forfeited and confiscated lands of persons in rebellion against the United States. At the time the House acted, Julian had little positive knowledge of any quantity of land that had come into possession of the government, other than the forfeited lands in the Port Royal area of South Carolina, but he was optimistic that millions of acres would be forfeited or confiscated during the prosecution of the war. By a vote of 75 to 64 the House followed Julian's leadership and approved the measure on May 12, 1864.[4]

It was the Freedmen's Bureau Act of March 3, 1865, that came closest to meeting the wishes of the freedmen. Land abandoned by its rebel owners or confiscated through legal process was to be allotted in tracts of not more than forty acres to freedmen and refugees at a fair rent for three years, at the end of which time the tracts could be purchased by the occupants at the value

---

[3] LaWanda Cox: "The Promise of Land for the Freedmen," *Mississippi Valley Historical Review*, XLV (December 1958), 432 ff.; Randall: *Constitutional Problems*, pp. 275 ff., and P. S. Pierce: *The Freedmen's Bureau* (University of Iowa *Studies in Sociology, Economics, Politics and History*, III, no. 1, 1904), pp. 129 ff.

[4] *Cong. Globe*, 38 Cong., 1 Sess., 2253. *House Journal*, 38 Cong., 1 Sess., p. 540, gives the vote as 76–65.

placed on them in 1860 for tax purposes. Unfortunately from the freedmen's point of view, only 768,590 acres seem to have been acquired and held as abandoned or confiscated property, and before progress could be made in dividing it among the freedmen, Johnson issued pardons to the ex-leaders of the Confederacy and restored so much of their lands that there was little left for leasing or selling the freedmen.[5]

Julian's Southern Homestead Act of 1866, and the consideration given to a plan for the forfeiture of the land grants to Southern railroads, were additional efforts to provide a reservoir of land for freedmen and white refugees and to make the South a region of small farms. Forfeiture of railroad land grants in the South might be regarded as proper punishment for the people of that area and would provide some 9,000,000 acres, or 225,000 forty-acre tracts, for allotment. However, if Congress decided that Southern railroad grants could be forfeited, might this not place in jeopardy some of the grants given to Northern railroads whose officers had failed to meet the conditions of the donations? Julian won sufficient support for his Southern Homestead Act, but forfeiting land grants was too radical for railroad-minded members of Congress. It is interesting that some of the Southern grants which Julian proposed to have forfeited during the war were actually forfeited by special legislation at a later time.[6]

Like most, if not all, of the Reconstruction measures, the Southern Homestead Act was designed as a blow at the planter aristocracy of the South and at the same time as a reform measure to benefit the landless. It halted all cash sales in the five Southern public-land states and withheld the remaining public lands for homesteading only. Unfortunately, the 47,700,000 acres of public lands in these states were the refuse tracts after planters, small farmers, speculators, the states, and railroads had taken their pick. Much of the land was covered with yellow pine or cyprus, then a drug on the market. To make such land into successful farms called for labor and capital, and the latter the freedmen lacked.

---

[5] 13 *U.S. Stat.*, p. 508; Report of O. O. Howard in *House Ex. Doc.*, 41 Cong., 2 Sess., VI, no. 142, p. 10.
[6] D. M. Ellis: "The Forfeiture of Railroad Land Grants, 1867–1894," *Mississippi Valley Historical Review*, XXXIII (June 1946), 30 ff.

Between 1866 and 1876 when the Southern Homestead Act was the only route to ownership of the public lands in the five states, 67,609 original homestead applications were filed and 10,307 went to patent. By 1881 when the last of the entries for these years might have been proved up and ready for patent, 23,609—roughly one third of them—had been patented. Many entries were relinquished; others were forfeited. This ratio does not compare favorably with the ratio of original to final entries of homesteaders elsewhere. General O. O. Howard, head of the Freedmen's Bureau, said in 1870 that some 4,000 families, presumably freedmen, had "acquired homes of their own and commenced work with energy building houses and planting" on government land. If his figure is correct, we may conclude that the Southern Homestead Act was not of major aid in meeting the freedmen's desire for land.[7]

Though general and systematic redistribution of land in the South was not to be effected by Federal power, or indeed by any other force, some property of leaders of the rebellion was forfeited. The first step toward confiscation, however, came from the South, with the adoption by the Confederate Congress of the Sequestration Act of August 1861. This provided for the seizure of the property of enemy aliens. Under this act Jefferson's Monticello, owned by Uriah P. Levy, was seized and sold along with Levy's other land and slaves, and 33,000 acres in Florida owned by people in Boston, 480,000 acres in Texas, and numerous other pieces of land, as well as shares in banks, railroads, and steamboats, were sequestered and sold. Southern Unionists who had invested in public land in the North and who were ostracized, imprisoned, and in some instances deprived of their local possessions were Solomon Tifft of Jackson, Mississippi; William Aiken and William W. Boyce, both members of Congress from South Carolina on the eve of the Civil War; W. R. W. Cobb of Alabama, a former member of Congress; and William B. Stokes of Tennessee. Aiken's and Boyce's investments were in Superior,

---

[7] I have dealt with the Southern Homestead Act in "Federal Land Policy in the South," pp. 303 ff.; Commissioner of the General Land Office: *Reports*, 1870, p. 334, and 1874, p. 74. Peirce: *The Freedmen's Bureau*, p. 69, says that "thousands of families took advantage" of the Southern Homestead Act.

Wisconsin. Aiken, said to be the richest man in South Carolina, was confined in Libby prison, apparently for his failure to take the oath of loyalty to the Confederacy. Tifft, who had invested some $25,000 in Nebraska land just before the outbreak of the war, died in prison at Salisbury, North Carolina. Stokes, a prominent Tennesseean who had substantial investments in Minnesota, managed to stay out of the clutches of Secessionists. Efforts were made to expel Cobb, who was called a "Yankee nubbin," a "traitor congressman," from the Confederate Congress, but they failed. These and other actions taken against Unionists, of course, did nothing to extend ownership of land to the landless Negroes or whites.[8]

The Federal Confiscation Act of July 17, 1862, was weakly prosecuted in both North and South, because neither Attorneys General Edward Bates nor Orville H. Browning, or indeed Lincoln himself, believed in rigorous enforcement. As a result of public clamor from Northern radicals, property within Union lines by 1862 belonging to Judah P. Benjamin, General Pierre G. T. Beauregard, Duncan Kenner, Thomas J. Semmes, and John Slidell was confiscated. James G. Randall has assembled information showing that $129,680 was deposited in the Treasury from the sales of confiscated property, and he estimates that the government's total share may have been as much as $300,000. His figures, however, have been found substantially incomplete by Henry Shapiro, who discovered many more libels for the New York district alone than were known to Randall.[9]

---

[8] R. W. Shugg: *Origins of Class Struggle in Louisiana. A Social History of White Farmers and Laborers during Slavery and after, 1840–1875* (University, La., 1939), pp. 234 ff.; Atlanta *Southern Confederacy*, Oct. 17, 1861, Nov. 24, 1863; *Savannah Republican*, Dec. 25, 1863; *Mobile Advertiser and Register*, Dec. 13, 1864; Austin *State Gazette*, Nov. 18, 1863; *National Intelligencer*, Aug. 13, 1863; *Nashville Union*, Apr. 23, 1863; *Memphis Appeal*, Apr. 15, 1863, June 1, 1864; Huntsville *Daily Confederate* (Marietta, Ga.), Nov. 30, 1863; *Charleston Courier*, June 8, Nov. 22, 1864; Raleigh *Daily Confederate*, May 11, 1864.

[9] *Nashville Union*, Aug. 27, 1863; Randall: *Constitutional Problems*, pp. 289–91; H. D. Shapiro: *Confiscation of Confederate Property in the North* (Ithaca, N.Y., 1962), *passim*, and in more detail his master's thesis with the same title in the Cornell University Library. For the investments of Southerners in the North see P. W. Gates: "Southern Investments in Northern Lands before the Civil War," *Journal of Southern History*, V (May, 1939), pp. 155 ff. For a partial list of the property and the owners

On August 5, 1861, and June 7, 1862, Congress provided for a direct tax on property; if not paid, the property was to be sold for what it would bring and an absolute fee simple title was to pass after a brief period of grace. Under this legislation, proceedings were brought against property in Alexandria, Virginia, and against planters of the Beaufort–Port Royal region, which was captured in November 1861 and held by Union forces thereafter. The planters having fled, and being unable or unwilling to pay the taxes assessed against their land and slaves, their property was sold and much of it was taken by the government. Included were choice Sea Island plantations which belonged to prominent members of the aristocracy of the Palmetto state. Some plantations were bought or rented from the government by men who had come down from Massachusetts to help the freedmen and to aid in the reconstruction of the area. One Bostonian—Edward S. Philbrick—bought eleven plantations, rented two more, and proceeded to divide them into small tracts to rent to freedmen. The low cost of the land—about one dollar an acre for an absolute title—combined with an abundant supply of cheap labor, the use of such confiscated tools and equipment as remained, and the extremely high price of cotton, enabled him to make large profits in 1863 and 1864. The Negro workers on these plantations may have been treated well, though their pay or share of crops was small and they were able to make little or no progress toward ownership.[1]

Of the 37,000 acres offered in the Beaufort region in 1863, 18,000 were sold to private individuals for $19,000 and the balance was bid in for the United States at 52¢ an acre. Of the forty-odd plantations sold in 1863 no more than six, and possibly only four, fell to Negroes, who were said to have banded together and pooled resources for their purchase. A private in a Connecticut regiment protested against the sales which he had

against which confiscation proceedings were successfully completed see *Sen. Ex. Doc.*, 40 Cong., 2 Sess., 1868, II, no. 58. For the confiscation proceedings against John Slidell see the *New Orleans Picayune*, Apr. 9, 1863.
[1] 12 *U.S. Stat.*, pp. 304, 422; *National Intelligencer*, July 23, 1864;

P. J. Staudenraus (ed.): "Occupied Beaufort, 1863: A War Correspondent's View," *South Carolina Historical Magazine*, LXIV (April 1963), 143; W. H. Pease: "Three Years among the Freedmen: William C. Gannett and the Port Royal Experiment," *Journal of Negro History*, XLIII (April 1957), 107.

witnessed, declaring that there was no opportunity for competition for any but government officials, army officers, and a few Northern sharpers who by agreement secured favored tracts at low prices. A new group of aristocrats was thus being formed to replace the previously discredited planters, and little redistribution of the land among small holders was being achieved.[2]

In June 1862 it was reported that there were 5,000 acres in cotton and 3,000 in corn, potatoes, and other vegetables in the captured areas around Port Royal. Negroes were allowed 1¼ acres of land for their own planting, were given rations of bread, hominy, molasses, and some meat (but less food than was allowed Union soldiers), and were advanced one dollar an acre for all land they planted. The received no regular wages. Government operations in the Port Royal area in 1862 were unsuccessful. The weather was bad, the cotton crop was light, and vacillating government policy did not encourage the Negroes to work hard. Also, the hands were needed for army work elsewhere. But, asked the *Merchants Magazine* of January 1863, if cotton could not be raised profitably by freedmen at Port Royal, where could it be?

On January 16, 1865, General William T. Sherman issued an order that captured, abandoned, and confiscated land on the Sea Islands and for a distance of thirty miles inland and south of Charleston should be reserved for the Negroes who had attached themselves to his army as it had marched through Georgia. The land was to be assigned to the freedmen in small tracts under possessory titles, though Sherman seemed to suggest that these might become freehold grants. Some 40,000 Negroes thus received allotments. Congress tried to validate the titles in the second Freedmen's Bureau bill of January 1866 but was defeated by Johnson's veto. His pardon and amnesty policy amounted to an outright reversal of Sherman's order. To the great regret of General O. O. Howard, the former owners of these lands, no

---

[2] *National Intelligencer,* Apr. 21, 1863, Jan. 2, Mar. 31, 1864; *London Economist,* XXII (February 1864), 199–200; J. T. Trowbridge: *The South: A Tour of Its Battlefields and Ruined Cities* (Hartford, Conn., 1866), p. 567; *House Ex. Doc.,* 45 Cong., 3 Sess., 1879, XVI, pp. 1–4; V. C. Holmgren: *Hilton Head. A Sea Island Chronicle* (Hilton Head Island, S.C., 1959), p. 110.

matter how deeply involved they had been in the rebellion, were permitted to recover possession and ownership, and freedmen who had served in the Union army or who had cooperated with Union officers in raising cotton were downgraded to tenants or sharecroppers and were ejected if they refused to accept the change. Few actions could have been as disillusioning to the freedmen as this. The allotment policy with its promise of ultimate ownership had given the freedmen a great uplift and when General Howard had to notify them at a public meeting that Johnson had ordered the return of the land to the former owners, their reaction was tragic. In Johnson's mind reconciliation with the whites came before the welfare of the freedmen.[3]

In Louisiana and Mississippi, where Union forces early acquired an important foothold, there seemed for a time a greater opportunity to bring about a major change in the pattern of land ownership by means of the Confiscation Act and the property-taxing law of 1862. Many planters fled before approaching Union forces, while others tried to maintain relations with both sides to avoid the threatened confiscation and pillaging. After the capture of New Orleans, Federal troops overran a number of the principal sugar- and cotton-producing parishes. But with Banks's withdrawal from his ill-planned Red River campaign, the area held by the Federals contracted. Many places adjacent to the Mississippi and nominally under Union control were subject to raids by Confederate guerillas, and terrible punishment was meted out to those who had cooperated with the Federals. Confiscation was carried out in New Orleans more vigorously than anywhere else. Close to a million dollars was raised from sales of Confederates' property, but how much more went to those whom General Butler entrusted with carrying out the Confiscation Act cannot be determined. President Johnson's efforts to conciliate the South led him to order much of the property thus confiscated to be returned. Elsewhere in Louisiana and Missis-

[3] *The Merchants Magazine*, XLVIII (January 1863), 190; O. O. Howard: *Autobiography* (2 vols., New York, 1907), II, 238 ff.; F. B. Simkins and R. H. Woody: *South Carolina during Reconstruction* (Chapel Hill, N.C., 1932), p. 228; Benjamin Quarles: *The Negro in the Civil War* (Boston, 1953), pp. 282 ff.

sippi, confiscation was not achieved to any substantial extent because of the awkwardness of the legal process and Johnson's tenderness toward the whites.

A good deal of captured and abandoned property did come into the possession of the Union forces and was turned over to the Treasury Department for administration. In New Orleans it was reported that people who were not unfriendly to the North were officially declared to be enemy aliens and were forced to pass into the Confederate lines to make it possible for the Union forces to seize their property. General Banks issued notice that all plantations in his military district in Louisiana which were not in cultivation on February 1, 1864, would be considered abandoned and would be rented by the government to those who would operate them. Every effort was made to restore the agricultural operations of the plantations within Union lines, for both cotton and sugar were in great demand and brought high prices. In some instances the Union forces operated plantations, perhaps to make sure that a crop was harvested, but generally they resorted to leasing.

Leases were negotiated only with men of known Union sentiment. They were required to have for each 100 acres they contracted to operate five or six mules, one wagon, four plows, hoes and other equipment, and food, provisions, and clothing for the Negroes—whose pay would be $7 a month for men, $5 for women. To protect the lessees from being harassed by Confederate guerillas, Federal officers were authorized to seize the property of nearby disloyal people for indemnification. If a lessee were killed, a levy of $10,000 was to be collected from disloyal people within 30 miles of the offense.[4]

Wherever the army went in the South, there followed contractors, brokers, and speculators who were anxious to buy cotton for shipment to the North, where premium prices prevailed. Other foresighted investors were convinced there were equally good opportunities for making fortunes in the purchase and op-

---

[4] B. F. Butler: *Autobiography and Personal Reminiscences* (Boston, 1892), p. 522; *National Intelligencer*, Feb. 4, 1864; *New York Weekly Tribune*, Jan. 16, 1864; *New Orleans Picayune*, May 19, 1864; I. A. Hamilton: "The United States Court of Claims and the Captured and Abandoned Property Act of 1863," Ph.D. dissertation, 1956, University of North Carolina Library.

eration of plantations. An agent of the U. S. Treasury Department who was examining and leasing captured and abandoned plantations in Mississippi in early 1864 was followed by a "swarm of hungry devils" from Wisconsin and Iowa with plows and other farming utensils, hopeful of gaining control of some of the rich land of the Delta. There is little evidence that the speculations of these Northerners in Southern plantations—and few thought of them as anything more than a get-rich-quick investment— had any substantial result in breaking up the large holdings into small ownerships.[5]

From the outset there was trouble over the employment of freedmen under Federal supervision on these leased plantations. The freedmen did not understand the wage system, they wanted ownership, not the status of a hired hand, and they showed little more interest in their work than they had as slaves driven by the lash. To set forth the rights and obligations of the freedmen the army issued an order declaring: "Labor is a public duty, and idleness and vagrancy a crime." All freedmen not having jobs in town or city were required to work on plantations; those who refused were compelled to work for the government without compensation other than board. Having made their selection of the plantations on which they preferred to work, freedmen were bound to them for a year. Their day's work was ten hours in summer and nine in winter. In addition to comfortable clothing, quarters, fuel, healthy rations, and instruction for their children, first-class hands were to be paid $8 a month, second-class hands $6, third-class hands $5, and fourth-class hands $3. In addition the freedmen were to be permitted to use small allotments of land. Wages and rations were to be deducted when sickness was feigned. Indolence, insolence, disobedience, and crime were to be punished by forfeiture of pay and disciplinary action allowed in army regulations.

Although the Freedmen's Bureau was not to be an agency through which its wards could acquire ownership of land, it provided the ex-slaves with relief until they could be induced to

---

[5] I. S. Robinson, Jan. 24, 1864, to Gov. Pettus, Gov. Corr., Miss. Arch.; Bliss Perry: *Life and Letters of Henry Lee Higginson* (Boston, 1921), pp. 248 ff., for Higginson's difficulties and final failure in managing his investment in a Georgia plantation.

return to the plantations as tenants, and saw that their interests were safeguarded in the signing and enforcing of contracts made with the landlords. For most freedmen there was no alternative but return to the land, for most of them knew no occupation other than farming. Freedmen complained that the landlords did not provide the full rations, charged unduly high prices for supplies, did not meet contractual obligations, gouged the Negroes in determining shares of crops, resorted to physical punishment, and kept them in a state of peonage. Planters found the freedmen unstable, dishonest, destructive of equipment, and unwilling to perform the amount of work expected of them. They complained that officials of the Bureau had encouraged the Negroes to the point of insubordination. Doubtless there were dishonest officials in the Bureau, as there were in most public offices of the time, North and South, East and West. But the least that can be said for the Bureau is that it eased the path of the disillusioned freedmen on the way to tenant and sharecropper status. Schools had been late in coming to the South. It was the Freedmen's Bureau that instituted them for the poorer whites as well as for Negroes. Inadequately financed and poorly staffed as these schools were, they enabled the Negro to take one step forward on the long march to education and improvement.[6]

Few planters were prepared to deal with the Negroes as freedmen, but wished them to be so bound by legal contracts as to be virtual peons controlled by patrols and police juries. Planters restored to or left in charge of their land continued to regard the freedmen as forced to work, subject to discipline, tied to the land, and having no rights. The contract wage system broke down everywhere, and gradually leasing to tenants or

---

[6] *New Orleans Picayune*, Feb. 20, 1863, quoting *The Era; New York Weekly Tribune*, Mar. 12, 1864; *National Intelligencer*, Feb. 8, 1864; *O.R.*, ser. 1, XXXIV, part 2, p. 229; F. H. Harrington: *Fighting Politician: Major General N. P. Banks* (Philadelphia, 1948), p. 105; J. C. Sitterson: *Sugar Country. The Cane Sugar Industry in the South, 1753–1950* (Lexington, Ky., 1953), pp. 205 ff.; Peirce: *Freedmen's Bureau*, pp. 142 ff.; John Cox and LaWanda Cox: "General O. O. Howard and the 'Misrepresented Bureau,'" *Journal of Southern History*, XIX (November 1953), 427 ff. The Freedmen's Bureau does not even appear in the index of P. H. Buck: *The Road to Reunion, 1865–1900* (Boston, 1937).

sharecroppers was substituted. At this point the planters declared that they would not rent to the freedmen, nor would they take them on as croppers "except that they be directly under our control and fed by us." Only under such control, they maintained, could the Negroes be expected to perform their work properly. Planters who rented to Negroes under conditions that would permit the tenants to control the land were considered enemies of the country's interests.[7]

Nowhere in the South could it be said that plantation management under the army or the Treasury Department worked well. Leased plantations near Vicksburg were reported to have made less than one fourth of a crop of cotton, notwithstanding the good weather. Difficulty with the freedmen under the rules Federal authorities insisted the planters should follow in dealing with them led many lessees to abandon their leases as unprofitable. The decline in operations may be seen by comparing the production of 175 sugar plantations within the Union lines in Louisiana in 1861 with the same plantations' production in 1864; in the former year they produced an average of 356 hogsheads of sugar; in the latter year, an average of 39 hogsheads. Farther north, in the vicinity of Vidalia, Louisiana, only 20 out of 100 leased plantations were having their crops gathered, the larger number having been "broken up" by guerillas. So serious were these raids in driving off the lessees and freedmen, killing some who were too openly cooperative with the other side, and carrying off the mules, that the St. *Louis Republican* declared in 1864 that the scheme of working plantations by leasing them was a failure. Not a dozen plantations on the river would produce a crop that year, it maintained.

A more optimistic picture of the leased plantations was given by the superintendent of the Bureau of Free Labor on February 1, 1865. According to this report there had been 1,500 plantations in Louisiana under cultivation by military orders, with some

---

[7] *Hinds County Gazette*, Nov. 25, 1865; J. C. Sitterson: "The Transition from Slave to Free Economy on the William J. Minor Plantations," *Agricultural History*, XVII (October 1943), 216 ff.; F. A. Shan-non: *The Farmer's Last Frontier* (New York, 1945), pp. 76 ff. For the position of the Negro cropper in the eighties see T. S. Stribling: *The Store* (New York, 1932).

50,000 freedmen on them. It declared that labor difficulties were small; on only 12 had it been necessary to intervene between planter and freedmen to protect the latter. This optimistic report was soon shown to be quite false.[8]

Given rigorous prosecution of the Confiscation Acts, the Captured and Abandoned Property Act, and the taxing measures both during the Civil War and in the immediate postwar years, it is conceivable that an agrarian revolution could have been achieved whereby large holdings would have been divided into small allotments for owners, not for croppers or tenants. Julian thought there was much sentiment in behalf of such action in the midst of the war. In 1864 he tried to get the Republican Party to adopt a plank favoring confiscation of the fee of the land of rebel leaders. He even suggested that Lincoln had come to approve the idea. A subcommittee of the Committee on Resolutions of the Republican Party did report favorably on such a plank, but it was dropped by the full committee. After Appomattox, the angry emotions of the war quickly subsided. The radical Republicans, other than Julian, became more concerned with political than social reform and soon forgot the truly radical proposals they had championed. Johnson, who had little liking for the Negro, placed reconciliation with the white leadership above the welfare of the freedmen. The expression Barton J. Bernstein applied to later circumstances applies here as well: "The Negro was sacrificed 'on the altar of reconciliation, peace and prosperity.' " Negroes had obtained their freedom and were given citizenship—that is, second-class citizenship—but their lot as sharecroppers was not to be much better than it had been as slaves. Nor was it possible to see that their children might move onward to something better through education.[9]

Agrarian revolutions, if the Russian and Cuban models are considered as typical, have not achieved efficiency, expanded

---

[8] Adjutant General Thomas, report to Secretary Stanton, *Nashville Dispatch,* Nov. 15, 1863, May 20, 1864; *National Intelligencer,* Nov. 18, 1864 (quoting the *Vicksburg Herald*), Dec. 1, 1864; *New Orleans Price Current,* Feb. 17, 1865; J. D. Winters: *The Civil War in Louisiana* (Baton Rouge, La., 1963), p. 395; *O.R.,* ser. 1, XLIV, part 2, p. 954.

[9] B. J. Bernstein: "Plessy v. Ferguson: Conservative Sociological Jurisprudence," *Journal of Negro History,* XLVIII (July 1963), 204; G. W. Julian: *Political Recollections, 1840–1872* (Chicago, 1884), pp. 242 ff.

production, and created better standards of living for the beneficiaries in a short time. The South was badly demoralized without any such revolution and was to take years to recover. In few instances has war's destruction been so intensive or its effects so long-lasting as in the sugar and rice parishes of Louisiana and South Carolina. In this area a great amount of capital had been invested in agricultural operations, including steam-operated sugar mills, rice hulling and grinding mills, and an elaborate system of ditches, levees, bridges, and pumps. On the larger plantations investments in equipment and improvements ran into the tens of thousands of dollars, and greatly enhanced the value of the rich alluvial land on which they were placed. Warfare destroyed many of the sugarhouses and the rice hulling and grinding machines, breached the levees, demolished the bridges, freed the slaves, scattered the horses and mules, and permitted

PRODUCTION OF STAPLE CROPS*

YEAR	CANE SUGAR (pounds)	COTTON (bales)	TOBACCO† (pounds)
1859	230,000,000	5,387,000	434,000,000
1860		3,841,000	404,000,000
1861	459,000,000	4,491,000	
1862	87,000,000	1,597,000	
1863	78,000,000	449,000	
1864	10,000,000	299,000	
1865	18,000,000	2,094,000	
1866	41,000,000	2,097,000	316,000,000
1867	40,000,000	2,520,000	260,000,000
1870	144,000,000	4,352,000	345,000,000
1875		4,631,000	609,000,000
1880	218,000,000	6,606,000	469,000,000
1890	380,000,000	8,653,000	647,000,000
1894	710,000,000	9,901,000	766,870,000

* Blank spaces indicate that information is unavailable.
† Included in the tobacco figures is the production of northern states.
SOURCE: *Historical Statistics of the United States* (Washington, 1960); J. C. Sitterson: *Sugar Country. The Cane Sugar Industry in the South, 1753–1950* (Lexington, Ky., 1953); E. M. Coulter: *The Confederate States of America, 1861–1865* (Baton Rouge, La., 1950); F. A. Shannon: *The Farmer's Last Frontier* (New York, 1945).

EFFECTS OF WAR ON SOUTHERN AGRICULTURE

STATE	IMPROVED ACREAGE (in thousands)		VALUE OF FARMS (in thousands)		VALUE OF FARM MACHINERY (in thousands)		VALUE OF LIVESTOCK (in thousands)	
	1860	1870	1860	1870	1860	1870	1860	1870
Alabama	6,385	5,062	$175,824	$ 67,739	$ 7,433	$3,286	$43,411	$26,690
Arkansas	1,983	1,859	91,649	40,029	4,175	2,237	22,096	17,222
Florida	654	736	16,435	9,947	900	505	5,553	5,212
Georgia	8,062	6,831	157,072	94,559	6,844	4,614	38,372	30,156
Louisiana	2,707	2,045	204,789	68,215	18,648	7,159	24,546	15,929
Mississippi	5,065	4,209	190,760	81,716	8,826	4,456	41,891	29,940
N. Carolina	6,517	5,258	143,301	78,211	5,873	4,082	31,130	21,993
S. Carolina	4,572	3,010	139,652	44,808	6,151	2,282	23,934	12,443
Tennessee	6,795	6,843	271,358	218,743	8,465	8,199	60,211	55,084
Texas	2,650	2,964	88,101	60,149	6,259	3,396	42,825	37,425
Virginia*	11,437	10,745	371,761	314,624	9,392	7,036	47,803	45,362

* The data for West Virginia for 1870 have been included with those of Virginia.
SOURCE: *U.S. Censuses* of 1860 and 1870.

the fields to be overrun with weeds. Rice cultivation in South
Carolina and Georgia was never to recover from these fearful
times, and the production of sugar in Louisiana was to recover
more slowly than that of cotton or tobacco.

The table of production of the three Southern staples reflects
to some extent the travail through which the South went during
the war and the slow rate of recovery in the following years. The
long-lasting effect of war's destruction on Southern agriculture
may be seen equally vividly in the census figures. They show
that the acreage in cultivation diminished in the sixties in every
Southern state, except Florida and Texas; the value of farms fell
by $772,000,000, or 41 per cent; the value of farm machinery
and equipment fell by 37 per cent; and the value of livestock fell
by 28 per cent. The number of hogs fell by 38 per cent and the
number of beef cattle by 15 per cent.

The decline in land values in the Southern states is also
evidence of the damage the war did to the agricultural economy.

AVERAGE PER ACRE VALUE OF LAND IN FARMS IN
REPRESENTATIVE SOUTHERN STATES

STATE	1860	1870
Alabama	$ 9	$4
Louisiana	22	9
Georgia	6	4
South Carolina	8	3

SOURCE: *U.S. Censuses* of 1860 and 1870.

The value of all farmland in the ten cotton states fell 48 per
cent in this decade. It was to take a generation for the South to
recover.

Substitution of the tenant and sharecropper systems for
the contract wage system was fairly rapid, for the latter did not
satisfy the freedmen, who felt they were little better off under
it than they had been as slaves. Crop sharing was the plan most
widely followed with workers who had no credit and no resources.
Everything, including land, plow, mule, provisions, and cabin,
was provided by the planter, who technically allowed the cropper
one third of the crop. If the renter furnished his own rations

and half the feed for the animals, his share was half. Tenancy was generally limited to persons who had some equipment and some other resources of their own and who agreed to pay either a cash rent or a fixed amount of cotton. Although the census report of 1880 shows a huge increase in the number of farms in the Southern states, there was an actual 7,137,000 acre decline of land in farms, if we exclude Texas and Florida. Both Roger Shugg and Fred Shannon have pointed out, moreover, that this increase in the number of farms is the result of division of the plantations into small operating units being farmed by croppers and tenants; it in no way indicates division of ownership.

The one-crop system, with continued planting of cotton or tobacco year after year, was no innovation in the postwar South, but the tenant cropper–planter relationship fastened it upon much of the better land suitable for these staples. Diminishing fertility and ever-increasing debts produced the tragedy of Southern agriculture.[1]

Northern farmers likewise had problems which were partly the result of the war. They related, however, more to the expansion of agriculture and to the wartime prosperity that made the expansion possible. The wool growers, who nearly doubled their output of wool during the war, found it impossible after 1865 to compete with foreign-produced wool without major tariff aid—obtained, as has been seen, by cooperating with the wool manufacturers. Prairie agriculture, with its huge outpouring of wheat, corn, and pork, had a strong influence on the farm practices in the older states, for they were compelled to make painful adjustments. Hill farms that were no longer profitable had to be abandoned, and grain growers had to turn to dairy farming and truck gardening. In the sixties three New England states—New Hampshire, Massachusetts, and Rhode Island—lost 10,999 farms and their improved land in farms fell by 424,656 acres.

---

[1] Willard Range: *A Century of Georgia Agriculture, 1750–1850* (Athens, Ga., 1954), pp. 77 ff.; Shugg: *Origins of Class Struggle in Louisiana,* pp. 196 ff.; Shannon: *Farmer's Last Frontier,* pp. 76 ff.; Oscar Zeichner: "The Transition from Slave to Free Agricultural Labor in the Southern States," *Agricultural History,* XIII (January 1939), 23 ff.; R. P. Brooks: *The Agrarian Revolution in Georgia, 1865–1912 (Bulletin of the University of Wisconsin, History Series,* III, no. 3), *passim.*

A glance at the map of rural townships in Vermont and New Hampshire showing declines in population reveals that a large part of the southern half of these states was losing farmers.[2]

A new wheat belt running from Ohio through Iowa, Missouri, and Minnesota had come into existence, and its prosperity depended on foreign markets and the world price of wheat. Many farmers in these states, coming to rely on wheat for their principal crop, had increased the acreage sowed to it and bought the essential harrows, drills, reapers, and threshers. The abrupt decline in the volume of exports in 1865–7 and the equally rapid fall in the price of wheat occurred when thousands of new farms were being created in rich virgin soil in Minnesota, Iowa, and California. The output of the grain was spiraling upward from 148,000,000 bushels in 1865 to 210,000,000 in 1867, 289,000,000 in 1869, and 321,000,000 in 1873. Exports expanded again in 1870, but not to the extent that production had grown. Not until World War I was the price of wheat to rise to the $1.50 and $2.50 levels of the Civil War. The downward slide of prices seemed to result in even greater expansion of output. The picture of prosperous farmers with money in their pockets, their credit good, taxes paid, and debt burden, if any, lightly carried, was to change in a few years' time to one of farmers hounded by their creditors, unable to meet their taxes, angered by the exactions of railroads and elevators, and trying to get along with broken-down equipment.

On the whole, Northern farmers more than held their own financially during the war. Where many were "drowning in debt" in 1860, within a few years their obligations were retired, new equipment was acquired, and improvements were made, including draining, tiling, fencing, and clearing or breaking additional land. Permanent improvements, combined with the increasing pressure of population on the supply of land both in the older states and in the newer communities to which migration was flowing, boosted farm and wild land values. The average value of New York farms, for example, increased from $4,452 in 1860 to $5,668 in 1870. In the Middle Western states the demand for

---

[2] H. F. Wilson: *The Hill Country of Northern New England* (New York, 1936), p. 49.

GROWTH OF AGRICULTURE IN PRINCIPAL NORTHERN FARM STATES

STATE	IMPROVED ACREAGE (in thousands)		VALUE OF FARMS (in thousands)		VALUE OF FARM MACHINERY (in thousands)		VALUE OF LIVESTOCK (in thousands)	
	1860	1870	1860	1870	1860	1870	1860	1870
California	2,468	6,218	$ 48,726	$ 141,240	$ 2,558	$ 5,316	$ 35,585	$ 37,964
Illinois	13,096	19,329	408,944	920,506	17,235	34,576	72,501	149,756
Indiana	8,242	10,104	356,712	634,804	10,457	17,676	41,855	83,776
Iowa	3,792	9,396	119,899	392,662	5,327	20,509	22,476	82,987
Kentucky	7,644	8,103	291,496	311,238	7,474	8,572	61,868	23,173
Michigan	3,476	5,096	160,836	398,240	5,819	13,711	23,714	49,809
Missouri	6,246	9,130	230,632	392,908	8,711	15,596	53,693	84,285
New York	14,358	15,627	803,343	1,272,857	29,166	45,997	103,856	175,882
Ohio	12,625	14,469	678,132	1,054,465	17,538	25,692	80,384	120,300
Pennsylvania	10,463	11,515	662,050	1,043,481	22,442	35,658	69,672	115,647
Wisconsin	3,746	5,899	131,117	300,414	5,758	14,239	17,807	45,310

INCREASE IN PRODUCTION OF STAPLE CROPS

CROP	1860	1870
Wheat	173,104,925 bu.	287,745,626 bu.
Oats	172,643,185 bu.	282,107,157 bu.
Wool	60,264,813 lbs.	100,102,387 lbs.
Potatoes (white)	111,148,807 bu.	143,337,473 bu.
Butter	459,681,372 lbs.	514,092,683 lbs.

SOURCE: *U.S. Censuses* of 1860 and 1870.

farmland sent prices upward even more rapidly. In Illinois the average value of farms increased in this decade from $2,774 to $4,480 and in Iowa from $1,982 to $3,350. Farmers and others who had acquired more land than they could reasonably expect to cultivate were able to dispose of their surplus holdings at profitable prices.[3]

AVERAGE PER ACRE VALUE OF LAND IN FARMS

STATE	1860	1870
Iowa	$12	$25
Illinois	19	35
Ohio	32	48
Wisconsin	16	26
United States	16	22

SOURCE: *U.S. Censuses* of 1860 and 1870.

A serious threat to the prosperity of Northern farmers, however, was the prospect of deflation. Prices of agricultural commodities, particularly wheat, were falling sharply. If, in addition, it was decided to withdraw the greenbacks from circulation and return to the gold standard, the well-being of farmers who had gone deeply into debt to develop new farms or expand old ones would be seriously threatened.

Outside the South farmers found themselves in a different world in postwar America. The demands of the market had encouraged farmers to specialize, to concentrate their capital and labor upon the production of fewer items and to be less concerned with near self-sufficiency. Specialization and dissatisfaction with their share of the consumers' dollars had led them to experiment with wool marketing groups and joint-stock cheese factories and to talk about constructing farmers' grain elevators, warehouses, and ships. State and national organizations of wool and hop growers, sorghum producers, cattle and sheep breeders, and dairymen had come into existence, and they had established

[3] *Historical Statistics* (Washington, 1960); G. F. Warren and F. A. Pearson: *Wholesale Prices for* 213 *Years, 1720–1932* (Ithaca, N.Y., 1932). Also see *Prairie Farmer*, V (Mar. 20, 1860), 194.

their journals, annuals, and herdbooks. No longer could politicians in state capitals and in Washington ignore farmers and their problems, for they had learned to organize and to arouse support for their objectives. Government had come to their aid by liberalizing land policies, by making possible the establishment of land-grant colleges—which, however, were still in the experimental state—by granting protection to wool growers, and, above all, by creating the Department of Agriculture to conduct research into the numerous problems relating to farming.

The generous aid the government had given railroads while the South was out of the Union in the form of land grants and financial subsidies, as well as the political decline of the forces opposed to immigration from abroad, opened the way for the last great rush of settlers into the New West beyond the Missouri River. In the eight years following the war the railroad mileage of the country doubled and 2,735,000 immigrants entered the country. Many of these immigrants, together with discharged soldiers and others who were tired of trying to farm worn-out and poor lands in the East, swept over the Great Plains and within a generation had carved up the remaining territories into states.

Northern farmers emerged from the war prosperous for the time being. Markets were easier of access, credit was more obtainable, and conditions favored specialization. A demand for land, improved or unimproved, made it possible for them to sell at favorable prices and go west to get a free homestead or to finance more intensive farm practices. Some of their hardest labor was now done by machines, though their workday still remained long and at times exhausting. Their labor costs were high, but many farmers were able to hire help in haying and harvesting time. Tenancy was emerging in the richer areas of the West in somewhat undesirable forms, but was vastly different from what it was in the South.

Southern planters had taken huge losses from the destruction wrought by both armies and from the repudiation of Confederate bonds and state obligations for cotton, grain, and meat that they had sold or that had been impressed. Credit for the purchase of new equipment and supplies was available, if at all, at high cost. Their former slaves, encouraged by Northern humanitarians, were reluctant to accept the economic and political status to which all Southern whites consigned them and for a time were restless and mobile. Negroes became share tenants wholly subject to the landlord by crop liens, vagrancy laws, and other local regulations. Their condition was, perhaps, little worse than that of the thousands of poor whites who slipped into the share tenancy status, though the latters' political rights might be assured. Staple crop production revived slowly and for years continued on a low-yield basis, a result of row cropping, failure to rotate, and soil depletion. The rural South remained a land of poverty not greatly touched by the industrialism which was to produce the New South. Negro and white croppers and tenants were to wait long years for better times.

Note on
Sources and Acknowledgments

The historian of agriculture in the Northern states during the Civil War has available rich materials in the numerous widely circulated and well-edited farm journals, chief of which are the *Rural New Yorker,* the *Country Gentleman,* the *American Agriculturist,* and the *Prairie Farmer.* These, with the *New York Tribune,* provide excellent coverage of agricultural problems. In addition the proceedings and publications of the state agricultural societies and state boards of agriculture and of the U.S. Department of Agriculture with its *Monthly* and *Bi-Monthly Reports* and its *Annual Reports* are full and most useful. Also, the Federal land system continued to operate from Michigan to California, monthly reports of land entries were made regularly and published in the *Annual Reports* of the Commissioner of the General Land Office, and letters descriptive of Western problems exist in abundance in the National Archives. These, plus a host of contemporary printed and manuscript materials, state census data, and *Reports* of the Secretary of the Treasury concerning exports and imports, leave little ground for complaint about the paucity of source materials.

For the South the story is different. The *Southern Cultivator* limped along on meager support and rising costs, but touched lightly if at all the great changes in agriculture which war made necessary. There was little more than this: no publications of state or Confederate boards of agriculture, no census data, few or no publications on agriculture or land problems. Fortunately, the newspapers of Richmond, Raleigh, Charleston, Atlanta, Mobile, Memphis, Nashville, New Orleans, and many smaller communities allotted space to farm problems because food became so pressing an issue throughout the war. One of the finest collections of Confederate newspapers is in the Boston Athenaeum, where I used them in the quiet splendor overlooking the Granary Burying Ground. Other collections of newspapers in the Library of Congress, the University of Texas and Tulane University libraries, and the state departments of archives and history of North Carolina, Georgia, Mississippi, and Alabama, admirably supplemented the Athenaeum collection. Confederate materials in the National Archives and, of course, the *War of the Rebellion Records* provided much useful information.

The richest source available to me on Southern agriculture proved to be the letters to the governors of Mississippi, Alabama, Georgia, and North Carolina. They tell of the hardships of the planters resulting from the impressment of their slaves, the difficulties in maintaining plows, harrows, and reapers in effective working condition, and the plight of the small farmer's family when the draft took the farmer and his older sons. Custodians were altogether helpful and cooperative in making known their treasures and in facilitating my use of them. My visit in the South was made memorable by delightful associations with Joe B. Frantz, J. Frank Dobie, Mrs. Walter Webb, Fletcher Green, Bingham Duncan, and the members of the departments of history of the University of Texas and of Emory University. Gracious Southern hospitality in Jackson, Montgomery, and elsewhere almost led me to forget for the moment the tragedy of color.

Mrs. Mary Conn Bryan of the Georgia Department of History and Archives not only gave me many excellent suggestions and shared some delightful experiences with me but opened her facilities to me in the evening so that I could make the best use of my time. What a loss Georgia suffered in her passing just at the time the new Archives building was coming into use. Peter Brannon of the Alabama State Department of Archives and History, Christopher Crittenden of the North Carolina Department of Archives and History, and Miss Charlotte Capers of the Mississippi Department of Archives and History provided excellent facilities for work and allowed me to impose frequently on their staffs. Frederick Merk and Allan Nevins generously lent notes gathered in their research.

A Faculty Research Fellowship of the Social Science Research Council enabled me to have fifteen months of freedom from all other obligations to concentrate on the research and writing for this study.

Careful readers will easily recognize how heavily dependent I have been on the writings of a host of Southern historians who have illuminated so many features of the Civil War. Without the scholarship of Messrs. Bettersworth, Bragg, Cathey, Coulter, Fleming, Green, Hill, Johns, Moore, Owsley, Quarles, Range, Robert, Silver, Sitterson, Todd, and Wiley, Miss Lonn, Miss Massey, and Miss Tatum, and, indeed, many others, my task would have been far greater. L. C. Gray surely belongs high on this list. Among the Northern writers the most helpful have been Messrs. Brown, Merk, Nevins, Ross, Shannon, Shugg, and Mrs. Cox.

My wife accompanied me on a ten weeks' research jaunt through the South, taking notes in an indecipherable hand and aiding constantly in stimulating discussion. She has read the manuscript at least three times and suggested many improvements.

Portions of Chapters 10 and 11 have appeared in somewhat different form in *Agricultural History, Michigan History,* and Howard W. Ottoson (ed.): *Land Use Policy and Problems in the United States.*

Index

Academy of Medicine, on contaminated milk, 189

Addison County, Vt., leader in Merino sheep, 162, 164–5

Agricultural College Act: introduced by Morrill, 251; Morrill's speech for, 262; sectional attitudes toward, 262–3; vetoed by Buchanan, 263; adopted in 1862, 264; selection of beneficiaries, 264–5

agricultural college scrip, 264–6

agricultural colleges: beginnings of, 267–70; early disillusionment with, 271

agricultural machines, *see* farm machinery

Agriculture, Department of: movement for, 302, 306; act creating, 307; Newton appointed commissioner of, 309; reports of, 310–13; seed importation and distribution, 149, 314; work in entomology, 316–17; investigations of, 317–18; experimental garden, 318; Monthly Reports, 320

Aiken, William, 361–2

Alabama: taxation of excessive cotton planting, 18; dissatisfaction with price fixing, 55; relief work, 87–8; use of food crops for distilling prohibited, 97; food crisis in, 116–17; shrinkage of farm land in, 118; migration from, 281; land policy of, 296–8; stay laws, 329

Alabama & Tennessee Railroad, 298

Aldrich, A. P., 336

Alexander, John T., cattle drover, 179

Allen, Charles, planting operations of, 20

Allen, Lewis F., *New American Farm Book*, 217

American Agriculturist, 148, 258, 261, 270

American Dairymen's Association, 213

American Emigrant Company, 289

American Farmer, 303

American Institute, 322

Anaconda plan, 28

animal diseases, losses from, 257–258

anthrax, 92

anti-monopoly league, 351

apples, 141

Arkansas: restriction on cotton planting, 18; depletion of food in, 37; land policy of, 298

Atkins, *see* reaper

Atlanta, 115, 124, 156; food riot in, 39

Augusta *Chronicle & Sentinel*, 19, 335

Augustana College, 252

Austria, agricultural science in, 255

Ayrshire cattle, in Massachusetts, 215

Bacon, 105, 107

Bailey, Liberty Hyde, 182

Banks, Nathaniel P., 365; and abandoned plantations, 366

Barry, Patrick, contributor to *Rural New Yorker*, 164

Bates, Edward, 362

Beaufort, 156

Beauregard, P. G. T., 362

beet sugar, *see* sugar beets

Belcher's Sugar Refinery, 149

Benjamin, Judah P., 362

Bennett, Henry, 254

Bernstein, Barton, 370

Bingham, A. L., 167

Bingham, Alonzo, sheep breeder, 162

Bingham, Merrill, sheep breeder, 162, 164, 165, 166

Blackburn College, 252
Bladensboro, N.C., food riot in, 39
Borden, Gail, milk condensery, 193
Boston, adulterated milk in, 196
Bowdoin College, 252
Boyce, William W., 361
Bragdon, Charles D.: contributor to *Rural New Yorker*, 164; currency reformer, 354-5
Bragg, General Braxton, 31
Brannon, Sam, sheep rancher in California, 167
Breck, Joseph, 141
Brewer, William H., 269
breweries, 133; and dairies, 188, 189
Brown, Amos, president of People's College, 259, 308
Brown, Harry E., 169, 170, 172, 174
Brown, Joseph E.: urges doubling of corn crop, 17; provides refuge for his slaves, 25; favors restrictions on cotton, 32; on sacrifices of the poor, 35; on food impressment, 46; on impressment abuses, 48-9; on tithing tax, 65; on distilling, 97-8; on speculators, 100; on exhaustion of provisions, 114; on devastation in Georgia, 114; embargo of food exports, 115; on stay laws, 334-335
Brown, Simon, 260
Brown University, 269
Browne, Daniel Jay, head of Agricultural Branch, 302-3; arranges seed imports, 309-10
Buchanan, James, 253; orders sale of public lands, 282; vetoes Homestead bill, 284
Buckeye mower, 235
Bureau of Free Labor, 369-70
Butler, Benjamin F., 365
butter: New York as major producer, 201; dasher churn, 202; produced on most farms, 203; western product generally poor, 214

California: encourages experiments with new crops, 154; sheep in, 159; Merino sheep in, 166-7; cattle industry ruined by drought, 178; large dairy operations, 215; agricultural expansion, 223, 228; homestead entries in, 292; warfare between settlers and rancho owners, 342-3; wheat production, 375
California Farmer, 178
Campbell, Alexander, currency reformer, 353
Canfield, Flora, *Hop Picking*, 140
canning, commercial, 141
Capron, Horace, 315
Carroll, William T., 289
Cary, Freman G., 259
Case, Jerome I., 236
cattle: Southern, 7-8; driving to New York, 180; beef, 182; *see also* various breeds, dairy farming
Central Pacific Railroad, 300
charbon, *see* anthrax
Charleston, flight to, 25
Charleston Courier, 28, 76
Charleston Mercury, 30, 83
cheese: chief centers, 207-8; cooperatives, 206-15; exports of, 210-11; skim, low quality of, 210; faults of American, 213
Chenery, William, Holstein importer, 216-17
Cherokee Reserve, 344
Chesnut, Mrs. James, class attitudes toward war, 36
Cheves, Langdon, 337
Chicago: as pork-packing center, 184; regulation of dairies, 192; as center of farm-machinery industry, 239
Chicago Board of Trade, 348, 352
Chicago, Burlington & Quincy Railroad, 345
Chicago Mercantile Association, 352
chinch bugs, 224
cider, 141
Cincinnati, unsanitary dairies in, 193
Clark, Charles, 118
Clemson, Thomas C.: advances agricultural work of government, 303-4; favors agricultural department in Confederacy, 305; favors a Confederate university, 306
Cobb, Williamson R. W., 361-2
Coe College, 252
coffee, brought in by blockade runners, 105

Colfax, Schuyler, 170

Collamer, Jacob, 307

Colman, Henry, *European Agriculture and Rural Economy*, 102, 256

Commissary Department, Confederate: prices, 44; staffing problems, 71–2

Confederacy: defaults on cotton control, 33; Impressment Act, 47; Revenue Act of 1863, 63; modification of Revenue Act, 69; Produce Loan Act, 84; shrinkage of area of, 85; refusal to ban whiskey distilling, 96; ineffectiveness of propaganda, 109–10; foraging of troops of, 113; lack of agricultural branch, 305

confiscation: of rebel-owned property, 358–9, 362–5; of Unionist-owned property, 361–2; *see also* Sequestration Act

Congress, Federal, concern for flax and hemp production, 153–4

Connecticut: tobacco in, 143; emigration from, 274

conscription, Confederate, 34, 122

contagious abortion, 218, 258

cooperatives, cheese, 206–15

corn: Southern efforts to increase production of, 16–22, 30; as major food of Confederate soldiers, 101; exports of, 226–7

corn belt, feeder cattle business of, 178

corn planter, 238

Cornell, Ezra, 220, 313; on sale of impure milk, 190; supports pure-bred stock, 217–18; founder of Cornell University, 268

cotton: superiority of American, 13 *n.*; Southern policy on, 13–21, 30; efficiency of production, 14; reduction of output, 74; burning, 84–5; trading through the lines, 105–6, 107, 125–6, 156; revival of planting in 1865, 107; efforts to raise in the North, 151–3; in Utah, 154; in Kentucky, 154

Country Gentleman, 184, 270, 309

Countryman, 43

Cox, LaWanda, 359

credit, on the frontier, 282–3

creditors, opposition to stay laws, 328, 329, 331, 333, 335, 338–9

Cumming, Kate, 118

currency: Confederate, 45, 51–4; shrinking value of, 54; refused as medium of trade, 125; Federal, contraction of, 377; *see also* greenbacks

Curti, Merle, *Making of an American Community*, 291–2

Dabney, Thomas Smith Gregory, 31

Dadd, George H., writer on veterinary practices, 216; author, *Modern Horse Doctor*, 258

Daily Confederate, 43

dairy farmers: turn from butter to fluid milk, 195; tolerate unsanitary conditions, 204–5; in Wisconsin, opposition to sanitary legislation, 205; in New York, opposition to standardization of firkins, 205; replacing grain production in East, 198; and improvement of farmers' welfare, 200

Dallas County, Ala., tenancy in, 280

Dartmouth College, 252

Davis, Jefferson, denounces speculation, 43

De Bow's Review, 5, 28

Deere, John, 236

Delano, Columbus, supporter of wool tariff, 174

Delaware Reserve, 344

Delta, Mississippi, levee breached, 121

Democratic Party, 295

Des Moines River, land grant to improve, 341

Devon cattle: widely raised, 180; highly regarded by dairymen, 215

Dickson, Daniel, 68

Dickson, T. G., 68

Diseases of Cattle, 216

distilleries, 133; and swill dairies, 188; unsanitary conditions of, 189; efforts to outlaw swill dairies, 192

distilling, Southern efforts to control, 96–100

Dix, Dorothea, 253

Dodge, Grenville, raids Alabama, 92

Dodge, Jacob R., 182, 244

dogs, as sheep killers, 158
Douglas, Stephen A., 294, 295
Downing, Andrew Jackson, 141
drought: destructive in the South, 86; in Georgia, 113; in Alabama, 116; decimates cattle in California, 167, 178
Dunkin, B. F., 337
Dunlap, M. L., 152
Durham cattle, *see* shorthorn cattle
Dutchess County, N.Y., 195
dysentery, 29

education, government aid to, 251
Ellsworth, Henry L., 301
Ellwanger & Barry, 140, 319
England: imports of American cheese, 210–11; dairies in, 214; poor wheat crops, 224; wheat imports, 225
entomology, studies by Department of Agriculture, 316–17
Erie Canal, enlargement proposed, 349–50
Erie Railroad, milk transportation of, 194
Erni, Henry, 317
Europe, importation of American meat, 226

farm implements: scarcity of, 22–23; destroyed by Northern troops, 92
farm labor: Southern draft of, 23; drawn into the armies, 130, 229, 271; scarcity of, 231–2; replaced by machines, 232, 234; use of immigrants, 242; attracted by free land
farm machinery: hay presses, 131–2; reapers, 232–5; mowers, 235–6; horse rake, 236; patent applications for, 236; threshers, 237; drills, 238; centers of manufacture, 239; manufacturers, 353
farmers, Southern, condemned for exorbitant prices, 41–2; *see also* yeoman farmers
Farmers' Club of the American Institute, 322
farmers' conventions: urge Niagara ship canal, 350; in Ohio, on railroad rates, 351; in Ottawa,

advocate currency reform, 353–354
farmers' organizations, 377–8; cheese cooperatives, 208–15; proposals for cooperatives, 348–349
farms: management of, 33; diminishing productivity of in the South, 95; management of livestock on, 102; diversification of, 130–56; in the Northeast, 130, 131; number of new farms in the 1850's and 1860's, 222–3; 228; letdown of good practices during the war, 243–4; borrowing for expansion of operations, 246–7; careless and wasteful practices, 254–5; population on, 274; turnover on, 274; specialization in the North, 377
Fawkes, J. W., 352
fence rails, destruction of, 78–80
fertilizer, manufacture of, 240–1
Fessenden, William Pitt, 307
Fish, Carl Russell, 10
Fitch, Asa, 313
flails, 237
flax: efforts to adapt to cotton machines, 154–5; production of, 155
Fleischmann, Charles Lewis, 256
Fleming, Walter, 119
Flint, Charles L., 259; *Milch Cows and Dairy Farming*, 202
Flint-Bixby Company, California sheep ranch of, 167
Florida: food supplies in, 122; land policy of, 298–9; stay laws, 339
food: riots, 38–40; wastage, 72; destruction of, 92; losses, 94; sent through lines, 107
Foot, Solomon, 253
Ford, Paul Leicester, 192
Fort Donelson, 192
France, poor wheat crops of, 224, 225
Frank Leslie's Illustrated Newspaper, exposes distillery dairies, 190
free land: opponents of, 281, 286; movement for, 284–5
freedmen, *see* Negroes
Freedmen's Bureau: Act for, 359; aid to Negroes, 367–8
Freeman, Daniel, 290

Freemantle, Colonel, 18, 24

French, Henry F., 235, 266; and greater farm production, 243

frost, 177, 183, 184; in Georgia, 113; effects sorghum production, 148; reduces Illinois cotton output, 153

fruit growing, expansion of, 141

fuelwood: scarcity of in the South, 82–3; prices, 137; demand for, 138

Funk, Isaac, land holdings of, 279, 347, 348

Galena & Chicago Union Railroad, 198

Geneva, N.Y., as farm machinery center, 239

Gennert Brothers, 150

George, Henry, 283

Georgia: restrictions on cotton planting, 18; grain production of, 21; food wastage in, 67; clash with Confederacy over distilling, 98; drought in, 113; shrinkage of farm land, 114; ravaged by Sherman, 115; lack of aid to agricultural education, 305; see also Brown, Joseph E.

Germania Sugar Co., 150

Germans, immigration of, 241

Germany, agricultural science in, 255

Gillett, John Dean, land holdings of, 279

Glover, Townend, entomologist: dismissal of, 303; warns of foreign plant insects and diseases, 316; museum of insects, 317

Gorgas, Josiah, 124

Goshen butter, see Orange County butter

Gould, John Stanton, on sorghum claims, 148–9

grain: used by Confederacy for distilling, 98–9; diminishing yield, 116; prices of, 244; cradles, 239; dealers, 350; drills, adoption of, 238; weevil, 314

Greeley, Horace, 340; on land grabbing, 272; on speculators, 276; advocates free land, 283–4

Green County, Ala., tenancy in, 280

greenbacks: preferred to Confederate currency, 54; farmers' convention on, 353, 354

Greenville, Ala., food riot at, 38

Grinnell, James S., 321

Grinnell, Josiah B., supporter of wool tariff, 174

Grinnell College, 252

Grow, Galusha, advocate of Homestead Law, 286

guerillas, Confederate, 365

Guernsey cattle, 216

Gulf & Ship Island Railroad, 298

Hale, John P., 260, 307

Hammond, Edwin, Merino sheep breeder, 162, 164–5, 166, 167

Hammond, James H., dislike of appraisal procedures, 50

Hannibal & St. Joseph Railroad, 281, 289

Harlan, James, 307

Harlem Railroad, heavy milk traffic on, 195

Harper's Weekly, 320

hay: presses, 131–2, 237; urban demands for, 133–4; prices, 134–5; shortsighted sales of, 135; forks, 236; tedders, 236

Hell's Kitchen, 191

Helper, Hinton Rowan, The Impending Crisis, 357

hemp, 154–5

Hereford cattle, 182, 216

Herkimer County, N.Y., as leading cheese producer, 208

Hillsborough Recorder, 35

hoarding, 42

Hoffman, Francis, 242

hogs: Southern, 6–7, 11; Southern losses of, 91–2; decline in numbers, 183; cholera, causes heavy Southern losses, 91–3; need for scientific investigation of, 183, 258

Hohenheim, German Agricultural School, 267

Holstein cattle, neglected in America, 216

Homestead Law: provisions of, 285; defects in, 286; limitations of, 287; and land speculation, 288; applied to lands beyond railroads, 290; early applications under, 290; original and final entries, 293; and historians, 293–4; influence of, 294

Homestead National Monument, 290

Hop Grower's Journal, 139

hop louse, aphis, 140

hops, New York as largest producer, 139

horse rake, 236

horses: impressment of, 58; captured, impressed, or killed, 59; government purchases of, 184–186

Howard, General O. O., 361–2

Hussey reaper, *see* reaper

Illinois, 289; cotton grown in 151–3; sheep in, 158–60; expansion of farms in, 222–3; railroad construction in, 246; migration from, 281; average value of farms, 377

Illinois & Lake Michigan Canal, proposal to deepen, 349

Illinois Central Railroad: use of fuelwood, 137; encourages sugar-beet production, 150; promotes cotton growing, 151–3; prizes for farm machines, 236; promoter of European emigration, 241–2; and homestead policy, 289; land policy of, 345–6; rates, 350; payments in kind to, 352

Illinois State Agricultural Society, on cotton cultivation, 152

Illinois State Horticultural Society, 312

Illinois Wool Growers Association, 171

immigrants, as farm laborers, 277

immigration, 241

impressment, Confederate: troubles of, 46–52; appraisal procedure, 47; Acts, 47–8; improvements in administration, 55; errors, 55–6; resisted in mountain areas, 59; of tools, 62–3

Index, 85

Indian Affairs, Office of, 343

Indian country, 282

Indian lands, 287; acquisition by railroads, in Kansas, 343

Indiana: sheep in, 158–60; expansion of farms in the 1850's, 223; migration from, 281

inflation, 35–6, 40

Interior, Department of the, 306

Iowa: sheep in, 158–60; expansion of farms in the 1850's, 223; wheat crop of 1860, 223–4; railroad construction in, 246; migration from, 281; stay law, 340; wheat production, 375; farm values, 377

Iowa State Agricultural College, beginnings of, 268

Jackson, Andrew, advocates free land, 283

Jackson, Charles T., 304

Jackson, Miss., Yankee devastation around, 120–1

Jersey cattle, 215–16

Jewett, Solomon W., Merino sheep breeder, 162; trailed sheep to California, 166; sheep ranch of, 166

Johnson, Andrew, vetoes second Freedmen's Bureau bill, 364; favors reconciliation with whites, 370

Johnson, Benjamin Pierce, 308, 313

Johnson, Samuel W., 260, 269

Johnson on Manures, 258

Johnston, James F. W., 257

Jones, J. B., 31, 37

Judd, Orange, 169

Julian, George W., advocates free land, 283, 285; as land reformer, 286; on confiscation of rebel property, 357, 359; proposes forfeiture of railroad land grants, 360; author, Southern Homestead Act, 360–1; social reformer, 370

Kankakee Valley, tenancy in, 279

Kansas: homesteading in, 292; bans Texas longhorns in summer, 182; public lands ordered sold in, 282; and land speculation, 282

Kasson, John A., 288

Kean, Robert G. H., 51, 74

Kelley, Oliver Hudson, 291

Kenner, Duncan, 362

Kennicott, John F., cautions on over-optimistic views of cotton cultivation, 152; mentioned for Commissioner of Agriculture, 308

Kent's Commentaries, 336–7

Kentucky: refugees from, 26; lost to Confederacy, 122; aid to agricultural education, 305; emigration from, 274; stay law, 339
Ketchum mower, 235
Kickapoo Reserve, 344
Kirby-Smith, Edmund, 101
Klippart, John H., studies European technical education, 266–267; qualified to be Commissioner of Agriculture, 308
Knox College, 252

labor problems, on farms and plantations, 23
LaCrosse land district, 292
LaCrosse *Republican*, 142
Lacy, H. K., 131
Lampard, Eric, 205
land clearing, 273
land grants: for education, 251; railroad, sold at high prices, 276; to states, 287; acreage of, 287; railroad and agricultural expansion, 294–5; opposition to, 345
land hunger, 272
land monopoly, fear of, 275
Land Ordinance, 251
land reformers: advocate free lands, 283–5; disappointment with Homestead Law, 286
land speculation: extent of in Old Northwest, 275–6; farmer participation, 276; in Kansas struggle, 282; and Homestead policy, 288
land speculators, engrossment of, 277
land warfare: in Iowa, 341–2; in California, 342–3; in Kansas, 343–4; in Wisconsin, 344
Lane, James, 307; secures Federal aid for cotton in Kansas, 153
leather: scarcity of in the South, 81; brought in by blockade runners, 105
Lee, Robert E.: reluctance to use impressment, 95–6; sanctions movement of food through the lines, 106–7
levees, breached, 120
Levy, Uriah P., 361
Liebig, Justus von: *Organic Chemistry in Its Application to Agri-*

culture and Physiology, 256; Americans study under, 257
Lincoln, Abraham: and border-state loyalty, 11; recommends a bureau of agriculture, 306; and Isaac Newton, 309; on Confiscation Act, 358, 362
Lindley, Daniel C., *Morgan Horses*, 303
Little Falls, N.Y., 213, market center for cheese, 208
livestock, number of, 177
Logan County, Ill., tenants in, 347–8
longhorns, 182
Loomis, Dr. Silas L.: on milk, 197; argues for Ayrshires, 217
Louisiana: relief activities in, 88; restrictions on liquor manufacture, 97; land policy of, 298; stay laws, 337–9; turmoil on plantations, 365
Lovejoy, Owen, 306, 307

Malmborg, Oscar, 241
Manny reaper, *see* reaper
Mapes, James J., 135
maple sugar, production of, 138–9
Mark Lane Express, on England's dependence on American wheat, 225
Marshall, John, 326, 337
Massachusetts: unsafe milk sold in, 192; Ayrshire cattle in, 215; pleuropneumonia in, 219; abandonment of farms in, 374
Massachusetts Institute of Technology, 269
McConnell, James, large sheep owner, 158–9
McCormick, Cyrus, 233, 236, 325; *see also* reaper
McCoy, Joseph G., *Historic Sketches of the Cattle Trade of the West and the Southwest*, 179
Memphis, Tenn., 156
Memphis Appeal, 44, 49, 50, 99, 101
Merchants Magazine, 364
Meridian, Miss., Federal occupation of, 121
Merinos, French, 167; Vermont leader in, 162; *see also* sheep
Merk, Frederick, 344

Metropolitan Board of Health, New York City, 191
Miami University, 253
Michigan: homesteading in, 292; sheep in, 158–60; railroad construction in, 246
Michigan Agricultural College, beginnings of, 267
Michigan Central Railroad, 137
middlemen, farmers' complaints against, 348
Milbank, Jeremiah, 193
Milk: adulterated and impure, 189–92; condensed, 193; hauled to New York City, 195
milk trains, 194
milksheds, extended by railroads, 198
Milton, John, on impressment abuses, 48
Milwaukee, as farm machinery center, 239
Minnesota: wheat crops of, 223, 224, 226; railroad construction in, 246; public lands ordered sold, 282; early Homestead entries in, 290–1; wheat production, 375
Minnesota Farmer, 234
Mississippi: restricts cotton planting, 18; penalties for distilling from grain, 97; laxness of courts, 100; starvation in, 119; flight of Negroes of, 119; plantations laid waste, 121; migration from, 281; land policy of, 298; stay laws, 327–9; turmoil in the Delta, 365
Mississippi Central Railroad, trades cotton through the lines, 105
Mississippi Valley, Upper: economic ties with the South, 4; hurt by break with the South, 5
Missouri: lost to the Confederacy, 122; sympathy with the South, 151; farm expansion of, 223; few homesteads during the war, 292; stay law, 340
Mitchell, Donald Grant, on farm ownership, 129–30; description of farm laborers, 230, 231
Mobile: inflation in, 38; starvation prices in, 116; food needs of, 118
Mobile Advertiser and Register, 14, 19, 22, 90

Mobile & Ohio Railroad, 38
Moline, as farm machinery center, 239
Montgomery, Ala., 124
Montgomery Advertiser, 58, 116
Montgomery Convention, on cotton reduction, 14
Monticello, confiscated, 361
morale, Southern, at low ebb, 124
Morgan horses, favored by War Department, 185
Morrill, Justin Smith: advocate of agricultural education, 253; dislike of free homesteads, 285; friendly to wool growers, 174; works with wool manufacturers, 176; bill to aid agricultural colleges, 261; speech in behalf of land-grant bill, 262
Morrill Act, see Agricultural College Act
Morris, Lewis G., 259
mortgages, farm: retirement of, 245; foreclosures in Minnesota, 283
Mot, Maurice, experiments with sugar beets, 150
mowing machines: in the Northeast, 235; rising cost of, 244–5

Nashville, Tenn., 156
Nashville Union, 94
Natchez Courier, 89
National Association of Wool Manufacturers, 170
National Bank Act, 353
National Intelligencer, 85, 320
National Wool Growers' Association, 173
Nebraska: Buchanan orders lands sold in, 282; homesteading in, 292; and tax exemption of land grants, 346
Negroes: most efficient on Southern staples, 23; flight of, 119; follow Northern armies, 356; and land redistribution, 357; on Sea Island plantations, 363–4; disillusionment of, 365; abandoned land leased to, 366; friction on leased land, 367–9; Freedmen's Bureau aid to, 368; subordinated to white reconciliation, 370; become share croppers, 379
New England: war prosperity and the sheep industry, 161; aban-

New England (*continued*)
donment of farms in, 255; contraction of agriculture, 374–5
New England Farmer, 194
New Hampshire: bans feeding distillery refuse to cows, 192; emigration from, 274; abandonment of farms in, 374
New Orleans: food imports, 9–10; Federals supply food, 122; hay imports, 133–4; capture of, 145, 156; stay law, 338; confiscation in, 365
New Orleans *True Delta*, 338
New York: maple-sugar crop, 138; investigation of cottonized flax, 154; flax production, 155; attacks sale of adulterated milk, 190–1; bans skim milk in cheese manufacture, 212; quarantine and slaughter of diseased cattle, 220; farm expansion, 223; average value of farms of, 375
New York & New Haven Railroad, milk traffic on, 195
New York Central Railroad, 137
New York Cheese Manufacturers' Association, 212, 213
New York Sheep Breeders and Wool Growers Association, 172
New York State Medical Society, on infant mortality and contaminated milk, 189
New York Times, 194, 196, 200
New York Tribune, 180, 202, 283
Newton, Isaac: as Commissioner of Agriculture, 309; reports of, 310; ignores controversial questions, 311; improprieties of, 312; useful articles, 313; obtains budget increase, 315; favors protection for wool, 320; on agricultural education, 321; pressure for removal of, 322
Niagara ship canal, proposal for, 350
North Carolina: farmers accused of hoarding, 37; soldiers' relief, 87; raids in, 112; stay laws, 330–34
North Carolina Standard: on Richmond food riot, 39; on corrupting influence of whiskey, 99
Northhampton Beet Sugar Co., 150
Northrop, Colonel L. B.: as Confederate Commissary General,

12; charges Georgians with planting unneeded cotton, 31; merits fair consideration, 56; problems of tithing tax, 66; trade through the lines, 125
Norton's Scientific Agriculture, 258
Norwegians, immigration of, 241
nurserymen, 312

Oberlin College, 252
Ohio: maple-sugar output increased, 138; flax production in, 155; sheep in, 158–60, 167; expansion of farms in the 1850's, 223; wheat crops in, 224–5; stay law, 340
Ohio Farmer, 309, 322
Ohio University, 253
Omaha, Neb., 295
Oneida County, N.Y., as center of hop production, 139–40
Orange County, N.Y.: as rich dairying area, 195, 200; Goshen butter, standard of perfection, 202–3
Osborn, William H., president of the Illinois Central Railroad: encourages sugar-beet industry, 150; promotes cotton production, 151–3; advocates ship canal, 349–50
Overland Monthly, 215
oxen, impressment of, 58

Pacific railroad: projects for, 295; Act passed, 295
Panic of 1857, 280
passes, railroad, 351
Patent Office, Agricultural Branch, 302; *Annual Report, Agriculture*, 303
Pemberton, John C.: orders noncombatants from Vicksburg, 26; monopolizes railroads, 38
Pennsylvania: sheep in, 158–60; expansion of farms in the 1850's, 223
People's College, failure of, 268
Pettus, John J., 118
Philbrick, Edward S., and Sea Island plantations, 363
Piedmont, N.C., near exhaustion of food supplies, 111–12
Pierce, Franklin, 253
Pitt thresher, 237
plant diseases, ravages of, 257

plantations: diminishingly productive, 95; plundered in Louisiana, 122

planters: evasion of military service, 33–4; accused of hoarding, 41–2; defense of, 43–4; dislike of slave impressment, 60–2; effects of war on, 77; save cotton from burning, 105–6; and stay laws, 327, 329; and freedmen, 357; recovered land, 365; and Negro rights, 368–9

pleuropneumonia, 183, 217, 218–219, 258

plows: sent through Confederate lines, 107; improvements in, 237; steam, 352

pork: Southern substitutes for, 102; increased exports of during the war, 176–7

Port Royal, S.C., 364

potatoes: in farmers' economy, 141–2; blight, 258

Pottawatomie Reserve, 344

Prairie Farmer, 183, 242, 270, 285, 322, 350

prairies: farmers' adjustment to, 275; landlord estates in, 279

Pratt, Zadock: dairy operations of, 205; profits of, 206

Preemption Law, 291

Prince, W. R., 140, 319

Produce Loan Act, Confederate, 84

property tax, results in the South, 363

public lands: elusive character of cheap land, 281; in the Confederacy, 296

Pugh, Evan, 259, 266

Putnam County, N.Y., as part of New York milkshed, 195

pyrethrum, 316

Racine, Wisc., as farm machinery center, 239

Radicals, Northern, and land redistribution, 357

raiders, Federal, lay waste great areas, 111

railroad farm mortgages, in Wisconsin, 344

Railroads: reverse trade routes, 4; breakdown in the South, 38, 110; and farmers' market economy, 131; extend milksheds, 132; bring country milk to the city, 194; and marketability of wheat, 245; construction during the war, 246, 296; and agricultural expansion, 294–5; land grants, 296; opposition of settlers to grants, 345; tax exemption of grants, 346; land grants and tenancy, 347; obtain alternate reserve sections, 343; acquire Kansas Indian reserves, 343; rate controversies of, 349, 351; farmers' concern about rates of, 351; aids to settlers, 352; forfeiture of land grants proposed, 360

Raleigh, N.C., food riot at, 40

ranchos, in California, drought contributes to break up of, 178

Randall, Henry S.: and sheep industry in the South, 81; *Fine Wool Sheep Industry*, 162; *Sheep Husbandry in the South*, 162; *The Practical Shepherd*, 162–3; Merino sheep breeder, 162; editor, 163; plan for wool growers, 171–2; president of New York Sheep Breeders and Wool Growers Association, 171; cooperation with wool manufacturers, 172; president of the National Wool Growers' Association, 173; lobbies for wool tariff, 174; *Sheep Husbandry*, 258

Randall, James G., 362

Reading Railroad, 137

reapers: manufacture of, 232–3; frequency of breakdown, 233, 355; rise in price of, 244–5

rebates, railroad, 351–2

refugees, 26

Republican Party, free-land policy of, 284

Rich, Charles, Merino sheep breeder, 162, 166

Richmond: population of during the war, 25; suffering in, 29; inflation, 37; food riot in, 39; effects of impressment in, 51; dram shops, 96; prices, 124; Union Benevolent Society of, 88

Richmond Enquirer, 19, 39

Richmond Whig, 41, 90, 111, 123

rinderpest, 182; fear of spread of, 219; European cattle banned to prevent spread of, 220

Robinson, Solon, reporter, *New York Tribune*, 180, 190, 197, 219, 260
Rockford, Ill., as farm machinery center, 239
Ross, Earle D., *Democracy's College*, 259
Rotch, Francis M., 216, 312
Ruffin, Thomas, on stay laws, 331
Rural New Yorker, 152, 157, 163, 173, 202, 243, 270, 309, 310, 314, 322; on currency reform, 354–5
rust, 224
Rutgers, agricultural studies, 269

St. Cloud land office, 291
St. Paul Pioneer and Democrat, 290–1
Salisbury, N.C.: food riot at, 39; Confederate distillery in, 98–9
salt, scarcity of, 24, 80
San Joaquin Valley, 292
Sanford, William R., Merino sheep breeder, 162, 166
Santa Barbara County, Cal., 178
Saunders, William, 318
Savannah, Ga., 115
Schapiro, Henry, 362
Scioto Valley Shorthorns, 8
Scott, Matthew T., 279
scrip, agricultural college, 261, 263, 264–6
Scully, William, land holdings of, 279, 348
scurvy, 101
scythes, brought in by blockade runners, 105
Sea Islands: capture of, 113; plantations sold, 363
Seddon, James A.: on impressment, 47, aware of waste of supplies, 72; on Confederate whiskey distilling, 99; on trade through the lines, 105
seeds: brought in by blockade runners, 102; distribution by Department of Agriculture, 314
Selma, Ala., 124
Semmes, Thomas J., 362
Sequestration Act, Confederate, 361
settlers, frontier: dependence on borrowed capital, 288; controversy with Burlington Railroad, 345
Shannon, Fred A., 374

share cropper system, 373
sheep: Southern, 8; killed by dogs, 81; in the 1850's, 157; increase in the Middle West, 158; breeding increased during the war, 161; coarse-wooled, 168; Merino, 168; Southdowns, 168; Rambouillet, 168; English breeds, 168–9; decline of breeding, 175; *see also* wool growers
Sheffield Scientific School, 269
Sheridan, Philip, destruction in Shenandoah, 93
Sherman, William T.: removal of non-combatants from Atlanta, 26; in Georgia, 115; and land for Negroes, 364
Shorter, John G., 31, 61
shorthorn cattle: in Scioto Valley, 8; dual-purpose, 181; most popular breed, 215
Shugg, Roger, 374
Simmons, James F., 306
slaves: removal of, 24; impressed, 59–62; mistreatment on defense work, 62; flight of, 78; freed by Sherman, 115
Slidell, John, 362
Smedes, Susan Dabney, 31
smut, 224
sorghum: as substitute for sugar, 103; efforts to promote production of, 145; production of, 147–148; poor quality of, 148–9; Wetherill's report on, 317
Sorgo Journal and Farm Machinist, 146, 313
South Carolina: restrictions on cotton planting, 18; planters' flight from coast, 113; emigration from, 274; stay laws, 336–337
Southern Confederacy, 41, 305
Southern Cultivator, 305
Southern Homestead Act, 359, 361–2
Spanish fever, 182
speculators: in food, condemned, 34–5, 41; in land, a deterrent to settlement, 280; in Illinois, 289; active after 1862, 294; blighting influence of, 347
squatters: borrow to protect claims, 282; in California, conflict with Mexican grantees, 292,

squatters (*continued*)
342–3; agrarian program in California, 343
Stanton, Edwin M., 180
starvation, fear of, 27, 37, 110
stay laws: use of, 324–6; in Mississippi, 327–9; in Alabama, 329; in North Carolina, 330–4; in Georgia, 334–6; in South Carolina, 336–7; in Louisiana, 338–9; in Texas, 339; in Arkansas, 339; in Virginia, 339; in Florida, 339; in Kentucky, 339; in Iowa, 340; in Ohio, 340; in Missouri, 340; in Wisconsin, 340–1
Stearns, Abel, drought and cattle losses, 178
Stevens, Thaddeus, on confiscation of rebel property, 357
Stokes, William B., 361–2
Story, Joseph, 326, 337
Strawn, Jacob, 348
Sturges, Solomon, 348
Subsistence Department, Confederate, 56
sugar: production of, 103; captured supplies flow to the North, 145; decline of plantations, 369; recovery of plantations, 371
sugar beets: European production of, 149; American experiments with, 150
Sullivan, Michael, 134, 348
Sumner, Charles, on confiscation of rebel property, 357
Supreme Court, U.S., 326–7
Surgeon General, Confederate, on whiskey distilling, 99
Surget, Mrs. E., 89
swamplands, 345
Swedes, immigration of, 241
swill dairies, *see* distillery dairies

Talladega, Ala., 39
tariffs: wood schedule of Walker Tariff of 1846, 169; Act of 1857, unsatisfactory to wool growers, 169; Act of 1861, wool growers critical of, 169; Act of 1864, disliked by wool growers, 172; Wool and Woolens Act, 174
Taussig, Frank W., 174
Taylor, Richard, criticism of impressment, 50
tenancy: decline of in New York

and Pennsylvania, 129; in the West, 275; immigrants move into, 279; in Illinois, 279; spread of, 280; in ante-bellum Alabama, 280; speculators contribute to, 289; conditions of, 347; and railroad land grants, 347
Tennessee: food areas lost to the Confederacy, 122; emigration from, 274; little aid to agriculture, 305
Tennessee Valley, 116
Texas: cattle shipments to war zone, 10, 12; as reservoir of cattle, 181–2; land policy of, 299; stay laws, 339
Thoreau, Henry David, 197
threshing machine, 237–8
Tifft, Solomon, 361–2
tithing tax, Confederate: on farm products, 63; regions where applied, 64; administration of, 64; housing of goods, 66; losses in handling, 67; evasion of, 68; results of, 69; revision, 71
tobacco: Virginia's limitations on, 18; planting, 32; bonded, not taxable, 68; prices, 142–3; Northern centers of production, 143–4; Northern exports of, 145; recovery of, 371
Toombs, Robert: condemned for planting cotton, 19; on Joseph E. Brown, 20*n.*
treadmill, 237
Trempealeau County, Wisc., 290, 291
trichinae, 184
Turner, Jonathan Baldwin: plan for industrial university, 259; authority on agriculture, 308
twenty-Negro law, 33
Tyrell, W. D., plantation ruined by Sherman's forces, 93

Union Pacific Railroad, 300; tax exemption of lands, 346–7
United States Agricultural Society, 306
United States Economist, denounced by wool growers, 171
Utica Weekly Herald, 214

Vance, Zebulon B.: criticizes administration of tithing tax, 65; troubled by Confederate distil-

Vance, Zebulon B. (*continued*) lery, 98–9; bans food exports from North Carolina, 100–1; fears exhaustion of food supplies, 110, 112; on stay laws, 333

vegetables: scarcity of in the South, 28, 101; prices of, 102

Vermont: leader in Merino sheep breeding, 162–7; butter production of, 201; abandonment of farms in, 255, 374; emigration from, 274; sale of agricultural college scrip, 265

Vicksburg, Miss., 38

Vicksburg & Meridian Railroad, 298

Virginia: limitations on tobacco, 18; farmers accused of hoarding, 37; wet season, 86; bans distilling from grain, 97; food supplies exhausted, 123; lack of aid to agriculture, 305; stay law, 339

Wabash Valley, tenancy in, 279

Wadsworth estate, tenancy, 129

Walkill Creamery Association: cooperative dairy, 206; business of, 207

Walkill Valley, dairy region of Orange County, N.Y., 195

Warren, James L. L. F., welcomed destruction of Spanish cattle, 178

Washington, D.C., efforts to ban adulterated milk in, 192

Watts, Thomas H., on impressment abuses, 49

Weed, Thurlow: lobbyist of wool manufacturers, 171; opposed Homestead law, 286

weevil, damage to wheat, 51

Wentworth, John, and Merino sheep, 159

Westchester County, N.Y., 195

westward migration: from newer states, 281; rush of, 378

Wetherill, Charles M., 317

wheat: Northern, 8; inadequacy of Georgia crop, 114; affected by weather and parasites, 223; exports of, 226–7, 375; bumper crop in 1860, 223; belt: moving west, 244

whey, 209

whiskey: Confederate soldiers' use of, 49; efforts to ban use of grain for, 96–100; profits in, 99

Wilder, Marshall Pinckney, 259, 308, 319

Wiley, Bell I., 76

Willard, Xerxes A.: *Practical Dairy Husbandry*, 202; authority on cheese making, 206, 313; investigates English cheese making, 214

William and Mary College, 252

Williams, Joseph R., 259

Wilmington, N.C., blockade runner plundered at, 40

Wilson, Harold, *Hill Country of Northern New England*, 175

Winnebago land office, 291

Wisconsin: land speculators in, 289; growth of hops in, 240; wheat crop of 1860, 223–4, 225; appraisement law, 340–1; railroad farm mortgages in, 344

Wisconsin Farmer, on heartless creditors, 341

women: burdens lightened by cheese factories, 214–15; work in fields, 75, 242–3

wood, *see* fuelwood

wood mower, 235

wool: Southern need for, 106; exported from Texas, 106; imports of, 159; production in major countries, 170

wool growers: establish depots, 170; create national association, 171, 173; move for tariff protection, 169, 173; and tariff protection, 374

wool manufacturers: and tariffs, 169; create national association, 170

Working Farmer, 322

Wright, Chester, 159

Yale College, scientific studies in, 257, 269

Yates, Richard, on railroad rates, 349

yeoman farmers, 4; constitute bulk of Confederate army, 74; wartime burdens of families of, 75; pinched by debts, 327; and stay laws, 327

Youatt on the Hog, 258

A NOTE ON THE TYPE

The text of this book was set on the Linotype in a new face called PRIMER, designed by RUDOLPH RUZICKA, earlier responsible for the design of Fairfield and Fairfield Medium, Linotype faces whose virtues have for some time now been accorded wide recognition.

The complete range of sizes of Primer was first made available in 1954, although the pilot size of 12 point was ready as early as 1951. The design of the face makes general reference to Linotype Century (long a serviceable type, totally lacking in manner or frills of any kind) but brilliantly corrects the characterless quality of that face.

Composed, printed, and bound by
The Haddon Craftsmen, Scranton, Pa.

Typography and binding design by

W A R R E N ⧎ C H A P P E L L